asis

Volume

16

1981

Annual Review of Information Science and Technology

MARTHA E. WILLIAMS, Editor

Published by
KNOWLEDGE INDUSTRY PUBLICATIONS, INC.
for
AMERICAN SOCIETY FOR INFORMATION SCIENCE

ISSN: 0066-4200
CODEN: ARISBc

Knowledge Industry Publications, Inc.
701 Westchester Avenue
White Plains, New York 10604

LC Catalog Card Number: 66-25096
ISBN: 0-914236-90-3
ISSN: 0066-4200
CODEN: ARISBc
Printed in the United States of America

The opinions expressed by contributors to publications of the American Society for Information Science do not necessarily reflect the position or official policy of the American Society for Information Science.

ASIS Publications Staff

Linda (O'Brien) Holder, Graphic Compositor

Contents

iv

Preface

This is the 16th volume of the *Annual Review of Information Science and Technology* (*ARIST*) produced by the American Society for Information Science (ASIS). ASIS (formerly American Documentation Institute) initiated the series in 1966 with the publication of Volume 1. ASIS is the owner of *ARIST*, maintains the editorial control, and has the sole rights to the series.

Through the years several organizations have been responsible for publishing and marketing *ARIST*. Volumes 1 and 2 were published by Interscience Publishers, a division of John Wiley & Sons. Volumes 3 through 6 were published by Encyclopaedia Britannica, Inc. Volumes 7 through 11 were published by ASIS itself, and with Volume 12 Knowledge Industry Publications, Inc. assumed the role of publisher for *ARIST*.

Policy. *ARIST* is an annual publication that reviews numerous topics within the broad field of information science and technology. No single topic is treated on an annual basis; it is the publication of the book that occurs annually. Inasmuch as the field is dynamic, the contents (chapters) of the various *ARIST* volumes must change to reflect this dynamism. *ARIST* chapters are scholarly reviews of specific topics as substantiated by the published literature. Some material may be included, even though not backed up by literature, if it is needed to provide a balanced and complete picture of the state of the art for the subject of the chapter. The time period covered varies from chapter to chapter, depending on whether the topic has been treated previously by *ARIST* and, if so, on the length of the interval from the last treatment to the current one. Thus, reviews may cover a one-year or multiyear period. The reviews aim to be critical in that they provide the author's expert opinion regarding developments and activities within the chapter's subject area. The reviewer guides the reader to or from specific publications, and these expert opinions should be substantiated. Chapters aim to be scholarly, thorough within the scope defined by the chapter author, up to date, well written, and readable by an audience that goes beyond the author's immediate peer group to researchers and practitioners in information science and technology in general and ASIS members in particular.

Purpose. The purpose of *ARIST* is to describe and to appraise activities and trends in the field of information science and technology. Material presented should be substantiated by references to the literature. *ARIST* provides an annual review of topics in the field. One volume is produced each year. A master plan for the series encompasses the entire field in all its aspects, and topics for each volume are selected from the plan on the basis of timeliness and an assessment of reader interest.

References cited in text and bibliography. The format for referring to bibliographic citations within the text involves use of the cited author's name instead of reference numbers. The cited author's surname is printed in upper case letters. The reader, wishing to find the bibliographic references, can readily locate the appropriate reference in the bibliography (alphabetically arranged by first author's last name); the author's last name again appears in upper case letters in the text. A single author appears as SMITH; coauthors as SMITH & JONES; and multiple authors as SMITH ET AL. If multiple papers by the same author are cited, the distinction is made by indicating the year of publication after the last name (e.g., SMITH, 1975), and if a further distinction is required for multiple papers within the same year, a lower case alpha character follows the year (e.g., SMITH, 1975a). Except for the fact that all authors in multi-authored papers are included in bibliographic references, the same basic conventions are used in the chapter bibliographies. Thus, the reader can easily locate in the bibliography any references discussed in the text.

Because of the emphasis placed on the requirement for chapter authors to discuss the key papers and significant developments reported in the literature, and because *ARIST* readers have expressed their liking for comprehensive bibliographies associated with the chapters, more references are listed in the bibliographies than are discussed in the text.

The format used for references in the bibliographies is based on the *American National Standard for Bibliographic References*, ANSI Z39.29. We have followed the ANSI guidelines with respect to the sequence of bibliographic data elements and the punctuation used to separate the elements. Adoption of this convention should facilitate conversion of the references to machine-readable form as need arises. Journal article references follow the ANSI guide as closely as possible. Conference papers and microform publications follow an *ARIST* adaptation of the format.

Structure of the volume. In accordance with the *ARIST* master plan, this volume's eleven chapters fit within the basic framework: I. Planning Information Systems and Services; II. Basic Techniques and Tools; III. Applications; IV. The Profession. Chapter titles are provided in the Table of Contents, and an Introduction to each section highlights the events, trends, and evaluations given by the chapter authors. An Index to the entire volume is provided to help the user locate material relevant to the subject content, authors, and organizations cited in the book. An explanation of the guidelines employed in the Index is provided in the Introduction to the Index.

Acknowledgments. Appreciation should be expressed to many individuals and organizations for their roles in creating this volume. First and foremost are the authors of the individual chapters who have generously contributed their time and efforts in searching, reviewing, and evaluating the large body of literature on which their chapters are based. The *ARIST* Advisory Committee Members and *ARIST* Reviewers provided valuable feedback and constructive criticism of the content. Major contributions toward the production of this publication were made by Mary W. Rakow, Copy Editor; Elaine Tisch Dunatov, Bibliographic Editor; and Laurence Lannom, Index Editor. Appreciation is expressed to all of the members of the *ARIST* technical support staff who are listed on the Acknowledgments page.

Martha E. Williams

Acknowledgments

The American Society for Information Science and the Editor wish to acknowledge the contributions of the three principals on the editorial staff and the technical support staff.

Elaine Tisch Dunatov, Bibliographic Editor

Laurence Lannom, Index Editor

Mary W. Rakow, Copy Editor

Technical Support Staff

Scott E. Preece, Technical Advisor

Dorothy Saxner, Technical Advisor

Laurel P. Preece, Proofreader and Data Input Technician

Margery Johnson, Editorial Assistant

Molly McLellan, Secretary

Advisory Committee for *ARIST*

Contributors

Marcia J. Bates
Graduate School of Library and
    Information Science
University of California at Los
    Angeles
Los Angeles, CA 90024

David Becker
Information Sciences
IIT Research Institute
10 West 35th Street
Chicago, IL 60616

Karl Brimmer
United States Department of
    Commerce
National Telecommunications and
    Information Administration
1800 G Street, NW, Room 770
Washington, DC 20504

Sarah K. Burton
North Carolina State University
Raleigh, NC 27607

Elaine Caruso
Graduate School of Public and
    International Affairs
1E 16 Forbes Quadrangle
University of Pittsburgh
Pittsburgh, PA 15260

Arthur Elias
BioSciences Information Service
2100 Arch Street
Philadelphia, PA 19103

Glyn T. Evans
SUNY Central Administration
State University Plaza
Albany, NY 12246

Gerry Goldsmith
Computation Department
UMIST, Box 88
Manchester, ENGLAND M60 1QD

Donald T. Hawkins
Bell Laboratories
600 Mountain Avenue
Room 6A-311
Murray Hill, NJ 07974

Thomas Hickey
OCLC Online Computer Library
    Center, Inc.
6565 Frantz Road
Dublin, OH 43017

W. David Penniman
OCLC Online Computer Library
    Center, Inc.
6565 Frantz Road
Dublin, OH 43017

Joseph Raben
Computers and the Humanities
Queens College
Flushing, NY 11367

Elaine Svenonius
Graduate School of Librarianship
  and Information Management
University of Denver
Denver, CO 80208

Howard Turtle
OCLC Online Computer Library
  Center, Inc.
6565 Frantz Road
Dublin, OH 43017

Nancy Vaupel
BioSciences Information Service
2100 Arch Street
Philadelphia, PA 19103

Philip W. Williams
Computation Department
UMIST, Box 88
Manchester, ENGLAND M60 1QD

Rutherford Witthus
Graduate School of Librarianship
  and Information Management
University of Denver
Denver, CO 80208

Edward K. Zimmerman
United States Department of
  Commerce
National Telecommunications and
  Information Administration
1800 G Street, NW, Room 770
Washington, DC 20504

Chapter Reviewers

Henriette D. Avram

John Bennett

Wesley T. Brandhorst

Walter Carlson

Carlos A. Cuadra

Douglas Ferguson

Margaret T. Fischer

Stephen E. Furth

Charles M. Goldstein

Glynn Harmon

Laurence B. Heilprin

Madeleine M. Henderson

Donald W. King

Joseph H. Kuney

Lois F. Lunin

Susan K. Martin

Richard H. Orr

Scott E. Preece

Howard L. Resnikoff

Tefko Saracevic

Linda C. Smith

Donald Walker

Herbert S. White

I

Planning Information Systems and Services

The chapter in this section is "National Planning for Data Communications." Edward K. Zimmerman and Karl Brimmer of the National Telecommunications and Information Administration describe the complex interaction of private and government sector forces and technological and economic changes that shape the data communications arena in the United States and fill the role taken by central planning in more regulated countries. The chapter is divided into three sections, describing the players in the data communications arena, the forces that shape planning by those players, and the prospects for developments in the 1980s. The players are the corporate, governmental, and consumer entities that provide, use, regulate, resell, and support data communications. The private sector players include the telecommunications industry (local facilities and services, long-distance facilities and services, and equipment), the computer industry, the information industry, users, and the standards-setting organizations. The government-sector players include the Federal Communications Commission (FCC), Congress, the executive branch, judicial organizations, state and local governments, and international organizations. Most, whether private or governmental, fill more than one of those roles.

Planning is based on player responses to changes in the technological, economic, and regulatory environment. The most apparent changes are the recent trend toward deregulation and increased competition, the continual advances in technology for providing and using communications services, and the likelihood of major changes in the Communications Act of 1934. The prospects are for an increased blurring of distinctions among data communications, general telecommunications, and other information activities as internetworking, electronic messaging, and competitive offerings increase. The governmental players will face continuing changes in the nature of the arena they regulate and an ever greater need for coordination with international requirements. The thrust of the U.S. national policy in the telecommunications common carrier industry is toward deregulation and open competition— a combination that many people believe will meet the diverse needs of Americans. However, the industry is highly concentrated, and a truly competitive and deregulated industry is not yet here. This chapter will be continued next year in Volume 17.

1

National Planning
for Data Communications

EDWARD K. ZIMMERMAN
U. S. Department of Commerce

KARL W. BRIMMER
U. S. Department of Commerce

INTRODUCTION

Definition and Scope

National planning. Many observers of U. S. efforts toward rational management of our national data communications and other telecommunications resources have pointed out that the United States does not plan per se. Nevertheless, the seemingly strange and sometimes loose amalgam of U. S. competition, regulation, federal and state government oversight has produced what is still the best telecommunications system in the world.

With the Morse telegraph, the transmission of encoded information preceded the development of the voice telephone service that dominates telecommunication service in the United States today. One hundred years after Morse, a new instrument—the computer—envisaged by his contemporary, Charles Babbage, has reversed the trend back toward encoded information, albeit in a much more sophisticated form and with a new name—data communications.

This chapter focuses on the recent evolution of U.S. national planning as it concerns telecommunications in general and data communications in particular. It seems impractical to separate the latter from the former, especially with respect to telephony, for the purposes of this chapter. While the regulatory differences are obvious and troublesome, the continuum that

The authors express their appreciation to Vera Whisenton, Janet Baxter, and Jeannette Kidd for their work in information gathering and preparing the bibliography for this chapter.
This chapter is in the public domain.

is obvious from even a cursory study of the physical science and technology involved suggests that these differences will tend to disappear over time.

The national planning process for telecommunications in the United States is unique in many respects. In most other countries, national planning falls under the direct control of the government and is therefore highly centralized. In addition, national governments of other countries often own, operate, and manage telecommunications facilities and services on an exclusive basis. Nevertheless, at least in Germany and England, this highly centralized process is being questioned (HOFFMAN; LAMOND). The U. S. federal government primarily and the states concomitantly through their respective legislative and regulatory processes establish broad goals, policies, and procedures, but they leave the ownership, operation, and management of telecommunications facilities and services to the private sector. Thus, in most countries the government determines the services and facility offerings, including price and quality, but in the United States the private sector does this, subject to regulatory oversight.

Even within this basic policy of relying on the private sector, the United States national planning process is evolving from reliance on a regulated monopoly market to reliance on a competitive and often deregulated market to meet its telecommunications needs. We focus on this recent evolution with an overview beginning with the 1956 Consent Decree and ending with events and issues as they stand in early 1981.

Data communications. SIPPL defines data communications as "the movement of computer-encoded information by means of electrical transmission systems." Data communications is generally thought of in terms of communications among computers and between computers and terminals. Some services that depend on data communications include airline reservation systems, electronic mail (EM), electronic funds transfer (EFT), and online database services. This chapter considers data communications in this context. Please note however that because computer and communications technologies are merging, Sippl's definition could be construed to subsume other forms of digital electronic communications, such as telephone and video, that have not been considered data communications.

Perspective on Data Communications

Data communications today is and will continue to be a fraction of total electronic communications. In 1979 less than 6% of the $69.2 billion earned by providers of communications facilities and services was attributable to data communications (*DATAMATION*, 1980a). Most of the revenue came from voice service, with data communications a distant second and video last. For the foreseeable future this relative ranking will continue to hold. These figures are not definitive because the accounting for data communications revenues differs from one provider to another and is difficult to estimate. After all, much data communication takes place over the dial-up telephone network, and thus a considerable amount of it is indistinguishable from voice communications for accounting purposes. In addition data communications surveys do not take into account the growing use of intracompany networks for non-voice traffic. As local area networks and private packet networks proliferate, undercounting in this hard-to-measure area will become more significant.

As part of a study done for the National Aeronautics and Space Administration (NASA), STAELIN & HARVEY (p17) give figures from an International Telephone and Telegraph (ITT) traffic forecast that show that the percentage of long-distance electronic communications attributable to data communications (narrowly defined) will actually fall from about 20% in 1980 to about 12% by the year 2000. However, because the overall volume of communications will grow substantially, data communications volume will actually increase. If we took the definition of SIPPL literally, which appears to classify all computer-encoded communications as data communications, then data communications would probably dominate as long as we classify microprocessors as computers and digital communications as data communications.

Because data communication is a relatively new phenomenon and is of relatively low volume, overall planning for it is constrained by voice communications. This is important because efficient data communications is tied to the types of technologies used. Unfortunately, the technologies used for most current telecommunications are optimized for voice communications—viz., analog transmission and circuit switching, which do not efficiently meet the needs of data communications. These needs can often be met more efficiently with digital transmission and packet switched technology. However, as BERGLUND notes, it is still an analog world. Even some recent key policy questions confronting the Federal Communications Commission (FCC), such as those posed by the Carterfone and Execunet decisions, were the result of demands for more flexible voice communications capability and not the result of demands of data communications users or providers.

As some of these key policy questions are being resolved and, more importantly, as the technology for voice communications increasingly relies on data communications concepts, such as digital transmission, the distinction between the two seems to be disappearing. Therefore, this chapter does not distinguish between national planning for data vs. voice communications. To the contrary, present technological and regulatory trends suggest that this ought to be the first and last *ARIST* review of national planning for data communications per se.

Organization of Chapter

This chapter is divided into three main sections: Players, Planning, and Prospects. In the Players section we describe the major players in the national planning process in both the private and the government sector. In the Planning section we briefly describe the technological changes that are occurring in telecommunications and computers as well as the confluence of these technologies. We then discuss the economic changes that have resulted from the technological changes, we discuss the major regulatory changes brought about by these economic changes, and finally we discuss recent legislative efforts to rewrite the Communications Act of 1934. In the Prospects section, we discuss some unresolved issues and current events and predict what data communications may look like in the 1980s.

Several good overviews of recent events, processes, motivations, and reasonings have been written. L. L. JOHNSON and R. B. JOHNSON provide insightful, if slightly dated overviews, and PEARCE provides a comprehensive and up-to-date overview, which is both insightful and predictive. Pearce's work also covers broadcast and mobile radio. R. B. Johnson's work also treats broadcast and cable TV.

PLAYERS

The players in the national planning process are many, they represent diverse interests, and they vary in size and influence. The important thing is that there has been a dramatic increase in the number of firms providing telecommunications equipment and services, especially those associated with long-distance telephone services and terminal equipment. The players fall into two groups—the private sector and the government sector. CROMBIE describes the roles of each.

Private Sector Players

Telecommunications industry. The telecommunications common carrier (telephone and telegraph), cable TV, and broadcast (TV and radio) industries are the three major components of the telecommunications industry; the telephone portion of the common carrier industry is by far the largest economically and has the greatest effect on data communications. The cable TV industry has a great potential effect on data communications, but there are obstacles to be overcome (discussed later). The broadcast industry has the least potential impact on data communications and is not discussed extensively.

The telecommunications industry can be divided into three major segments: local facilities and services, long-distance facilities and services, and equipment. The big players in the telecommunications common carrier industry tend to be involved in all three segments—i.e., they tend to be vertically integrated—while small common carriers, cable TV providers, and broadcast station operators tend to confine their activities to local operations.

The telecommunications common carrier industry is divided into: 1) the established common carriers, which include American Telephone and Telegraph (AT&T), independent telephone companies, and Western Union (WU); 2) other common carriers (OCCs), which include specialized common carriers (SCCs), value added networks (VANs), and domestic satellite carriers (domsats); 3) international carriers, which include the international record carriers (IRCs) and the Communications Satellite Corp. (Comsat); 4) mobile telephone companies, which are referred to as radio common carriers (RCCs); and 5) telecommunications equipment manufacturers, which include terminal and switching equipment. A report by the U. S. GENERAL

ACCOUNTING OFFICE (1979a) provides an excellent, if slightly dated, overview of the domestic telecommunications common carrier industry. The UNITED STATES DEPARTMENT OF COMMERCE gives the present and projected outlook for telephone and telegraph equipment and services, and the U. S. FEDERAL COMMUNICATIONS COMMISSION (1979d) provides comprehensive statistics on AT&T and the larger independent telephone companies.

Of the established common carriers, AT&T is the largest—in fact, it is one of the largest nonfinancial institutions in the world. AT&T dominates telephone service with more than 80% of the total local, long-distance, and telephone equipment markets. On the other hand, AT&T's dominance in data communications is not as complete (DATAMATION, 1980a). In 1979 AT&T's share of total data communications revenues of about $3.98 billion was estimated at only $2.31 billion, about 58% of the market. This figure represents only 5% of AT&T's total revenues in 1979 of $46.18 billion. SARASOHN discusses AT&T's corporate structure.

Although there are more than 1,500 independent telephone companies (U. S. GENERAL ACCOUNTING OFFICE, 1979d), they have less than 20% of the total telephone market. Much of this remaining market goes to General Telephone and Electronics (GTE), United Telecommunications, and Continental Telephone. The 1,500 remaining companies are often owned municipally or cooperatively. In 1979 five of the independent telephone companies— GTE, United Telecommunications, Continental Telephone, Central Telephone, and Rochester Telephone—generated about $900 million in data communications revenues, with GTE (through Communications Networks Systems Resources, which includes Telenet) generating almost 90% of that amount (DATAMATION, 1980a).

WU Corp. is the established common carrier for telegraph service (telegram message service, telegraphic money order service, Mailgram, and Telex/TWX) and has moved heavily into data communications. In 1979 WU generated almost $500 million in data communications services, which represented almost 12% of total data communications revenues and about 62% of its total revenues (DATAMATION, 1980a).

The SCC segment of the OCC industry provides long-distance telephone, data, and facsimile communications. For the long-haul portion of these services they usually use their own terrestrial microwave facilities. The local loops that connect the SCCs' networks to customers are usually leased from the local telephone company—i.e., established common carriers. Two of the better known SCCs are Southern Pacific Communications and MCI Communications Corporation (MCI). These companies had combined revenues of $227 million in 1979 (DATAMATION, 1980a). Only about 8% of that revenue, however, was for data communications. Hence, less than 0.1% of total data communications revenues were generated by these two SCCs.

The VAN segment of the OCC industry leases facilities from common carriers, adds specialized services, and markets this package to the final user. Among these services is one that allows dissimilar computer equipment to communicate. Tymnet, Graphnet, and GTE's Telenet are VANs. EDWARDS

(1980) describes VANs and assesses their contribution to improved data communications services.

Domsats are similar to SCCs except that they use satellite transmission facilities instead of terrestrial microwave facilities, and they appeal to different market segments. American Satellite Corp., WU, RCA American Communications (Americom), Comsat General, and Satellite Business Systems (SBS) are domsats. The broadband transmission characteristics used by satellite carriers make satellites an advantageous digital data communications medium, and their traffic tends to reflect this.

There are five international record carriers: 1) ITT World Communications, 2) RCA Global Communications (Globcom), 3) Western Union International (WUI), 4) TRT Telecommunications Corp., and 5) FTC Communications. IRCs generally provide international telex, telegraph, and other data services including facsimile. Some of these companies or their parent companies also offer domestic telecommunications services and manufacture switching and terminal equipment.

The telecommunications equipment industry has many participants, including foreign competition. Western Electric has dominated this field, with annual revenues in 1979 of about $10 billion. This entire industry has been experiencing rapid technological change and healthy growth. FRANK provides a good financial overview of the non-telephone company data communications equipment suppliers.

The cable TV industry is today primarily an entertainment medium. Nevertheless, the technical potential for cable as a two-way data communications medium is great. Because cable is a broadband medium, this potential extends beyond data to all facets of telecommunications—e.g., the use of cable for videotex systems. BLOOM ET AL. give a comprehensive and up-to-date discussion of various videotex systems as well as policy, economic, and technical questions surrounding the use of this technology. The cable TV industry to date has been reluctant to provide much in the way of programming other than entertainment although there have been limited experiments with voice and data services.

The broadcast industry has only a limited role in providing data communications. There is some potential for providing data service to the home using a one-way videotex system called teletext, which is based on specially equipped television receiver display of alphanumeric or graphic information that is transmitted as a part of the broadcast video signal but is not visible on the screen of conventional TV sets.

Computer industry. The big difference between the computer industry and the telecommunications industry is that the former has not been directly regulated while the latter has. It is generally agreed that this is one of the major reasons for the greater diversity in the computer industry, which has been characterized by explosive growth and technical change. The computer or data processing industry can be divided into five markets: 1) mainframes, 2) minicomputers, 3) peripherals and terminals, 4) service and software, and 5) media and supplies. A recent survey (*DATAMATION*, 1980b), estimates that in 1979 the 100 largest data processing firms generated more than $45 billion in revenues in these markets. With International Business Machines (IBM) leading the way with 38%, the top eight companies captured more than 70% of all data processing revenues. The survey goes on to give a fairly complete financial performance picture and characterization of the computer industry, including descriptions of firms and their participation in the five markets listed above. SOMA describes the technical and economic growth of the industry. The computer industry has a vital stake in the national planning process for data communications in that the flexibility and utility of the computer, as well as the continued penetration and growth of the computer industry, depend on data communications.

Information industry. The information industry also is not directly regulated, and it overlaps the computer industry considerably. The information industry merges telecommunications and computer technology to provide information services and products such as online databases, EFT, time-sharing services, EM, and marketing information. These products and services and the companies that provide them are growing daily. Network information services comprise a growing segment of the information industry. DORDICK ET AL. discuss the characteristics and benefits of network information services and describe specific services and applications. This segment of the information industry has potentially profound effects on society and the economy, yet most of the impact of these services will be confined to large-to medium-sized business users for the foreseeable future.

According to a report by the INFORMATION INDUSTRY ASSOCIA-TION, this industry as tightly defined by them generates $10 billion a year and is growing annually at 20-25%. This is the first report that comes close to a comprehensive and accurate survey of the information industry by the industry itself. Adequate data communications is the backbone of this industry and is vital to its continued growth.

Information-intensive industries, such as credit, finance, and insurance, are also undergoing rapid change. Issues such as personal privacy and changed business patterns (e.g., stronger central control of banking) are surfacing as new computer and telecommunications technologies are adopted.

Users. With the increasing penetration of computers, the number of data communication users is growing. In the more competitive computer industry marketplace, it is fairly easy for the user to obtain the appropriate hardware, software, and services, but the less competitive telecommunications marketplace has been a choke point in meeting the overall data communications needs of the user. SANDERS & MCLAUGHLIN estimate that communications capability may lag as much as 20 years behind computer capability. Right now most data communications users are medium- to large-sized companies. Fully adequate data communications services do not exist even for these companies, let alone for small business and residential users. Although the need for these types of services for small business and residential users has not been fully determined, one would expect that data services, such as burglar alarm systems, automatic utilities monitoring, and the like, would be in demand if adequate facilities were available.

Standards-setting organizations. These organizations include the Institute of Electrical and Electronics Engineers (IEEE), the American National Standards Institute (ANSI), and Electronics Industries Association (EIA). These organizations along with governmental bodies, such as the FCC, the National Bureau of Standards (NBS), the National Telecommunications and Information Administration (NTIA), and the National Communications System (NCS), in coordination with international standards groups, such as International Telegraph and Telephone Consultative Committee (CCITT) and International Organization for Standardization (ISO), attempt to achieve standards that balance the need for them with their inhibiting effects. For example, HARDEMAN describes work by EIA on a communications standard, while mentioning collateral efforts to coordinate with ANSI on their interface for public data networks. The proceedings of the TRANSPORTATION DATA COORDINATING COMMITTEE illustrate their efforts to develop electronic data interface standards.

Most civilian equipment standards for telecommunications in the United States are voluntary. Agreements are reached in such standards organizations as those above for industry, but manufacturers cannot be legally forced into compliance. Nevertheless, where equipment is to be used in the Department of Defense (DoD) or in other areas of the federal government, clear and unambiguous specifications may be established, and standards can and do become enforceable. "Milspecs" (military specifications) are the published specifications for federal procurements in telecommunications equipment. They are at the "nuts and bolts" level and set test standards for maintenance and for life-cycle characteristics. LEBDUSKA outlines efforts to develop fiber optic standards and in the process illustrates the standards-setting activities of the government and other organizations including those listed above.

Government Sector Players

The government has many roles in the telecommunications planning process (CROMBIE). At all levels, government is involved to some degree as policy maker, regulator, manager, user and purchaser, coordinator of public sector requirements, and supporter of key technological developments.

FCC. Usually the most important player, the FCC is primarily responsible for oversight of the interstate telecommunications industry through entry and rate regulation within the constraints of the Communications Act of 1934. The FCC, however, often has some latitude because of its mandate "to regulate in the public interest." Since the late 1960s the FCC has been moving inexorably, if at times haltingly, to reduce regulatory barriers to entry in providing telecommunications services and at the same time has been conscientiously avoiding the spread of its regulatory umbrella over the computer industry. A recent report by the U. S. GENERAL ACCOUNTING OFFICE (1979c) describes the FCC's organizational structure, while CROTTS & MEAD discuss the FCC from a sociological point of view.

Congress. At any time Congress is potentially the most important player. It determines the constraints under which regulators will regulate. Over the past few years the House Subcommittee on Telecommunications, Consumer

Protection and Finance (chaired in the 97th Congress by Rep. Timothy Wirth) and the Senate Subcommittee on Communications (chaired in the 97th Congress by Sen. Barry Goldwater) have been trying to rewrite all or part of the Communications Act of 1934. Other subcommittees and committees of the House and Senate involve themselves in matters affecting data communications, including government use and procurement of telecommunications and data processing equipment and services. The most active committee in this regard is the House Committee on Government Operations (chaired in the 97th Congress by Rep. Jack Brooks). Although the congressional role is dominant in principle, other branches of government and the FCC have exerted far more influence on telecommunications policy (GELLHORN).

The Executive branch. The NTIA of the Department of Commerce is the President's chief advisor on domestic and international telecommunications policy. Details of the birth of NTIA are given in two references (SIDEL & MOSCO; U. S. CONGRESS. HOUSE. COMMITTEE ON GOVERNMENT OPERATIONS, 1977). Another Department of Commerce agency, NBS, takes the lead in setting data processing equipment standards, while NCS, (which is a coordinating office within DoD and not a proprietor of communications facilities as its name implies), takes the lead in setting federal telecommunications standards. These agencies interact with each other as well as with other government agencies, the private sector, and international standards-setting organizations.

The Justice Department, primarily through its enforcement of antitrust laws, has an important role. The State Department plays the lead in international negotiations regarding telecommunications facilities and law. In this latter area there is a complex interaction among NTIA, the FCC, and the State Department recently described in several reports by the U. S. GENERAL ACCOUNTING OFFICE (1977b; 1978c) and by House committee hearings (U. S. CONGRESS. HOUSE. COMMITTEE ON GOVERNMENT OPERATIONS, 1980a).

Finally, several executive branch agencies are involved in various aspects of managing federal telecommunications facilities, estimated by CROMBIE to total $50 billion and to involve purchases totaling $10 billion per year. This $10 billion includes all telecommunications procurement, such as radio and radar. A recent report of the U. S. GENERAL ACCOUNTING OFFICE (1980b) conservatively estimates that the federal government spends $100-$200 million annually on wireline data communications, relatively small when compared with overall expenditures on telecommunications, but growing. We recommend this report for the insight it gives into federal government use and management of its data communications resources, including government concerns surrounding data communications privacy and security. However, its estimate of government data communications expenditures is likely to be woefully small. The General Services Administration (GSA) is soon to sponsor a new study of federal government data communications needs and how they should be met. Perhaps better estimates will emerge from this study.

Here we briefly describe how the federal government divides the responsibility for managing its telecommunications resources, as defined in Executive Order No. 12046 (U. S. EXECUTIVE OFFICE OF THE PRESIDENT). (For a listing of laws, policies, and regulations pertaining to the management of federal data processing and related telecommunications activities see a report by the U. S. OFFICE OF MANAGEMENT AND BUDGET (OMB).) Essentially executive branch responsibilities are divided among OMB, which has policy responsibility, GSA, which has procurement and supply responsibility, and NTIA, which has advisory responsibilities to OMB and GSA. Note that OMB enunciates policies regarding federal government management of its telecommunications resources, while NTIA not only advises OMB on these policies but also advises the President and the FCC on private sector telecommunications policies. GSA often delegates its procurement authority to other government agencies, notably DoD.

The agencies concerned with government procurement sometimes find themselves at odds with the federal agencies that make policy for private sector telecommunications. For example, NTIA has supported the FCC decisions on resale and shared use, which has led to AT&T's proposed elimination of Telpak service. GSA opposes Telpak's demise because it could lead to a 28% increase in the government's phone bill.

Further discussion of the federal government's role in managing its own telecommunications resources is beyond the scope of this paper, but the preceding example shows that there can be interaction between the concerns of federal telecommunications managers, particularly those in DoD, and those who develop private sector policy. One manifestation of this interaction is CROMBIE's view that the government's tremendous buying power could be used to encourage the private sector to advance technology, to lower costs, and to help set standards.

For more insight into the federal government's management of its own telecommunications resources, one should consult the reports of the U. S. GENERAL ACCOUNTING OFFICE (1969; 1975; 1977a; 1978b; 1979b; 1980a; 1980b). CHISMAN (1978) discusses various alternatives to the current executive branch organization of policy and operational function in the communications field.

Judicial. Through hearings and review, the judiciary primarily interprets the legal freedoms, definitions, and constraints that Congress has placed on the FCC and the Justice Department. Decisions of the FCC are subject to review by the United States Court of Appeals for the District of Columbia, which in turn is subject to review by the United States Supreme Court. The court of appeals, using the Communications Act of 1934 and the subsequent body of regulatory and judicial precedent, determines the appropriateness of FCC decisions and the applicability of antitrust laws.

In several instances the court has played a key role in circumscribing attempts by the FCC and AT&T to prevent competition. Nevertheless, courts are bound not by the desirability of promoting competition or changed technical and economic circumstance, but rather by rules of law, legislation, and precedent. Hence, court decisions that are consistent with promoting competition are not a given. In the absence of new legislation, the court of appeals will face increasing litigation and play an increasingly important role in determining the eventual structure of the telecommunications industry. GARAY and GELLER give perspectives on the relationship of the court of appeals to the FCC. ROBINSON (1978b) discusses and evaluates judicial reviews of FCC decisions from a legal and philosophical perspective.

State and local. States have jurisdiction over intrastate telecommunications services except those such as radio, television, and land mobile radio. States universally regulate nearly all aspects of intrastate telephone service including long distance. Usually state assertion of jurisdiction is allowed as long as it does not conflict with FCC policy. Few states actually regulate cable TV (DORDICK, 1975; KALBA); this is usually left to local governments through their franchising authority. RODGERS provides a history of state utility regulation from the perspectives of state regulators and gives some insight into the relationship and the basic tension between federal and state regulatory efforts.

The National Association of Regulatory Utility Commissioners (NARUC) is often the focal point of state commission representation concerning matters before the FCC and Congress. The Federal-State Joint Board, however, is the main focal point for decisions that are of joint concern to the FCC and state regulators. This usually deals with matters surrounding the allocation of cost between intrastate and interstate telephone services, referred to as separations. States tend to favor lowering or at least not increasing local telephone service costs. Therefore, they tend to oppose competition in terminal equipment and long-distance service because they believe (as asserted by established common carriers) that it will lead to higher rates for local telephone services.

Other. There are several other important government players. Although they lack direct control over telecommunications, their influence in some cases stems from the fact that they provide or acquire specific services. This influence is felt most dramatically in some of the newer data communications services, such as the U. S. Postal Service's proposed EM service and the Federal Reserve's EFT service. Government provision of these services may chill the initiative of the private sector in these areas and poses a fundamental policy question of under what conditions, if at all, should the government provide these services. In some other cases, policy interests in areas such as defense, national security, and reconstitutability of communications lead to an involvement of agencies such as the Federal Emergency Management Agency (FEMA) and the National Security Agency (NSA).

International organizations. International considerations are important to the U. S. national planning process for several reasons. First, important allocation decisions are made in international fora that affect both domestic and international telecommunications facilities and services—e.g., the allocation of satellite orbital slots. Second, because of trade considerations, international standards can affect standards for domestic telecommunications equipment and services. Third, as more and more data flow across international borders, questions are raised about the resulting economic, political, and social impacts. Not only are more international organizations addressing these issues, but various governments are already acting on them, especially those countries that are more centrally planned than the United States.

One important international organization that is addressing these issues is the International Telecommunications Union (ITU), which is a United Nations (U. N.) organization concerned with international technical standards for both wire and radio telecommunications. ITU's two main standards-setting organizations are the International Telegraph and Telephone Consultative Committee (CCITT) and the International Radio Consultative Committee (CCIR). CODDING explains the overall history, role, structure, and purpose of ITU; BUTLER explains ITU's role in data communications, while HUMMEL explains the role of the CCITT in data communications. Other international organizations include: United Nations Educational, Scientific, and Cultural Organization (Unesco), which is another U. N. organization that is examining the mass media (radio, TV) aspects of international communications issues; the Organisation for Economic Cooperation and Development (OECD), which is concerned with a broad range of issues involving information, computer, and communications policy, such as transborder data flow; and International Telecommunications Satellite Consortium (INTELSAT), which, with Communications Satellite Corp. (Comsat) as a U. S. representative, is concerned with planning and management of international satellite communications facilities (GOLDBERG); ISO, which is concerned with data communications standards; and the Intergovernmental Bureau for Informatics (IBI), which is also concerned with a broad range of international information, computer, and communications issues, especially as they relate to developing countries. Unesco, OECD, IBI, and ITU are described briefly in a government publication on international information flow (U. S. CONGRESS. HOUSE. COMMITTEE ON GOVERNMENT OPERATIONS, 1980a, p27-30).

PLANNING

Technological Change

In last year's *ARIST*, CAWKELL reviewed information technology and communications. Here we add a few references and give a different slant in the context of this chapter.

Telecommunications. Advances in telecommunications technology have been and are affecting three main areas: 1) transmission media ("twisted pair" copper wire, coaxial cable, terrestrial and satellite microwave, wave guide and fiber optics); 2) transmission methods (analog and digital); and 3) switching (circuit, message, and packet). MARTIN (1977) gives a now dated but still valuable assessment of future developments in telecommunications. For an excellent overall perspective on technological change in telecommunications technology for the 1980s see BAER (1978) and LANGLEY.

Essentially transmission media differ in information-carrying capacity (bandwidth), cost, and flexibility of application. In general the older "twisted pair" copper wire technology has the least information-carrying capacity, while the newer wave guide and fiber optic technologies have the greatest capacity; coaxial cable and microwave fall in between. (See MARTIN 1977).

The relative costs of these technologies are subject to change and are sensitive to their application. For instance, satellite transmission costs are insensitive to distance, and waveguide transmission costs are very sensitive to volume and distance. Twisted pair technology, because it is older, is by far the most extensively used for local telephone distribution. Because of its high bandwidth and because it is a relatively mature technology, coaxial cable is used most extensively for local TV distribution and high capacity telephone links. It is also used for highly localized data communications networks. Satellite and terrestrial microwave transmission technology is used primarily for long-distance telecommunications. LEMASTERS outlines the applications, growth, and future of satellite telecommunications. INTERNATIONAL RESOURCE DEVELOPMENT, INCORPORATED (1980a) assesses the market for digital microwave radio. Fiber optics has the greatest long-term potential for an almost limitless communications pathway into every business, home, and office. LUCKY feels that optical distribution at the local level is the key to low-cost information dissemination. MARSH discusses the commercial application of fiber optic technology.

There have also been advances in transmission methods. The two basic transmission methods are analog and digital; MARTIN (1977, Chapter 4) compares digital and analog transmission, analog currently being predominant. GREGG describes analog and digital communications and foresees a dramatic shift to digital transmission techniques for several reasons. First, digital transmission allows users to take advantage of relatively new time division multiplexing, packet and message switching, and other sharing technologies, all of which reduce transmission cost by allowing more intensive use of a physical circuit. Second, because computers are inherently binary in information representation, digital transmission technology is much better suited to the increasing demands for data communications. Third, the new transmission media are much better suited to digital transmission than the older transmission media. Fourth, digital transmission can efficiently meet the needs of voice, data, facsimile, and TV transmission services, thus giving a way to provide all these services in a dynamic and integrated manner. Fifth, digital transmission methods tend to be more robust than analog and thus usually provide more reliable communications. In addition, encryption is easier for digital transmission (BOMPER).

According to DOLL (1978, p144), a complete common carrier network being constructed today would probably use digital transmission techniques for economic reasons. Nevertheless, the heavy investment in analog transmission facilities makes complete conversion to digital technology in the near term economically impractical. VIGILANTE assesses AT&T's efforts in implementing digital networks.

Advances in switching technology have also been important. Both the speed and method of switching have improved to meet new communications needs. There are now three basic switching methods: 1) circuit switching, 2) message switching, and 3) packet switching. According to SIPPL, circuit switching, also referred to by MARTIN (1977) as line switching, is "a communications switching system that completes a circuit from sender to receiver at the time of transmission." Because circuit switching is most compatible with the needs of analog voice communications, its most common example is regular telephone switching.

Message switching is "a telecommunications application in which a message is received at a central location, stored on a direct-access device until the proper outgoing line is available, and then transmitted to the appropriate destination" (SIPPL). This definition makes message switching seem to be a highly technical new technology, but plain old telegram service as well as torn-tape Telex are good examples of message switching. However, this old form of switching, which has been overshadowed by circuit switching, has a new lease on life especially in such applications as non-real time dependent communication (ROBERTS).

Packet switching is defined by MCGLYNN as "a data transmission process utilizing addressed packets, whereby a channel is occupied only for the duration of transmission of the packet." Packets are actually portions of messages, broken down into short lengths with addressing and error-correcting information (DOLL, 1978; HOUSLEY). Without getting into more detail, packet switching allows for interactive communications applications through the full exploitation of many of the technologies associated with line sharing, such as various forms of multiplexing and alternative routing schemes. DOLL (1978, p404–405) explains the advantages and disadvantages of packet switching. We recommend the special issue on packet communications networks by WADE for those who want a deeper understanding of the subject.

Finally, advances in such technologies as frequency and time division multiplexing and concentrators have provided great potential and savings in telecommunications costs. The technologies of time division multiplexing and concentrators are primarily used for digital communications. A number of good books explain these technologies in detail (DOLL, 1978; GREGG; HOUSELY; MARTIN, 1976). For each new method cited here it is important to note that it is the computer's storage and switching capabilities that are making these new methods feasible for both voice and data communications.

Because advances in computer technology are better known than those in telecommunications technology, we only summarize briefly what has been occurring in the computer field.

Computers. While technical progress in the telecommunications industry has been great, the rate of technical innovation in the computer industry has been spectacular in terms of improved price/performance ratio and new technology. An entire issue of *SCIENTIFIC AMERICAN* gives an overview of the microelectronic technology that is at the heart of this technical innovation. According to RESNIKOFF & WEISS, relative computer processor price has decreased by a factor of 1,000 since the early 1950s while performance has increased by the same factor, yet the cost of computer main memory has decreased by a factor of 10-100. The inexpensive hand-held calculator, video games, word processors, microcomputers, and the like illustrate this phenomenon. The result of this innovation is that now users can put exactly the amount of computing power where it is needed with the result that processing elements are being decentralized with communications links to interconnect them (HOPEWELL). In a brief article M. JOHNSON describes the work of the Charles Babbage Institute in recording the history of the computer.

At the heart of the computer revolution is integrated circuit technology. BHANDARKAR gives a perceptive discussion of how this technology affects the computer. STEIN, using IBM as an example, indicates that significant improvements in integrated circuit technology are yet to come, and that they will improve the price/performance ratio. For those who predict that size and cost reductions are reaching their limits, a new concept in digital computer design is surfacing that may obviate that prediction. This new concept is an optical-digital computer. It uses solid-state lasers, prisms, and lenses in an optical equivalent of electronic integrated circuits to carry and process signals. A working computer may be ready within five years (*SCIENCE NEWS*; TIEN & GIORDMAINE, 1980; TIEN & GIORDMAINE, 1981a; TIEN & GIORDMAINE, 1981b).

Confluence of telecommunications and computer technology. The confluence of telecommunications and computer technology is manifested in two different but complementary ways. First, access to computers is generally dependent on the use of telecommunications—e.g., the concept of teleprocessing (HOUSLEY; MARTIN, 1972) manifests this. Second, telecommunications is becoming dependent on the use of computers—e.g., the concept of packet switching manifests this dependence. The result is a synergistic interdependence that expands the capability of each technology. As with any truly beneficial interdependence the whole is greater than the sum of the individual parts, and the solutions to problems which are posed by the needs of one technology are often obtained through the use of the other. At this point, however, the lag in application of new telecommunications technology is the limiting factor in the ultimate fruition of the advantages to be reaped from the confluence of computer and telecommunications.

LANGLEY and MARTIN (1976) provide insight into the use of computer technology in telecommunications. HOPEWELL ET AL. also provide insight into the interdependence of computer and communications technology. DOLL (1978) gives an excellent treatment of data communications, including such information as common carrier services and tariffs. MELVIN discusses the handling of telephone traffic using large-scale integrated (LSI) computer technology; MELVIN estimates that more than $300 million is being spent on integrated circuits for telecommunications applications and further estimates that this figure will reach $5 billion a year by 1985. GRAM notes that even the telephone handset is going digital. For a general overview of computer and telecommunications technology applications we recommend the articles by MOKHOFF and JURGEN.

Resulting Economic Change

Historic and economic perspective. Before 1968 the telecommunications common carrier industry consisted solely of the established common carriers —AT&T and independent companies for the telephone industry and WU for the telegraph industry. Because of the absolute dominance of the telephone industry we confine our discussion to AT&T. Prior to 1968 AT&T held a de facto monopoly on U. S. domestic and foreign telephone service that extended to all three segments of the industry—terminal equipment, local facilities and service, and long-distance facilities and service. All potential competitors were precluded from entry either by direct regulatory intervention or AT&T's tariffs, which prohibited or severely circumscribed resale and shared use, interconnection with private networks, and interconnection with terminal equipment. Unless users could justify, the expense of building their own facilities, they were forced to use AT&T's facilities and services for data communications. These facilities and services were based on a technology that best served the needs for voice service—i.e., a narrow band analog circuit switched technology, which was inefficient and costly for data communications.

All of this constrained the options open to those who were trying to meet their data communications needs. Matched against the needs of data communications users and others were AT&T's and others' countervailing arguments concerning, for example, economic efficiency, universal service, national security, and system integrity.

These constraints were not as serious in early data communications efforts, and from the early 1950s to the late 1960s many large-scale data communications needs were met through highly specialized data networks. FRISCH & FRANK trace the development of these networks as well as those in the 1970s. They begin with the Semiautomatic Ground Environment (SAGE) system, which they characterize as a milestone in computer communications. They go on to describe pioneering data communications efforts in the banking industry, the airlines industry (American Airlines SABRE I), and education [Dartmouth Time Sharing System (DTSS)]. They describe the emergence of computer-to-computer networks such as the U. S. Department of Defense's Automatic Digital Information Network (AUTODIN) and the Advanced Research Projects Agency Network (ARPANET). Frisch and Frank also provide references to more detailed explanations of data communications networking.

Rising economic pressures. Advances in computer and telecommunications technology, as well as their confluence, have been fueling consumer demand for a host of new telecommunications services including data communications, while at the same time providing the means for meeting these demands in a more efficient and less costly manner. AT&T has not been able to respond fully to those demands in a timely fashion and in some instances has been prohibited from doing so, either through outmoded regulatory policy, such as overlong depreciation schedules, or regulatory prohibition, such as cable TV/telephone company cross ownership restrictions. These factors are in addition to what some would point out as the overriding one—i.e., the inherent inertia of a monopoly. These factors increased the pressure for alternatives to traditional telephone technology. As pressure mounted, concern shifted from technical and economic feasibility to questions of regulatory policy.

Regulatory Issues Raised by Technological Change and Resulting Economic Change

Four main sets of issues have been raised as the result of technological and economic change in telecommunications. The first set of issues concerns appropriate market structure—i.e., the traditional telecommunications monopoly vs. a competitive market. The second and probably most important set of issues concerns regulation vs. deregulation—i.e., substituting competition for the entry and rate regulation usually associated with a monopoly. The third set of issues and the one that affects data communications most directly concerns the distinction between the traditionally regulated telecommunications services and the traditionally unregulated teleprocessing services —i.e., should the regulatory umbrella be extended to include teleprocessing or not. The first three sets of issues involve government policies; the fourth set of issues concerns the goals of those policies—i.e., universal service, reasonable rates, rapid and efficient communications, privacy, data security, national security and defense, and finally the appropriateness of current interpretations of what constitutes the public interest for regulatory decision making. The *FEDERAL COMMUNICATIONS BAR JOURNAL* provides an overview of common carrier issues as they appeared in the mid-1970s.

Monopoly structure vs. competitive structure. The set of issues involved in moving from a monopoly to a competitive market structure involves all three major telecommunications industry segments: telephone equipment, long-distance facilities and services, and local facilities and services. The move from a monopoly to a competitive market structure began with telephone terminal equipment. A series of FCC and court decisions that began in 1956 with Hush-a-Phone (*HUSH-A-PHONE CORPORATION* v. *UNITED STATES*) and continued in 1980 with Computer Inquiry II (U. S. FEDERAL COMMUNICATIONS COMMISSION, 1980d), progressively extended the competitive market structure of the terminal equipment industry by allowing the interconnection of competitive equipment into the existing telephone network. STONE ET AL. give a rationale for and an examination of the issues surrounding this move, which really began with the FCC's landmark 1968 Carterfone decision (U. S. FEDERAL COMMUNICATIONS COMMISSION, 1968) that opened the competition in the market for terminal equipment that is so important to data communications.

Competition next appeared in the long-distance telephone market. This market consists of two main sectors: private line long-distance facilities and service, and switched long-distance facilities and services. The private line sector was first exposed to competition in 1959 in the FCC's "Above 890" decision (U. S. FEDERAL COMMUNICATIONS COMMISSION, 1959) and eventually was made competitive as the result of the FCC's decision on

SCCs (U. S. FEDERAL COMMUNICATIONS COMMISSION, 1971a) and domsats (U. S. FEDERAL COMMUNICATIONS COMMISSION, 1972a). The FCC inadvertently exposed the long-distance switched sector to competition through its SCC decision. This decision did not anticipate MCI's exploitation of the decision to interconnect its private line offerings with local networks in such a way that it could offer long-distance switched service essentially equivalent to regular long-distance service.

The FCC's decision led to a series of important judicial and regulatory decisions, usually lumped together under the long-distance service offering called Execunet, which inspired them (BELL ET AL.). Although Execunet was not the final word, it was certainly important.

The local distribution market is just now being exposed to serious potential competition along several fronts: cable TV, cellular radio, and satellite and terrestrial microwave. Satellite and terrestrial microwave are the most immediate threat to local monopolies, but because of the relatively high cost and spectrum limitations, this threat appears to be limited mostly to the business rather than the residential local market. Because cellular radio is economically and spectrum efficient, it is likely to be more of a threat to the residential market; however, in the long term it is probably less a threat than broadband switched cable systems. HATFIELD (1981b) explains why competition for local distribution is emerging and the regulatory difficulties that this competition poses.

Regulation vs. deregulation. Although the traditional monopoly market structure of the telecommunication industry invited regulation, the increasing shift from a monopoly to a competitive market structure has invited deregulation. The FCC regulates with two powerful weapons: 1) entry and exit regulation—i.e., who gets into and out of the marketplace; and 2) rate regulation—i.e., how much money is made (rate of return) and how much is paid (tariffs). The problems regarding regulation vs. deregulation are probably the most important because regulation tends to stifle innovation and increase prices; therefore, the potential benefits of competition cannot be realized if regulation persists.

The issues can be boiled down to who gets regulated, to what extent, and how. AT&T has a special interest in this issue because the 1956 Consent Decree (*UNITED STATES* v. *WESTERN ELECTRIC CO.*) prevents AT&T, with limited exceptions, from offering unregulated services; therefore, any FCC moves to regulate or deregulate could essentially put AT&T into a business or take it out of a business and conversely affect the fate of some of its present or prospective competitors. Until recently most of the attention at FCC has been focused on market structure issues rather than deregulation. With many of the market structure issues resolved or nearing resolution, attention is shifting toward deregulatory efforts.

The trend toward competition and deregulation has brought other issues to the surface, such as technical and economic harm to established common carriers, the presence or absence of economies of scale, cost/variety tradeoffs, the appropriateness of regulating rate of return, value of service vs. flat rate pricing, cross subsidies, depreciation schedules, tariff filings, federal and state jurisdictional separation, interconnection standards and charges, predatory pricing, and oligopoly pricing. Some of these issues are discussed here, and STONE ET AL. and MEYER ET AL. give overviews.

Confluence of computers and telecommunications—the FCC's dilemma. At the risk of hyperbole this is probably the single most important issue that has ever faced the FCC. On the one hand, the extremely competitive and unregulated computer and information industries are known for explosive growth, change, and the rapid adoption of innovative ideas. On the other hand, the heretofore uncompetitive and heavily regulated telecommunications industry is known for moderate growth and constancy. Although Bell Labs is known for innovative ideas, the established telecommunications common carrier industry is not known for its rapid application of innovative ideas.

Nowhere are the issues of competition and deregulation drawn into sharper focus than in the dilemma that the confluence of computer and telecommunications technology poses for the FCC. While it has never had the power to regulate the computer or information industries directly, the Commission could use its regulatory power over telecommunications to justify regulation over at least some aspects of the computer and information industries. Should the FCC regulate even portions of those successful and competitive industries at the risk of stifling innovation and service offerings, or should it hold back and risk financial and technical damage to the established telecommunications industry and thus compromise its legislative mandate to ensure reasonably priced and widely available telephone service? Over the past few years the FCC has gone a long way toward answering this question in two computer inquiry proceedings: Computer Inquiry I (U. S. FEDERAL COMMUNICATIONS COMMISSION, 1966) and Computer Inquiry II (U. S. FEDERAL COMMUNICATIONS COMMISSION, 1976a; 1980d).

The two main issues facing regulators in this area are: 1) to what extent will the FCC extend its regulatory umbrella over traditionally unregulated teleprocessing equipment and services provided by the computer and information industry, and 2) how and to what extent will the FCC allow common carriers to provide teleprocessing services and equipment in competition with the computer and information industries (see LIPINSKI (1969a; 1969b) and KRAUSE). DUNN provides an overview of these issues. While they would be loathe to admit it for obvious reasons, some leading authorities feel that the distinction between data processing and data communications is more rhetorical than real and will eventually disappear in service offerings of the next millenium if we resolve market structure and regulatory issues by then.

Social and other issues. These issues unlike the preceding ones tend to represent goals, not policies. These goals are usually set through legislation and are not subject to change through judicial or regulatory proceeding. The broad goals contained in the COMMUNICATIONS ACT OF 1934 are to provide the American people with national and international communications services that are rapid and efficient, universally available, adequate, and reasonably priced. These goals and the public interest standard are the basis of regulatory and judicial policy and actions. The goals are broad and allow much latitude. The public interest standard, however, may not be an effica-

cious way of achieving these goals. The U. S. NATIONAL TELECOMMUNI-
CATIONS AND INFORMATION ADMINISTRATION gives a good rationale
for replacing this standard with the presumption that a competitive market
structure would best meet the above goals. CORNELL ET AL. present convincing arguments to support this. This thinking has been reflected in several
attempts to rewrite the Communications Act of 1934, in which competition
has been substituted for the public interest standard.

Legislation

Legislation is basic to the national planning process. From it come the
authority, constraints, and philosophy for the process. Considering the age of
present legislation—about 50 years—and the magnitude of changes since it was
enacted, it is not surprising that the presence or absence of a new legislative
mandate has become an issue itself. LOEB provides some perspectives on the
regulatory and legal problems surrounding the current legislative mandate.
Over the past few years Congress has been trying to rewrite all or part of the
Communications Act of 1934. Members of Congress who oversee communications realize that the 1934 act, which, in a testament to its anachronism,
borrows language from the 1887 Interstate Commerce Act, at least needs
amendment to reflect the changed circumstances surrounding modern telecommunications capability and its resulting economic and social impact.

Limited rewrite activities began with the Consumer Communications Reform Act of 1976 (CCRA). The CCRA, H.R. 12323 (U. S. CONGRESS.
94TH CONGRESS) was widely regarded as an attempt by AT&T to restrict
the pro-competition moves of the FCC that started with the 1968 Carterfone
decision. This effort quickly earned the name, the "Bell Bill." The CCRA
would have rolled back most of the FCC's pro-competition decisions. One
thing that CCRA did do was to heighten congressional awareness of the need
for revising the Communications Act. The U. S. FEDERAL COMMUNICA-
TIONS COMMISSION (1976f) provides a point-by-point critique of CCRA.

Since the CCRA both houses of Congress have been engaged in rewrite
efforts. The House Subcommittee on Communications took the lead by introducing the first full bill, the Communications Act of 1978, H.R. 13015
(U. S. CONGRESS. 95TH CONGRESS). After extensive hearings the bill was
revised heavily and reintroduced in early 1979 as the Telecommunications
Facilities and Services Act of 1979, H.R. 3333. Again after hearings, a new
bill was introduced in late 1979, the Telecommunications Act of 1980, H.R.
6121 (U. S. CONGRESS. 96TH CONGRESS, 1ST SESSION, 1979c), based
largely on an informal "primer" developed by NTIA (U. S. NATIONAL
TELECOMMUNICATIONS AND INFORMATION ADMINISTRATION). In
H.R. 6121 the House Subcommittee dropped controversial passages concerning broadcasting services and concentrated on telecommunications common
carrier services. In so doing, the subcommittee hoped for increased probability of passage. A comprehensive report on H.R. 6121 has been published
(U. S. CONGRESS. HOUSE. COMMITTEE ON INTERSTATE AND
FOREIGN COMMERCE. 96TH CONGRESS, 2ND SESSION).

Beginning in early 1979, the Senate Subcommittee on Communications also introduced two bills: S. 611 (U. S. CONGRESS. 96TH CONGRESS, 1ST SESSION, 1979a) and S. 622 (U. S. CONGRESS. 96TH CONGRESS, 1ST SESSION, 1979b). (For the extensive hearing record on these proposed pieces of legislation, see U. S. CONGRESS. SENATE.) Both bills addressed broadcast and common carrier services. COLEMAN provides a perspective of Capitol Hill thinking on communications legislation in mid-1979. By the middle of 1980, S. 611 and S. 622 were superseded by S. 2827 (U. S. CONGRESS. 96TH CONGRESS, 2ND SESSION). Thus, the two pending rewrite efforts in Congress for 1980 were H.R. 6121 and S. 2827. Although H.R. 6121 is limited to common carrier legislation, both bills are much more similar than dissimilar and indicate that a consensus may be near on the new legislation that will be up for consideration by the first session of the 97th Congress in 1981. BARRY compares both bills and gives the viewpoint of independent rural telephone companies. In overall terms both H.R. 6121 and S. 2827 reflect the principles articulated by HATFIELD (1979)—i.e., competition should be relied on unless proved unworkable, regulation should be applied only to the extent necessary, and congressional intent should be explicit.

Although many hurdles were cleared, disagreements over the details of the legislation prevented its passage. For instance, even though H.R. 6121 provided that it would not affect the current Justice Department antitrust suit against AT&T, the House Judiciary Committee effectively killed this bill because of its possible effects on the antitrust suit (U. S. CONGRESS. HOUSE. COMMITTEE ON THE JUDICIARY).

PROSPECTS

The current directions of competition and deregulation are likely to continue. Nevertheless, without legislation many of the specifics worked out under the interpretations of the Communications Act of 1934 may work against these overall directions. However, legislation will probably be passed in the near future. It will reaffirm the current trends and provide the mandate necessary to reduce regulatory uncertainty, litigation, and their possible deleterious effect on new and innovative data communications services and facilities. The biggest bottleneck will be local distribution, but this problem will be in large part successfully addressed for at least business applications.

What do these favorable regulatory prospects portend for data communications? For some perspective, SANDERS & MCLAUGHLIN look back to the promise of the early 1970s when the loosening of regulatory constraints began. They point out that the prospects for highly advanced data communications networks were bright. New companies and concepts such as Data Transmission Co. (DATRAN), MCI, ARPANET, AT&T's Advanced Communications System (ACS), and IBM's System Network Architecture (SNA) held out this promise. However, Datran died, MCI became a voice network, ARPANET remained a research network, ACS was withdrawn—it may yet appear—and SNA was changed conceptually. Thus, by the end of the 1970s, what we had were a few specialized private networks and even fewer public networks, including Tymnet, Telenet, and Graphnet. ADAM notes that private networks are less efficient than public networks and present inter-networking problems. In any event these networks currently capture only a fraction of total telecommunications revenue. For the 1980s, however, Sanders and McLaughlin take a more upbeat attitude, which is shared by ZIMMERMAN (1981a).

Now large companies such as IBM, Comsat, Exxon, and Xerox are throwing their hats into the ring. The 1980s will see true data communications net-working capability being provided along with a plethora of data communications services. DIBONA predicts explosive growth in revenues. SCC revenues are supposed to rise from $120 million in 1978 to about $1 billion in 1988; revenues for domsats will go from $70 million to $1.2 billion, and revenues from VANs will go from $30 million to $330 million. COMMUNICATIONS NEWS (1980a) predicts some of the industry leaders for the 1980s. BOTH-WELL predicts explosive growth—35% per annum through 1982—in the U. S. domestic satellite earth terminal market; revenues will increase from $60 million in 1978 to $200 million in 1982.

While DORDICK (1980) also sees strong growth—40% to 100% per year for information services—he believes that because there is no strong trend toward a universal network available to all economic levels, the gap between the information "haves" and "have-nots" will widen.

COMMUNICATIONS NEWS (1981) describes IBM's and Comsat's joint venture—SBS (p42)—describes Xerox's newest (XTEN) service offerings (p44), and goes on to describe the networking offerings of the current companies involved in telecommunications (p46). PRINCE also describes the major new service offerings—ACS, SBS, and XTEN.

HATFIELD (1981a) and NEWTON describe the changes in telephone service rates that will result from recent pro-competition deregulatory deci-sions and explains the effects on users. WAGNER discusses the future of local rates and discusses what independent telephone companies will have to do to meet changing cost allocation procedures.

We believe that three major thrusts will occur in planning for data com-munications (COMMUNICATIONS NEWS, 1981, p40-41). First, the emphasis will shift from long-distance networking to local networking, which is by far the most heavily used portion of a communications network. Second, instead of trying to achieve direct compatibility of hardware, software, and commu-nications protocols, networks will try to make these disparate components compatible (see DOLL, 1979). Third, integration of voice, data, video, and facsimile communications will begin to take place, resulting in more efficient use of underlying facilities. GRAY discusses the advantages of this approach. In addition, as ZIMMERMAN (1981a; 1981b) states, the issue of intercon-nection of similar services, such as EM, that are offered by different vendors will emerge and be resolved by the marketplace it is hoped, but if not, by regulatory fiat or legislative fiat.

CONCLUSION

The dominant thrust of U. S. national policy in the telecommunications common carrier industry is toward a competitive and deregulated market structure. The consensus among national policy makers is that this type of market structure is the most effective in meeting the diverse and changing communications needs of the American people. However, this industry remains highly concentrated, and the path to a truly competitive and deregulated industry is not clear. Nevertheless, certain things are clear.

First, telecommunications users in general and data communications users in particular are free to choose from competitive offerings or to strike out on their own to meet their communications needs.

In a diverse market, internetworking especially computer internetworking, will be a problem unless or until adequate yet flexible standards are developed. The United States must pay particular attention to international standards-setting efforts because they may effectively preclude or at least impede U. S. participation in international trade and information exchange. The usefulness and penetration of a data communications network will depend on its ability to support a wide variety of computer equipment; standards will help to ensure the utility of data communications networks.

The market power of giants such as AT&T and IBM must be acknowledged, and sufficient safeguards must be erected to prevent abuses. In addition, the United States telecommunications industry is in a period of transition where the waters are not clearly charted. Enhanced government oversight short of interference is needed to ensure a smooth and equitable transition.

The question of competition in local distribution will become more and more important. The conflict over federal, state, and local authority will be great, and the ultimate resolution of local competition may be decided by which level of government is given ultimate authority.

Some of the advantages of a telecommunications monopoly could be lost. For instance, internetworking is much less of a problem for a monopoly service provider who can often enjoy certain economies of scale, especially in reaching a large enough market to make a service viable. Because of the large markets afforded by their monopoly position, many countries with a centrally planned telecommunications industry will almost inevitably enjoy certain types of nationwide telecommunications service offerings before the United States.

Traditional telecommunications service providers will move more and more into computers and information services, while the computer industry will move more and more into telecommunications and information services. The information industry will increasingly use both computers and telecommunications and will challenge these industries in areas of perceived encroachment on its domain of providing information goods and services. This will create problems among all three industries as they compete with each other. No doubt the players in these industries will call on the government to referee or even to prevent serious interindustry competition.

Federal agencies such as the Postal Service and the Federal Reserve will continue to try to exploit the new computer and telecommunications technologies to provide services that compete with private sector offerings. The government will need to be cautious about the nature and extent of its competition here.

Even though the government will rely on the invisible hand of competition and will move to deregulate, it will still play an important role in ensuring that competitive conditions exist, in redefining boundaries and helping to solve disputes between formerly distinct industries, in representing U. S. interests before international standards bodies, and in preventing or at least reducing the effects of competition between government and private sector communications and information services.

For the data communications users there will be services that will allow users to satisfy their needs better at reduced cost, yet there will be such a bewildering and rapidly changing array of offerings that it will take intelligence and knowledge to make the best choice.

* * * * *

EPILOGUE

This chapter does not end here. A continuation chapter on this topic will appear next year in *ARIST*, Volume 17. By that time, another Congress will have tackled the legislative issues surrounding telecommunications policy, some of the key pending court cases may have been resolved, the shape of the Reagan administration's telecommunication and information policy will be more clear, and exciting new technological developments will have been announced.

BIBLIOGRAPHY

ADAM, T. W. 1975. Data Services. In: Flood, J. E., ed. Telecommunication Networks. Stevenage, Great Britain: Peter Peregrinus, Ltd.; 1975. 233–252. ISBN: 0-901223-65-4.

ALESCH, D. J.; SUMNER, G. C. 1972. Method of Evaluation for the Metropolitan Regional Council Telecommunication System. Santa Monica, CA: Rand Corp.; 1972. 46p.

AMERICAN FEDERATION OF INFORMATION PROCESSING SOCIETIES (AFIPS). 1979. Selected Documents on Data Protection. Arlington, VA: AFIPS; 1979 July. 205p.

AMERICAN FEDERATION OF INFORMATION PROCESSING SOCIETIES (AFIPS). 1980. FCC Makes Significant Changes in Computer Inquiry II Decision. AFIPS Washington Report. 1980 December; 6(12): 3–4. Available from: AFIPS, 1815 North Lynn Street, Suite 805, Arlington, VA 22209.

ARMED FORCES COMMUNICATIONS AND ELECTRONICS ASSOCIATION (AFCEA). 1979. Telecommunications in 1979: Proceedings of the Armed Forces Communications and Electronics Association Symposium; 1979 January 11; Washington, DC. Falls Church, VA: AFCEA; 1979. Unpaged. Available from: AFCEA, 5205 Leesburg Pike, Falls Church, VA 22041.

BACH, GABRIEL G. F. 1980. Data Privacy: Critical Issue of the 80's. Telecommunications. 1980 May; 14(5): 43–45, 48. ISSN: 0040-2494.

BAER, WALTER S. 1971. Interactive Television: Prospects for Two-Way Services on Cable. Santa Monica, CA: Rand Corp.; 1971 November. 88p. (R-888-MF). LC: CA-240-B145-in.

BAER, WALTER S. 1973. Cable Television: A Handbook for Decision-making. Santa Monica, CA: Rand Corp.; 1973 February. 229p. (Rand Corp. Cable Television Report no. R-1133-NSF).

BAER, WALTER S. 1978. Telecommunications Technology in the 1980s. In: Robinson, Glen O., ed. Communications for Tomorrow: Policy Perspectives for the 1980s. New York, NY: Praeger Publishers; 1978. 61–123. ISBN: 0-03-046546-X and 0-03-046541-9 pbk.

BARRY, T. MICHAEL. 1980. Part II: Evolution of a Telecommunications Act—Survival of the Fittest? Phone Call. 1980 September; 19(9): 18–21.

BEERE, MAX P. 1979. The User-Billpayer View. In: Electronic Industries Association. Telecommunications: Trends and Directions: An Electronic Industry Association Communications Division Seminar Program; 1979 May 22–24; Hyannis, MA. Washington, DC: Electronic Industries Association; 1979. 31–48.

BELL, JAMES; KIRBY, SHARON; WEISS, ROLAND G.; WATSON, STEVE. 1979. The FCC Public Message Services Policy Change: An ETIP Evaluability Assessment Report. 2 volumes. Washington, DC: U. S. Government Printing Office; 1979 September. 342p. CODEN: NBTNAE; GPO: 003-003-02117-2.

BERGLUND, RALPH G. 1980. It's Still an Analog World. Datamation. 1980 January; 26(1): 52–56. ISSN: 0011-6963.

BHANDARKAR, DILEEP P. 1979. The Impact of Semiconductor Technology on Computer Systems. Computer. 1979 September; 12(9): 92–98. ISSN: 0018-9162.

BLOCK, VICTOR. 1980. FCC Proposes a New Plan for Local Access Charges. Telephony. 1980 April 21; 18(16): 11. ISSN: 0040-2656.

BLOOM, L. R.; HANSON, A. G.; LINFIELD, R. F.; WORTEN DYKE, D. R. 1980. VIDEOTEX Systems and Services. Washington, DC: U.S. Department of Commerce; 1980 October. 158p. (NTIA Report 80-50).

BOBROFF, SARA A. 1974. United States Treaties and Other International Agreements Pertaining to Telecommunications. Washington, DC: U. S. Department of Commerce; 1974 January. 175p. (OT 74-26).

BOLTER, WALTER G.; IRWIN, DAVID A. 1980. Depreciation Reform: A Crucial Step in Transforming Telecommunications to a Free Market. Washington, DC: 1980 September. 429p.

BOMPER, W. J. 1980. Techniques and Equipment for Telecommunications Protection. Telecommunications Journal. 1980 June; 47: 410–412.

BORCHARDT, KURT. 1978. Actors and Stakes: A Map of the Compunications Arena (Computers-and-Communications). Cambridge, MA: Harvard University; 1978 June. 18p. (Program on Information Resources Policy Working Paper no. W-78-8).

BOTHWELL, JOSEPH C., JR. 1980. Telecommunications Growth in the

80s. Satellite Communications. 1980 June; 4(6): 32-35. ISSN: 0147-7430.

BRAUNSTEIN, YALE M.; KALBA, KONRAD K.; LEVINE, LARRY S. 1978. The Economic Impact of State Cable TV Regulation. Cambridge, MA: Harvard University; 1978 October. 75p. (Program on Information Resources Policy Working Paper no. W-78-7).

BUTLER, R. E. 1979. The International Telecommunications Union (ITU). In: Organisation for Economic Cooperation and Development (OECD). Information Computer Communications Policy: Transborder Data Flows and the Protection of Privacy: Proceedings of an OECD Symposium; 1977 September 20-23; Vienna, Austria. Paris, France: OECD; 1979. 197-201. Available from: OECD, Suite 1207, 1750 Pennsylvania Ave., Washington, DC 20006. ISBN: 92-64-01926-X.

CAPRON, WILLIAM M. 1976. Comments on Telecommunications Policy Developments. Cambridge, MA: Harvard University; 1976 March. 12p. (Program for Information Resources Policy Working Paper no. W-76-6).

CARRUTHERS, BRUCE R.; MANDANIS, GEORGE P. 1978. New Alignments in Intercity Telecommunications Services. San Rafael, CA: Systems Applications, Inc.; 1978 March 26. 85p. (Systems Applications, Inc. no. TF 78-19R1). NTIS: PB 2912-39.

CAWKELL, ANTHONY E. 1980. Information Technology and Communications. Annual Review of Information Science and Technology: Volume 15. 37-65. ISSN: 0066-4200; ISBN: 0-914236-65-2; CODEN: ARISBc.

CENTER FOR COMMUNICATIONS MANAGEMENT, INCORPORATED. 1973a. An Analysis of the Specialized Communication Common Carrier. Ramsey, NJ: Center for Communications Management, Inc.; 1973 December. 143p.

CENTER FOR COMMUNICATIONS MANAGEMENT, INCORPORATED. 1973b. Telecommunications Research Report: A New Private Line Rate Structure. Ramsey, NJ: Center for Communications Management, Inc.; 1973 April. 46p.

CENTER FOR COMMUNICATIONS MANAGEMENT, INCORPORATED. 1974. Planning Guide: Dedicated Digital Networks. Ramsey, NJ: Center for Communications Management, Inc.; 1974. 117p.

CERF, VINTON. 1977. Research Topics in Computer Communications. In: Hopewell, Lynn; Cerf, Vinton G.; Curran, Alex; Dunn, Donald A. Computers and Communications: Proceedings of the U. S. Federal Communications Commission; 1977 November 8-9; Washington, DC. Montvale, NJ: AFIPS Press; 1977. 39-90. Available from: American Federation of Information Processing Societies (AFIPS), 210 Summit Ave., Montvale, NJ 07645.

CHISMAN, FORREST P., ed. 1976. Refocusing Government Communications Policy. Aspen Institute for Humanistic Studies; 1976. 73p. (Aspen Institute for Humanistic Studies Series on Communications Occasional Paper). ISBN: 0-915436-35-3; LC: 76-53767.

CHISMAN, FORREST P. 1978. The Executive Branch. In: Robinson, Glen O., ed. Communications for Tomorrow: Policy Perspectives for 1980s. New York, NY: Praeger Publishers; 1978. 401-414. ISBN: 0-03-046546-X and 0-03-046541-9 pbk.

CLARK, E. F.; HARVEY, S. B.; ROBBINS, C. B.; TALL, R. S.; TYLER, S. S.; WEINBERT, G. R. 1975. Computer/Communications Networks on a

Communitywide Basis. New York, NY: The Singer Co.; 1975 June. 210p. NTIS: Com 75-10991.

CODDING, GEORGE, JR. 1979. International Constraints on the Use of Telecommunications: The Role of the International Telecommunications Union. In: Lewin, Leonard, ed. Telecommunications: An Interdisciplinary Survey. Dedham, MA: Artech House, Inc.; 1979. 1-38. ISBN: 0-89006-072-X; LC: 78-26665.

COLE, JACK E.; O'RORKE, RICHARD J., JR., comps. 1981. Profiles of International Private Lease, DATEL and Packet Switched. Washington, DC: National Telecommunications and Information Administration (NTIA); 1981 January 28. 19p. Available from: NTIA Office of International Affairs, 1800 G St., NW, Washington, DC 20504.

COLE, JACK E.; O'RORKE, RICHARD J., JR.; KOPINSKI, JOHN W.; PERRYMORE, GLYNETTA C. 1977. A Review of International Telecommunications Industry Issues, Structure, and Regulatory Problems. Washington, DC: U.S. Office of Telecommunications; 1977. 141p. (OT Special Publication 77-16). ERIC: ED 168573.

COLEMAN, RONALD D. 1979. The View from the Hill. In: Electronics Industries Association. Telecommunications: Trends and Directions: An Electronic Industries Association Communications Division Seminar Program; 1979 May 22-24; Hyannis, MA. Washington, DC: Electronic Industries Association; 1979. 15-22.

COLPITTS, ANDRE B.; WARREN, COLIN JOHN. 1974. International Patterns of Communications Usage: Postal, Telegraph, and Telephone Industries. Cambridge, MA: Massachusetts Institute of Technology; 1974. 42p. (MIT Report no. 14).

COMANOR, WILLIAM S.; MITCHELL, BRIDGER M. 1971. The Costs of Planning: The FCC and Cable TV. Stanford, CA: Stanford University; 1971 October. 47p. (Graduate School of Business Research Paper no. 49).

COMMUNICATIONS ACT OF 1934. Title 47, United States Code § 151 (1976).

COMMUNICATIONS NEWS. 1979. Forecast for 1979 Society's Needs Are Driving Telecom Revolution. Communications News. 1979 January; 17(1): 24-25. ISSN: 0010-3632.

COMMUNICATIONS NEWS. 1980a. Crystal Balling the 1980s. . .Industry Leaders Look Ahead to 1980s. Communications News. 1980 January; 17(1): 32-39. ISSN: 0010-3632.

COMMUNICATIONS NEWS. 1980b. Senator Schmitt Keynotes NTC 79 Calling for Comprehensive Legislation. Communications News. 1980 January; 17(1): 60-62. ISSN: 0010-3632.

COMMUNICATIONS NEWS. 1981. Communications News. 1981 February; 18(2): 103p. ISSN: 0010-3632.

COMPUTER AND BUSINESS EQUIPMENT MANUFACTURERS ASSOCIATION. 1979. Fourth State Legislation Status Report 1979. Washington, DC: Computer and Business Equipment Manufacturers Association; 1979. 20p.

CONSAD RESEARCH CORPORATION. 1978. Policy-Oriented Economic Research Issues in Telecommunications. Pittsburgh, PA: Consad Research Corporation; 1978 January. (Contract no. TP6AC026).

CORNELL, NINA W.; KELLEY, DANIEL; GREENHALGH, PETER R. 1980. Social Objectives and Competition in Common Carrier Communications: Incompatible or Inseparable. Washington, DC: U.S. Federal

Communications Commission; 1980 April. 67p. (Office of Plans and Policy no. 80-01).

CRINER, JAMES CRANFORD. 1972. Toward a Federal Computer Utility: Technological, Economic and Administrative Considerations. 1972. 118p. (Master's thesis). Available from: George Washington University Library, Special Collections Division, 2130 H Street, N.W., Washington, DC 20052.

CRINER, JAMES CRANFORD. 1975. History of Resale in Common Carrier Telecommunications. Washington, DC: U.S. Office of Telecommunications; 1975 December. 39p. NTIS: PB 2486-39.

CRINER, JAMES CRANFORD. 1977. An Analysis of Policy Options in the Regulation of Value Added Network Services. 1977. 330p. (Ph.D. dissertation). Available from: George Washington University Library, Special Collections Division, 2130 H Street, N.W., Washington, DC 20052.

CROTTS, G. GAIL; MEAD, LAWRENCE M. 1979. The FCC as an Institution. In: Lewin, Leonard, ed. Telecommunications: An Interdisciplinary Survey. Dedham, MA: Artech House, Inc.; 1979. 39-120. ISBN: 0-89006-072-X; LC: 78-26665.

CROMBIE, DOUGLASS D., ed. 1976. Lowering Barriers to Telecommunications Growth. Washington, DC: U.S. Government Printing Office; 1976 November. 260p. (U.S. Office of Telecommunications Special Publication 76-9). GPO: 003-000-00504-6.

DARBY, LARRY F. 1979. The FCC Policy-Maker's View. In: Electronic Industries Association. Telecommunications: Trends and Directions: An Electronic Industries Association Communications Division Seminar Program; 1979 May 22-24; Hyannis, MA. Washington, DC: Electronic Industries Association; 1979. 3-7.

DATAMATION. 1978. Communications: XTEN from Xerox. Datamation. 1978 December; 24(13): 52-53, 55. ISSN: 0011-6963.

DATAMATION. 1980a. Data Communications Carriers. Datamation. 1980 August; 26(8): 107-112. ISSN: 0011-6963.

DATAMATION. 1980b. The Datamation 100: The Top 100 U.S. Companies in the DP Industry. Datamation. 1980 July; 26(7): 87-182. ISSN: 011-6963.

DAVIES, DONALD W.; BARBER, DEREK L. A. 1973. Communications Networks for Computers. London, England: John Wiley & Sons; 1973. 566p. ISBN: 0-471-19874-9; LC: 73-2775.

DE SOLA POOL, ITHIEL. 1976. International Policy Dimensions: Background Report. In: Organisation for Economic Cooperation and Development (OECD). Proceedings of the OECD Conference on Computer/ Telecommunications Policy; 1975 February 4-6; Paris, France. Paris, France: OECD; 1976. 281-308. (OECD Informatics Studies 11). Also available as: DeSola Pool, Ithiel. 1975. The International Aspects of Computer Telecommunication. Cambridge, MA: Massachusetts Institute of Technology; 1975 February 4. 34p. (Research Program on Communications Policy Report no. 15).

DIBONA, RICHARD T. 1980. Data Communications Networks. In: Electronic Industries Association Telecommunications: Trends and Directions: An Electronic Industries Association Communications Division Seminar Program; 1980 May 27-29; Hyannis, MA. Washington, DC: Electronic Industries Association; 1980. 5-17.

DOLL, DIXON. 1978. Data Communications Facilities, Networks, and Systems Design. New York, NY: John Wiley & Sons, 1978. 493p. ISBN: 0-471-21768-9.

DOLL, DIXON. 1979. What's on the Horizon for Datacomm Systems. Communications News. 1979 June; 16(6): 60-61. ISSN: 0010-3632.

DORDICK, HERBERT S. 1975. The Roles Available to States in the Development of Cable Communications. Los Angeles, CA: Center for Communications Policy Research; 1975 February 12. 27p.

DORDICK, HERBERT S. 1980. Information Inequality. Computerworld. 1980 April 21; 14(6): In-depth, 1-14. ISSN: 0010-4841.

DORDICK, HERBERT S.; BRADLEY, HELEN G.; NANUS, BURT; MARTIN, THOMAS H. 1979. Network Information Services: The Emergence of an Industry. Telecommunications Policy (Great Britain). 1979 September: 3(3): 217-234. ISSN: 0308-5961.

DUNN, DONALD A. 1969. Policy Issues Presented by the Interdependence of Computer and Communications Services. Menlo Park, CA: Stanford Research Institute (SRI), 1969 February. 72p. (SRI Report no. 7379B-1).

EASTON, TERRENCE. 1979. International Aspects of Telecommunications Operations. In: Lewin, Leonard, ed. Telecommunications: An Interdisciplinary Survey. Dedham, MA: Artech House, Inc.; 1979. 351-390. ISBN: 0-89006-072-X; LC: 78-26665.

EDWARDS, MORRIS. 1979. International Carriers See Broader Choice of Data Services in 1980's. Communications News. 1979 September; (16)9: 52-55. ISSN: 0010-3632.

EDWARDS, MORRIS. 1980. Value-Added Carriers Lead Drive for Improved Datacomm Services. Communications News. 1980 May; 17(5): 64-69. ISSN: 0010-3632.

EGER, JOHN. 1979. Communications Revolution Faces a Crucial Juncture in World History. Communications News. 1979 January; 16(2): 36-37. ISSN: 0010-3632.

EINHORN, THERESA A. 1979. The Federal Government's Operational Role in EFT. University of San Francisco Law Review. 1979 Winter; 13: 431-447. ISSN: 0042-0018.

ELECTRONIC INDUSTRIES ASSOCIATION. 1979. Telecommunications: Trends and Directions: An Electronic Industries Association Communications Division Seminar Program; 1979 May 22-24; Hyannis, MA. Washington, DC: Electronic Industries Association; 1979. 157p.

ELECTRONIC INDUSTRIES ASSOCIATION. 1980. Telecommunications: Trends and Directions: An Electronics Industries Association Communications Division Seminar Program; 1980 May 27-29; Hyannis, MA. Washington, DC: Electronic Industries Association; 1980. 111p.

EWING, DONALD R.; SALAMAN, ROGER K. 1977. The Postal Crisis: The Postal Function as a Communications Service. Washington, DC: U.S. Office of Telecommunications (OT); 1977 January. 70p. (OT Special Publication no. 77-13.)

FEDERAL COMMUNICATIONS BAR JOURNAL. 1975. A Federal Communications Bar Association Seminar. Federal Communications Bar Journal. n.d. (Special combined issue; Reprint from 1975; 28(2-3): 113p.). ISSN: 0163-7606.

FEINMAN, STEPHEN. 1976. The Information Age: Past, Present and

Future. Jenkintown, PA: Gellman Research Associates, Inc.; 1976 November. 96p. (Contract TP6AC027).

FINLEY, MARION R., JR. 1980. The Wired City. International Fiber Optics and Communications. 1980 March; 1(2): 19-20, 30-32. ISSN: 0199-5820.

FISHMAN, WILLIAM L. 1980. Introduction to Transborder Data Flows. Stanford Journal of International Law. 1980 Summer; 16: 1-26. ISSN: 0081-4326.

FLOOD, J. E., ed. 1975. Telecommunication Networks. Stevenage, Great Britain: Peter Peregrinus, Ltd.; 1975. 431p. ISBN: 0-90122365-4.

FORTGANG, MORTON. 1980. Military Communications Networks: Key to Effective Operations. Telecommunications. 1980 June; 14(6): 63-64, 85. ISSN: 0040-2494.

FOSTER, RICHARD B.; SILVERSTEIN, HAROLD; HOEBER, FRANCIS P.; AILES, CATHERINE P.; STYLES, JAMES G. 1980. Basic Telecommunications Issues Affecting U.S. National Security and Survival. Arlington, VA: SRI International; 1980 September. (SRI Project 1232).

FRANK, HOWARD; GANTZ, JOHN. 1979. Network Strategy. In: International Information Technology Institute. Communication Networks 79: Conference Proceedings; 1979 January 30-February 1; Washington, DC. Newton, MA: International Information Technology Institute; 1979. 121-149.

FRANK, RONALD A. 1980. Alive and Well. Datamation. 1980 June; 26(6): 112-121, 125-142. ISSN: 011-6963.

FRIEDMAN, ELLIOT H. 1975. International Telecommunications from the American Perspective: International Record Carriers and International Telephone Tariffs. Cambridge, MA: Massachusetts Institute of Technology; 1975. 103p. (Report no. 11).

FRISCH, IVAN T.; FRANK, HOWARD. 1978. Computer Communications— How We Got Where We Are. In: Meier, Donald A., Chairman. Proceedings of the American Federation of Information Processing Societies (AFIPS) 1975 National Computer Conference (NCC): Volume 44; 1975 May 19-22; Anaheim, CA. Montvale, NJ: AFIPS Press; 1975. 109-117. LC: 75-44701.

GARAY, RON. 1979. The FCC and the U.S. Court of Appeals: Telecommunications by Judicial Decree? Journal of Broadcasting. 1979 Summer; 23(3): 301-318. ISSN: 0021-938X.

GELLER, HENRY. 1974. Communications Law. The Georgetown Law Journal. 1974 October; 63(1): 39-47.

GELLER, HENRY; BROTMAN, STUART. 1978. Electronic Alternatives to Postal Service. In: Robinson, Glen O. ed. Communications for Tomorrow: Policy Perspectives for the 1980's. New York, NY: Praeger Publishers; 1978. 307-349. ISBN: 0-03-046546-X and 0-03-046541-9 pbk.

GELLHORN, ERNEST. 1978. The Role of Congress. In: Robinson, Glen O., ed. Communications for Tomorrow: Policy Perspectives for the 80s. New York, NY: Praeger Publishers; 1978. 445-462. ISBN: 0-03-046546-X and 0-03-046541-9 pbk.

GILBERT, DAVID; PERRY, JAMES. 1979. The Significance of X.25. Mini-Micro Systems. 1979 September; 12(9): 61-70. ISSN: 0364-9342.

GOLDBERG, HENRY. 1978. International Telecommunications Regulations. In: Robinson, Glen O., ed. Communications for Tomorrow, Policy Perspectives for the 1980s. New York, NY: Praeger Publishers; 1978. 157-187. ISBN: 0-03-046546-X and 0-03-046541-9 pbk.

GRAM, M. W. 1979. Digital Telephones: A Reality at Jutland Tel. Telephony. 1979 June 25; 196(26): 62-69. ISSN: 0040-2656.

GRAY, JAMES S. 1980. A Theory of Digital Communications. Satellite Communications. 1980 December; 4(12): 23-25. ISSN: 0147-7439.

GREEN, PAUL E., JR.; LUCKY, ROBERT W., eds. 1974. Computer Communications. New York, NY: The Institute of Electrical and Electronics Engineers, Inc.; 1974. 615p. ISBN: 0-87942-041-3; LC: 74-82501.

GREEN, PAUL E., JR.; MCKENZIE, A. A.; SUNSHINE, C. A.; WECKER, S., eds. 1980. Computer Network Architectures and Protocols. IEEE Transactions on Communications. 1980 April; 28(4): 258p. (Special issue on title topic). ISSN: 0090-6778.

GREENAWALT, KENT. 1976. Legal Protections of Privacy. Washington, DC: Government Printing Office; 1976. 76p. (Final Report to the U.S. Office of Telecommunications Policy, Executive Office of the President). GPO: 041-001-00105-1.

GREENBERGER, MARTIN, ed. 1971. Computers, Communications and the Public Interest. Baltimore, MD: The Johns Hopkins Press; 1971. 315p. ISBN: 0-8018-1135-x; LC: 74-140671.

GREGG, WILLIAM DAVID. 1977. Analog and Digital Communication: Concepts, Systems, Applications, and Services in Electrical Dissemination of Aural, Visual, and Data Information. New York, NY: John Wiley and Sons; 1977. 603p. ISBN: 0-471-32661-5.

GTE SERVICE CORPORATION v. U. S. FEDERAL COMMUNICATIONS COMMISSION (FCC). 1973. 474 F. 2d 724 (2d Cir. 1973).

HARDEMAN, LYMAN. 1979. RS449: Communications Cornerstone for the 1980s...Now is the Time to Begin Planning for This Successor to RS232. Mini-Micro Systems. 1979 November; 12(11): 67-71. ISSN: 0364-9342.

HATFIELD, DALE N. 1979. The Administration View. In: Electronic Industries Association. Telecommunications Trends and Directions: Electronic Industries Association Communications Division Seminar Program; 1979 May 22-24; Hyannis, MA. Washington, DC: Electronic Industries Association; 1979. 9-14.

HATFIELD, DALE N. 1981a. Effects of Competition and Regulatory Reform on Design of Rates for Telecommunications Services. Remarks presented at: Rate Symposium on Problems of Regulated Industries; 1981 February 9; Kansas City, MO. Available from: the author, National Telecommunications and Information Administration, 1800 G St. NW, Washington, DC 20504.

HATFIELD, DALE N. 1981b. Long-Haul Services Overshadow the Crucial Local Distribution Issues. Communications News. 1981 February; 18(2): 56-57. ISSN: 0010-3632.

HIRSCH, PHIL. 1980. Geller Sees Cable TV Replacing Local Loops. Computerworld. 1980 May 26; 14(21): 86. ISSN: 0010-4841.

HOFFMAN, WOLFGANG. 1980. End of the Post's Omnipotence? Monopoly Commission Collects Ammunition Against the State Enterprise. Die Zeit (Germany). 1980 August 8.

HOPEWELL, LYNN. 1976. Computer Communications—An Introduction and Overview. In: Hopewell, Lynn; Cerf, Vinton G.; Curran, Alex; Dunn, Donald A. Computers and Communications: Proceedings of the Federal Communications Commission; 1976 November 8–9; Washington, DC. Montvale, NJ: AFIPS Press; nd. 1–38. Available from: American Federation of Information Processing Societies (AFIPS), 210 Summit Ave., Montvale, NJ 07645.

HOPEWELL, LYNN; CERF, VINTON G.; CURRAN, ALEX; DUNN, DONALD A. 1976. Computers and Communications: Proceedings of the Federal Communications Commission; 1976 November 8–9; Washington, DC. Montvale, NJ: AFIPS Press; nd. 127p. Available from: American Federation of Information Processing Societies (AFIPS), 210 Summit Ave., Montvale, NJ 07645.

HORODAS, ERIC DAVID. 1979. Ownership and Control of Electronic Funds Transfer Systems in the United States. Computer/Law Journal. 1979; 1: 501–516. ISSN: 0164-8756.

HOUGH, RICHARD R. 1979. Dealing with an Integrated World Network. Telephony. 1979 October 22; 197(17): 122–123. ISSN: 0040-2656.

HOUSLEY, TREVOR. 1979. Data Communications and Teleprocessing Systems. Englewood Cliffs, NJ: Prentice-Hall, Inc.; 1979. 262p. ISBN: 0-13-197368-1; LC: 78-22073.

HUMMEL, E. 1979. The Role of CCITT in Data Communications. In: Organisation for Economic Cooperation and Development (OECD). Information Computer Communications Policy: Transborder Data Flows and the Protection of Privacy: Proceedings of an OECD Symposium on Transborder Data Flows and the Protection of Privacy; 1977 September 20–23, Vienna, Austria. Paris France: OECD; 1979. Available from: OECD, Suite 1207, 1750 Pennsylvania Ave., Washington, DC 20006. ISBN: 92-64-01926-X.

HUSH-A-PHONE CORPORATION v. AMERICAN TELEPHONE & TELEGRAPH COMPANY. 1957. 22 F.C.C. 112 (1957).

HUSH-A-PHONE CORPORATION v. UNITED STATES. 1956. 238 F 2d 266 (D.C. Cir. 1956).

INFORMATION INDUSTRIES ASSOCIATION (IIA). 1981. Business of Information Report 1980. Washington, DC: IIA; 1981 February. Available for $950 from the IIA, 315 Pennsylvania Avenue, S.E., Washington, DC 20003.

INOSE, H., ed. 1978. Evolutions in Computer Communications: Proceedings of the 4th International Conference on Computer Communication; 1978 September 26–29; Kyoto, Japan. New York, NY: North-Holland Publishing Co.; 1978. 842p. ISBN: 0-444-85258-1.

INSTITUTE OF ELECTRICAL AND ELECTRONICS ENGINEERS (IEEE). 1979. ICC '79 Conference Record: Record of the Communications Society Conference Board (CSCB); 1979 June 10–14; Boston, MA. New York, NY: Institute of Electrical and Electronics Engineers, Inc.; 1979. 4 volumes (discontinuous paging). Available from IEEE Service Center, 445 Hoes Lane, Piscataway, NJ. LC: 72-194957.

INTERNATIONAL INFORMATION TECHNOLOGY INSTITUTE. 1979. Communication Networks 79: Proceedings of the Communication Networks Conference; 1979 January 30–February 1; Washington, DC. Newton, MA: International Information Technology Institute; 1979. 410p. Available from: The Institute, 60 Austin St., Newton, MA 02160.

INTERNATIONAL RESOURCE DEVELOPMENT, INCORPORATED. 1980b. Home Telecommunications in the 1980s. Norwalk, CT: International Resource Development, Inc.; 1980 April. 203p. (Report no. 150). Available from: International Resource Development, Inc., 30 High St., Norwalk, CT 06851.
INTERNATIONAL RESOURCE DEVELOPMENT, INCORPORATED. 1980b. Home Telecommunications in the 1980s. Norwalk, CT: International Resource Development, Inc.; 1980 April. 203p. (Report no. 150). Available from: International Resource Development, Inc., 30 High St., Norwark, CT 06851.
INTERNATIONAL TELEGRAPH AND TELEPHONE CONSULTATIVE COMMITTEE. 1979. Rural Telecommunications. Geneva, Switzerland: International Telecommunications Union; 1979. 318p. ISBN: 92-61-00821-6.
JOHNSON, LELAND L. 1978. Boundaries to Monopoly and Regulation in Modern Telecommunications. New York, NY: Praeger Publishers; 1978. 127-155. ISBN: 0-03-046546-X and 0-03-046541-9 pbk.
JOHNSON, MIKE. 1980. The Charles Babbage Institute: History Becomes a Database. Data Communications. 1980 January; 9(1): 18-19. ISSN: 0363-6399.
JOHNSON, RICHARD B. 1977. Federal Regulations Relevant to the Structural Development of Telecommunications Industries. Washington, DC: U.S. Department of Commerce; November 1977. (Office of Telecommunications Report no. 77-135). NTIS: PB-275 238.
JONES, W. T. 1980. Benefit or Burden? World Telecomm Standards—A Look at a Growing Need. Telephony. 1980 May 5; 198(18): 114-139. ISSN: 0040-2656.
JURGEN, RONALD K., ed. 1980. An Applications Review: Technology '81. IEEE Spectrum. 1981 January; 18(1): 122p. (Entire issue devoted to Applications Review). ISSN: 0018-9235.
KALBA, KONRAD K.; LEVINE, LARRY S.; BIRINYI, ANNE E. 1978. Regulatory Politics: State Legislatures and the Cable Television Industry. Cambridge, MA: Harvard University; 1978 August. 123p. (Program on Information Resources Policy Working Paper no. W-78-4).
KESTENBAUM, LIONEL. 1971. Common Carrier Access to Cable Communications: Regulatory and Economic Issues. Washington, DC: Sloan Commission on Cable Communications; 1971 March 19. 42p.
KIEBURTZ, BRUCE R. 1980. Network Standards and Protocols: Impact on User Needs Standards and Protocols in Data Communications. In: Waters, Maureen L., ed. Communications Network 80: Proceedings of the Communications Network Conference; 1980 January 28-30; Washington, DC. Newton, MA: International Information Technology Institute; 1980. 211-213. Available from: the Institute, 60 Austin St., Newton, MA 02160.
KIRBY, RICHARD C.; UTLAUT, WILLIAM F. 1975. Special Issue on Interactive Broadband Cable Systems. IEEE Transactions on Communications. 1975 January; 23(1): 184p. ISSN: 0090-6778.
KIRCHNER, JAKE. 1980a. Goldwater Proposed World Data Flow Congress. Computerworld. 1980 March 31; 14(13): 21. ISSN: 0010-4841.
KIRCHNER, JAKE. 1980b. Trade, Not Privacy Held Key to Data Flow Issues. Computerworld. 1980 March 31; 14(13):20. ISSN: 0010-4841.
KITTROSS, JOHN M. 1977. Documents in American Telecommunications Policy. New York, NY: Arno Press; 1977. 2 volumes. (Historical

Studies in Telecommunications Series reprint). ISBN: 0-405-07756-4; LC: 75-23904.

KLIE, ROBERT H. 1980. Compunications Network Management. Cambridge, MA: Harvard University; 1980 February. 72p.

KRAUSE, L. I. 1969. Analysis of Policy Issues in the Responses to the FCC Computer Inquiry. Menlo Park, CA: Stanford Research Institute; 1969 February. 199p. (Research Report no. 7379B-2).

LA BLANC, ROBERT E. 1979. The Common Carrier View. In: Electronic Industries Association. Telecommunications: Trends and Directions: An Electronic Industries Association Communications Division Seminar Program; 1979 May 22-24; Hyannis, MA. Washington, DC: Electronic Industries Association; 1979. 23-29.

LAMOND, FREDERIC E. 1979. The UK Telecommunications Monopoly: An Independent View. Telecommunications Policy (Great Britain). 1979 September; 3(3): 209-216. ISSN: 0308-5961.

LANGLEY, G. A. 1979. The Impact of New Technologies. Telephony. 1979 June 18; 196(25): 56-76, 111-112. ISSN: 0040-2656.

LEBDUSKA, ROBERT L. 1978. Standards for Fiber Optics. Laser Focus. 1978 July; 14(7): 44-47. ISSN: 0023-8589.

LECAROS, FERNANDO. 1979. Market Structure in a Computer Network. Stanford, CA: Stanford University; 1979 February. 149p. (Report no. 17).

LEMASTERS, JOHN N. 1980. Satellite Communications. In: Electronic Industries Association. Telecommunications: Trends and Directions: An Electronic Industries Association Communications Division Seminar Program; 1980 May 27-29; Hyannis, MA. Washington, DC: Electronic Industries Association; 1980. 41-46.

LEWIN, LEONARD. 1979. Telecommunications: An Interdisciplinary Survey. Dedham, MA: Artech House, Inc.; 1979. 670p. ISBN: 0-89006-072-X; LC: 78-26665.

LIPINSKI, A. J. 1969a. Decision Analysis of the FCC Computer Inquiry Responses. Menlo Park, CA: Stanford Research Institute; 1969 February. 56p. (Report no. 7379B-3).

LIPINSKI, A. J. 1969b. Digests of the Responses to the FCC Computer Inquiry. Menlo Park, CA: Stanford Research Institute; 1969 February. 234p. (Report no. 7379B-5).

LIPSCOMB, GREG. 1978. Private and Public Defenses Against Soviet Interception of U.S. Telecommunications: Problems and Policy Points. Cambridge, MA: Harvard University; 1978 April. 56p. (Program on Information Resources Policy Working Paper no. W-78-6).

LOEB, GUY HAMILTON. 1977. The Communications Act Policy Toward Competition: A Failure to Communicate. Cambridge, MA: Harvard University; 1977 October. 95p. (Program on Information Resources Policy Publication no. P-77-3).

LOTOCHINSKI, EUGENE B. 1980. Telecommunications: Converging with Data Processing. In: Electronic Industries Association. Telecommunications: Trends and Directions: An Electronic Industries Association Communications Division Seminar Program; 1980 May 27-29; Hyannis, MA. Washington, DC: Electronic Industries Association; 1980. 25-30.

LUCKY, ROBERT W. 1980. Can Cheap Bits Change Our Lives. In: Salz, Jack, ed. Computer Communications: Increasing Benefits for Society: Proceedings of the International Council for Computer Communications

(ICCC) 5th International Conference on Computer Communications; 1980 October 27–30; Atlanta, GA. Washington, DC: ICCC; 1980. 859–862. Available from: North-Holland Publishing Co., New York, NY. LC: 80-82549.

MAGNANT, ROBERT S. 1977. Domestic Satellite: An FCC Giant Step: Toward Competitive Telecommunications Policy. Boulder, CO: Westview Press; 1977. 296p. ISBN: 0-89158-226-6; LC: 76-30840.

MANDANIS, GEORGE P.; LANE, RICHARD N.; MYERS, JOHN R.; STANCK, PETER; MELNICK, MARTIN. 1974. The Domestic Telecommunications Industry: Economic Behavior, Competition, and Public Policy. San Rafael, CA: Systems Applications, Inc.; 1974 May. 436p. NTIS: PB-238 020.

MARSH, DONALD J. 1980. Optical Communications. In: Electronic Industries Association. Telecommunications: Trends and Directions: An Electronic Industries Association Communications Division Seminar Program; 1980 May 27–29; Hyannis, MA. Washington, DC: Electronic Industries Association. 1980. 47–58.

MARTIN, JAMES. 1972. Introduction to Teleprocessing. Englewood Cliffs, NJ: Prentice-Hall, Inc.; 1972. 267p. ISBN: 0-13-499814-6.

MARTIN, JAMES. 1976. Telecommunications and the Computer. 2nd edition. Englewood Cliffs, NJ: Prentice-Hall, Inc.; 1976. 670p. ISBN: 0-13-902494-8; LC: 75-37800.

MARTIN, JAMES. 1977. Future Developments in Telecommunications. 2nd edition. Englewood Cliffs, NJ: Prentice-Hall, Inc.; 1977. 668p. ISBN: 0-13-345850-4; LC: 76-40102.

MATHISON, STUART L.; WALKER, PHILIP M. 1970. Computers and Telecommunications: Issues in Public Policy. Englewood Cliffs, NJ: Prentice-Hall, Inc.; 1970. 270p. LC: 79-109108.

MCGLYNN, DANIEL R. 1978. Distributed Processing and Data Communications. New York, NY: John Wiley & Sons; 1978. 305p. ISBN: 0-471-01886-4; LC: 78-1117.

MCI TELECOMMUNICATIONS CORPORATION v. U.S. FEDERAL COMMUNICATIONS COMMISSION (FCC). 1977. 561 F. 2d 365 (D.C. Cir. 1977).

MCI TELECOMMUNICATIONS CORPORATION v. U.S. FEDERAL COMMUNICATIONS COMMISSION (FCC). 1978. 580 F. 2d 590 (D.C. Cir. 1978).

MELNICK, MARTIN. 1973. Data Communications Services by Local Coaxial Cable Networks: An Economic Analysis. San Rafael, CA: Systems Applications, Inc.; 1973 December 28. 53p. (Report no. R73-41).

MELVIN, DONALD K. 1980. LSI Helps Telephones Go Digital. IEEE Spectrum. 1980 June; 17(6): 30–33. ISSN: 0018-9235.

METELSKI, JOHN. 1978. Achieving Communications Privacy through Revision of the Eavesdropping Laws. Federal Communications Law Journal. 1978 September; 30(2): 135–147. ISSN: 0163-7606.

MEYER, JOHN R.; WILSON, ROBERT W.; BAUGHCUM, M. ALAN; BURTON, ELLEN; CAOUETTE, LOUIS. 1979. The Economics of Competition in the Telecommunications Industry. Boston, MA: Charles River Associates Inc.; 1979 August. 324p.

MITCHELL, MICHAEL R. 1971. State Regulation of Cable Television. Santa Monica, CA: The Rand Corp.; 1971 October. 65p. (R-783-MF).

38   EDWARD K. ZIMMERMAN AND KARL BRIMMER

MITRE CORPORATION. 1972. Digital Cable Communication. Bedford, MA: Mitre Corp.; 1972 January. 17p. (M71-113).
MOKHOFF, NICOLAS, ed. 1979. Communications Onward to the 80s. IEEE Spectrum. 1979 October; 16(10): 122p. (Special issue on Communications).
MUELLER, WILLARD F. 1970. A Primer on Monopoly and Competition. New York, NY: Random House, Inc.; 1970. 203p. LC: 71-93872.
NATIONAL ASSOCIATION OF REGULATORY UTILITY COMMISSIONERS (NARUC); FEDERAL COMMUNICATIONS COMMISSION (FCC). COOPERATIVE COMMITTEE ON COMMUNICATIONS. 1971. Separations Manual: Standard Procedures for Separating Telephone Property Costs, Revenues, Expenses, Taxes, and Reserves. Washington, DC: NARUC; 1971 February. 96p.
NEWTON, HARRY. 1980. Coming Soon: A Major Repricing of Telco Services. Business Communications Review. 1980 September/October; 10(5): 15-18.
NORTH CAROLINA UTILITIES COMMISSION v. U.S. FEDERAL COMMUNICATIONS COMMISSION (FCC). 1976. 537 F 2d 787 (4th Cir. 1976).
NORTH CAROLINA UTILITIES COMMISSION v. U.S. FEDERAL COMMUNICATIONS COMMISSION (FCC). 1977. cert denied, 434 U.S. 874.
OETTINGER, ANTHONY G. 1976. Performance, Politics and Policy in Computer/Communications: A Policy Agenda. Cambridge, MA: Harvard University; 1976 June. 13p. (Working Paper no. WP-79-2).
OETTINGER, ANTHONY G.; BERMAN, PAUL J.; READ, WILLIAM H. 1977. High and Low Politics: Information Resources for the 80s. Cambridge, MA: Ballinger Publishing Co.; 1977. 264p. ISBN: 0-88410-064-2; LC: 77-1685.
OETTINGER, ANTHONY G.; WEINHAUS, CAROL L. 1979. National Stakes in the Communications Revolution: Jurisdictional Cost Separations. Cambridge, MA: Harvard University; 1979 February. 75p. (Working Paper no. WP-79-2).
ORGANISATION FOR ECONOMIC COOPERATION AND DEVELOPMENT (OECD). 1973. Computers and Telecommunications: Economic, Technical and Organizational Issues. Paris, France: OECD; 1973. 222p. (OECD Informatics Studies no. 3). ISBN: 92-64-11063-1.
ORGANISATION FOR ECONOMIC COOPERATION AND DEVELOPMENT (OECD). 1979. Information Computer Communications Policy: Transborder Data Flows and the Protection of Privacy: Proceedings of the OECD Symposium on Transborder Data Flows and the Protection of Privacy; 1977 September 20-23; Vienna, Austria. Paris, France: OECD; 1979. 335p. (Information Computer Communications Policy Series). Available from: OECD, Suite 1207, 1750 Pennsylvania Ave., Washington, DC 20006. ISBN: 92-64-01926-X.
PARKHILL, DOUGLAS F. 1980. Universal Access to Computer/Communications Services—The Challenge to Society. In: Salz, Jack, ed. Computer Communications: Increasing Benefits for Society: Proceedings of the International Council for Computer Communications (ICCC) 5th

International Conference on Computer Communications; 1980 October 27–30; Atlanta, GA. Washington, DC: ICCC, 1980. 863–870. Available from: North-Holland Publishing Co., New York, NY. LC: 80-82549.

PEARCE, ALAN. 1981. The Telecommunications Policymaking Process and the Future Agenda: Implications for Service Providers, Manufacturers and Users. Waltham, MA: International Data Corporation; [1981]. 247p. manuscript. (To be published in early 1981.)

PELTON, JOSEPH N.; SNOW, MARCELLUS S., eds. 1977. Economic and Policy Problems in Satellite Communications. New York, NY: Praeger Publishers; 1977. 240p. ISBN: 0-275-23730-3; LC: 75-44937.

PRINCE, JEFFREY S. 1980. ACS, SBS, and XTEN: What's Happening with the Extended Networks. Administrative Management. 1980 February; 61(2): 38-40,46,50. ISSN: 0001-9376.

PRIVES, DANIEL. 1976. The Explosion of State Laws on Electronic Fund Transfer Systems: Its Significance for Financial Institutions, Non-Financial Institutions, and Consumers. Cambridge, MA: Harvard University Press; 1976 January. 69p. (Program on Information Technologies and Public Policy Publication no. P-76-1).

PRIVES, DANIEL. 1977. EFT Policy and Competitive Equality: The Roles of Courts and Congress. Harvard University, Cambridge, MA: Harvard University Press; 1977 January. 52p. (Program on Information Technologies and Public Policy Publication no. P-77-1).

READ, WILLIAM H. 1978. Rethinking International Communications. Cambridge, MA: Harvard University; 1978 April. 19p. (Program on Information Technologies and Public Policy Publication no. P-78-1).

RESNIKOFF, HOWARD L.; WEISS, EDWARD C. 1981. Adapting Use of Information and Knowledge to Enhance Productivity. In: Hogan, John D., ed. Dimensions of Productivity Research: Proceedings of the Conference on Productivity Research; 1980 April 21-24; Houston, TX. Houston, TX: American Productivity Center; n.d. 507–550. Available from: American Productivity Center, 123 North Post Oak Lane, Houston, TX 77024.

RICHARDSON, JOHN M.; GARY, ROBERT, eds. 1970. A Preliminary Survey of Data Communications in the United States. Washington, DC: U.S. Department of Commerce, Office of Telecommunications; 1970 October 19. 62p.

RICHER, IRA; MCKENZIE, PHILIP; MYER, THEODORE, H. 1979. Communications Technology Forecast. Cambridge, MA: Bolt Beranek and Newman, Inc.; 1979 January. 334p. NTIS: PB-292 697.

ROBERTS, LAWRENCE G. 1978. The Evolution of Packet Switching. Proceedings of the IEEE. 1978 November; 66(11): 1307–1313. (Special issue on Packet Communications Networks). ISSN: 0018-9219.

ROBINSON, GLEN O. 1976. January Perspectives on Communications Policy: Looking Back into the Future. Federal Communications Bar Journal. 1976; 29(2): 173–187. ISSN: 0163-7606.

ROBINSON, GLEN O., ed. 1978a. Communications for Tomorrow: Policy Perspectives for the 1980s. New York, NY: Praeger Publishers; 1978. 526p. ISBN: 0-03-046546-X and 0-03-046541-9 pbk.

ROBINSON, GLEN O. 1978b. The Judicial Role. In: Robinson, Glen O., ed. Communications for Tomorrow: Policy Perspectives for the 1980s. New York, NY: Praeger Publishers; 1978. 415–444. ISBN: 0-03-046546-X and 0-03-046541-9 pbk.

RODGERS, PAUL. 1979. The NARUC Was There: A History of the National Association of Regulatory Utility Commissioners. Washington, DC: NARUC; 1979. 507p.

SAFFO, PAUL L. 1980. Stanford Journal of International Law: Transborder Data Flow Volume XVI/Summer 1980. Stanford, CA: Stanford University Law School; 1980 Summer. 227p. ISSN: 0081-4326.

SALZ, JACK, ed. 1980. Computer Communications: Increasing Benefits for Society: Proceedings of the International Council for Computer Communications (ICCC) 5th International Conference on Computer Communications; 1980 October 27-30; Atlanta, GA. Washington, DC: ICCC; 1980. 870p. Available from: North-Holland Publishing Co., New York, NY. LC: 80-82549.

SANDERS, RAY W.; MCLAUGHLIN, R. A. 1980. Networks at Last? Datamation. 1980 March; 26(3): 122-128. (International edition). ISSN: 0011-6963.

SARASOHN, JUDY. 1980. Some Fear Competition: Telecommunications Rewrite Tries to Unfetter Industry. Congressional Quarterly. 1980 February 16: 38(7). 389-394. ISSN: 0010-5910.

SAXTON, W. A.; EDWARDS, MORRIS. 1979a. Datacomm Directions: Looking Beyond Xten. Infosystems. 1979 November; (26)1: 72-74.

SAXTON, W. A.; EDWARDS, MORRIS. 1979b. Datacomm Directions: The Integrated Network Movement. Infosystems. 1979 March; 26(3): 78-80.

SAXTON, W. A.; EDWARDS, MORRIS. 1980. Datacomm Directions: Home is Where the Action Is. Infosystems. 1980 January; 27(1): 62-63.

SCIENCE NEWS. 1980. Technology: Computing by Light. Science News. 1980 October 18; 118(16): 249. ISSN: 0036-8423.

SCIENTIFIC AMERICAN. 1977. Microelectronics. Scientific American. 1977 September; 237(3): 262p. (Entire issue on title topic). ISSN: 0036-8733.

SEITZ, NEAL B. 1980. Data Communication and Data Processing—A Basis for Definition. Telecommunications Policy (Great Britain). 1980 March; 4(1): 49-62. ISSN: 0308-5961.

SEITZ, NEAL B.; BODSON, DENNIS. 1980. Data Communication Performance Assessment. Telecommunications. 1980 February; 14(2): 35-45,89. ISSN: 0040-2494.

SELMON, JOHN. 1980. Telephone Equipment Registration Requirements. Phone Call. 1980 March; 19(3): 28-30.

SHERMAN, ROGER, ed. 1980. Perspectives on Postal Services Issues. Washington, DC: American Enterprise Institute for Public Policy Research; 1980. 228p. (AEI Symposia, no. 79J). ISBN: 0-8447-2173-5; LC: 80-12071.

SICHTER, JAMES W. 1977. Separations Procedures in the Telephone Industry: The Historical Origins of a Public Policy. Cambridge, MA: Harvard University; 1977 January. 146p. (Program on Information Resources Policy Publication no. P-77-2).

SIDELL, M. KENT; MOSCO, VINCENT. 1978. US Communications Policy Making: The Results of Executive Branch Reorganization. Telecommunications Policy (Great Britain). 1978 September; 2(3): 211-217. ISSN: 0308-5961.

SIPPL, CHARLES J. 1976. Data Communications Dictionary. New York, NY: Van Nostrand Reinhold Co.; 1976. 545p. ISBN: 0-442-27622-2; LC: 76-3739.

SOMA, JOHN T. 1976. The Computer Industry: An Economic-Legal Analysis of Its Technology and Growth. Lexington, MA: Lexington Books; 1976. 219p. ISBN: 0-669-00643-2; LC: 76-2989.

STAELIN, DAVID H.; HARVEY, ROBERT L. 1979. Future Large Broadband Switched Satellite Communications Networks. Cambridge, MA: Massachusetts Institute of Technology, Research Laboratory of Electronics; 1979 December. 270p.

STANFORD UNIVERSITY. CENTER FOR INTERDISCIPLINARY RESEARCH. 1973. Economics of Computer Communication Networks. Stanford, CA: Stanford University; 1973 December. 24p. (Report no. 7).

STANFORD UNIVERSITY. CENTER FOR INTERDISCIPLINARY RESEARCH. 1974. Economics of Computer Communication Networks. Stanford, CA: Stanford University; 1974 December. 26p. (Report no. 14).

STANFORD UNIVERSITY. ENGINEERING. ECONOMIC SYSTEMS DEPARTMENT. 1977a. Economics of Computer Communication Networks. Stanford, CA: Stanford University; 1977 January. 30p. (Report no. 2).

STANFORD UNIVERSITY. ENGINEERING. ECONOMIC SYSTEMS DEPARTMENT. 1977b. Economics of Computer Communication Networks. Stanford, CA: Stanford University; 1977 July. 35p. (Report no. 3).

STANFORD UNIVERSITY. ENGINEERING. ECONOMIC SYSTEMS DEPARTMENT. 1978. Economics of Computer Communication Networks. Stanford, CA: Stanford University; 1978 February. 28p. (Report no. 8).

STEIN, DAVID L. 1979. Price/Performance, Semiconductors and the Future. Datamation. 1979 November 25; 25(13): 14-20. (Special edition). ISSN: 0011-6963.

STEVENS, RICHARD K.; ROSE, KENNETH. 1973. Design of a Switched Broadband Cable Communications System. Troy, NY: Rensselaer Polytechnic Institute; 1973 October. 33p. (Rensselaer Polytechnic Institute Telecommunications Research Center no. TRC-102).

STINE, L. L.; PLUMMER, C. M.; LAMBERT, M. A. 1971. Local Distribution of Telecommunications: A Perspective. Bedford, MA: Mitre Corp.; 1971 August. 79p. (Report no. M71-91).

STONE, ROBERT F.; SCHANKERMAN, MARK A.; FENTON, CHESTER G. 1976. Selective Competition in the Telephone Industry: An Independent Appraisal Based on Responses to FCC Docket 20003. Cambridge, MA: Technology + Economics, Inc. (T + E); 1976 November. 47p.

TASCHDJIAN, MARTIN G.; CARRUTHERS, BRUCE; GRAY, M. B.; HATFIELD, DALE; JOYNER, VIRGINIA; MCADAMS, SUSAN; MYERS, KENNETH; NUSBAUM, WILLIAM; VILLAVICENCIO, JOSE. 1981. Evaluating Local Measured Telephone Service: Elements of a Benefit/Cost Approach. Washington, DC: National Telecommunications and Information Administration (NTIA), 1981 January 16. 66p. Available from: NTIA Office of Policy and Analysis Development, 1800 G St. NW, Washington, DC 20504.

TECHNICAL COMMUNICATIONS CORPORATION. 1969. The Adverse Effect of Data Transmissions on the Voice Telephone Network. Lexington, MA: Technical Communications Corporation; 1969 August. 18p.

42   EDWARD K. ZIMMERMAN AND KARL BRIMMER

TIEN, PING-KING; GIORDMAINE, JOSEPH A. 1980. Integrated Optics:
  Wave of the Future. Bell Laboratories Record. 1980 December; 58(11)
  371-378. ISSN: 0005-8564.
TIEN, PING-KING; GIORDMAINE, JOSEPH A. 1981a. Integrated Optics:
  The Components. Bell Laboratories Record. 1981 January; 59(1): 8-
  13. ISSN: 0005-8564.
TIEN, PING-KING; GIORDMAINE, JOSEPH A. 1981b. Integrated Optics:
  Putting It All Together. Bell Laboratories Record. 1981 February;
  59(2). 38-45. ISSN: 0005-8564.
TOWERS, ROBERT L. 1979. Wideband Is in the Future—But Whose?
  Telephony. 1979 August 13; 197(7): 36, 98. ISSN: 0040-2656.
TRANSCOMM, INCORPORATED. 1977. An Analysis of: "A Review of
  International Telecommunications Industry Issues, Structure, and
  Regulatory Problems". Falls Church, VA: Transcomm, Inc.; 1977 May.
  35p. (Draft analysis of a report by Jack E. Cole, Richard M. O'Rorke,
  Jr., John W. Kopinski, and Glynetta C. Perrymore). Available from:
  Transcomm, Inc., 6521 Arlington Boulevard, Falls Church, VA 22042.
TRANSPORTATION DATA COORDINATING COMMITTEE. 1980. Elec-
  tronic Interface for Business Systems Transactions: Proceedings of the
  Transportation Data Coordinating Committee 11th National Forum;
  1979 December 4-5; Washington, DC. Washington, DC: Transportation
  Data Coordinating Committee; 1980. 157p.
UNGER, J. H. W. 1976. Literature Survey of Communication Satellite Sys-
  tems and Technology. New York, NY: The Institute of Electrical and
  Electronics Engineers; 1976. 409p.
U. S. CABINET COMMITTEE ON CABLE COMMUNICATIONS. 1974.
  Report to the President: The Cabinet Committee on Cable Communica-
  tions. Washington, DC: Office of Telecommunications Policy; 1974.
  142p. NTIS: PB 2271-02.
U. S. CONGRESS. 94TH CONGRESS, 2ND SESSION. 1976. A Bill to
  Reaffirm the Intent of Congress with Respect to the Structure of the
  Common Carrier Telecommunications Industry Rendering Services in
  Interstate and Foreign Commerce, House Bill 12323, 94th Congress, 2nd
  Session. Washington, DC: Government Printing Office; 1976 March 4.
  10p. (Consumer Communications Reform Act of 1976; the "Bell Bill").
U. S. CONGRESS. 95TH CONGRESS, 2ND SESSION. 1978. A Bill to
  Establish Certain Requirements Relating to Interstate and Foreign Tele-
  communications, and for Other Purposes, House Bill 13015, 95th Con-
  gress, 2nd Session. Washington, DC: Government Printing Office; 1978
  June 7. 217p. (Communications Act of 1978).
U. S. CONGRESS. 96TH CONGRESS, 1ST SESSION. 1979a. A Bill to
  Amend the Communications Act of 1934, as Amended, to Provide for
  Improved Domestic Telecommunications and International Telecommu-
  nications, Rural Telecommunications Development, to Establish a
  National Commission on Spectrum Management, Senate Bill 611, 96th
  Congress, 1st Session. Washington, DC: Government Printing Office;
  1979 March 12. 115p.
U. S. CONGRESS. 96TH CONGRESS, 1ST SESSION. 1979b. A Bill to
  Amend the Communications Act of 1934 in Order to Encourage and
  Develop Marketplace Competition in the Provision of Certain Services
  and to Provide Certain Deregulation of Such Services, and for Other
  Purposes, Senate Bill 622, 96th Congress, 1st Session. Washington, DC:
  Government Printing Office; 1979 March 12. 37p.

U. S. CONGRESS. 96TH CONGRESS, 1ST SESSION. 1979c. A Bill to
Amend the Communications Act of 1934 to Make Certain Revisions in
the Provisions of Such Act Relating to the Regulation of Telecommuni-
cations Activities, House Bill 6121, 96th Congress, 1st Session. Wash-
ington, DC: Government Printing Office; 1979 December 13. 41p.
(Telecommunications Act of 1980).
U. S. CONGRESS. 96TH CONGRESS, 1ST SESSION. 1979d. A Bill to
Establish Certain Requirements Relating to Interstate and Foreign Tele-
communications, and for Other Purposes, House Bill 3333, 96th Con-
gress, 1st Session. Washington, DC: Government Printing Office; 1979
March 29. 238p.
U. S. CONGRESS. 96TH CONGRESS, 2ND SESSION. 1980. A Bill to
Amend the Communications Act of 1934 to Provide for Improved
Domestic and International Telecommunications, Rural Telecommuni-
cations Development, Senate Bill 2827, 96th Congress, 2nd Session.
Washington, DC: Government Printing Office; 1980 June 12. 129p.
U. S. CONGRESS. HOUSE. COMMITTEE ON GOVERNMENT OPERA-
TIONS. 91ST CONGRESS, 2ND SESSION. 1970. Reorganization Plan
no. 1 of 1970 (Office of Telecommunications Policy) Hearings before a
Subcommittee of the Committee on Government Operations, 91st
Congress, 2nd Session, 1970. Washington, DC: Government Printing
Office; 1970. 133p.
U. S. CONGRESS. HOUSE. COMMITTEE ON GOVERNMENT OPERA-
TIONS. 95TH CONGRESS, 1ST SESSION. 1977. Hearings on Re-
organization Plan no. 1 of 1977 (Executive Office of the President) be-
fore a Subcommittee of the Committee on Government Operations,
95th Congress, 1st Session, 1977. Washington, DC: Government Print-
ing Office; 1977. 221p. LC: 78-600902.
U. S. CONGRESS. HOUSE. COMMITTEE ON GOVERNMENT OPERA-
TIONS. 96TH CONGRESS, 2ND SESSION. 1980a. International
Information Flow: Forging a New Framework. 32nd Report by the
Committee on Government Operations Together with Additional Views,
House Report no. 96-1535, 96th Congress, 2nd Session. Washington,
DC: Government Printing Office; 1980 December 11. 61p.
U. S. CONGRESS. HOUSE. COMMITTEE ON GOVERNMENT OPERA-
TIONS. 96TH CONGRESS. 2ND SESSION. 1980b. Hearings on In-
ternational Data Flow before a Subcommittee of the Committee on
Government Operations, 96th Congress, 2nd Session, 1980. Washing-
ton, DC: Government Printing Office; 1980. 843p.
U. S. CONGRESS. HOUSE. COMMITTEE ON INTERSTATE AND FOREIGN
COMMERCE. 96TH CONGRESS, 2ND SESSION. 1980. Telecommu-
nications Act of 1980: Report together with Dissenting Views by the
Committee on Interstate and Foreign Commerce, House Report no. 96-
1252, 96th Congress, 2nd Session, 1980. Washington, DC: Govern-
ment Printing Office; 1980 August 25. 268p.
U. S. CONGRESS. HOUSE. COMMITTEE ON INTERSTATE AND FOREIGN
COMMERCE. SUBCOMMITTEE ON COMMUNICATIONS. 94TH CON-
GRESS, 1ST SESSION. 1975. Fundamental Changes Needed to Achieve
Effective Regulation of Communications Common Carriers. Washington,
DC: Government Printing Office; 1975 November 10. 18p. (Committee
Print).
U. S. CONGRESS. HOUSE. COMMITTEE ON INTERSTATE AND FOREIGN
COMMERCE. SUBCOMMITTEE ON COMMUNICATIONS. 95TH CON-

GRESS, 2ND SESSION. 1978. Hearings on the Communications Act of 1978 before the Subcommittee on Communications of the Committee on Interstate and Foreign Commerce, on H.R. 13015, 95th Congress, 2nd Session, 1978. Washington, DC: Government Printing Office; 1979. 5 volumes in 7. LC: 79-601853.

U. S. CONGRESS. HOUSE. COMMITTEE ON INTERSTATE AND FOREIGN COMMERCE. SUBCOMMITTEE ON COMMUNICATIONS. 96TH CONGRESS, 1ST SESSION. 1979. Hearings on the Communications Act of 1979 before the Subcommittee on Communications of the Committee on Interstate and Foreign Commerce, on H.R. 3333; 96th Congress, 1st Session, 1979. Washington, DC: Government Printing Office; 1980. 5 volumes in 8. LC: 80-602432.

U. S. CONGRESS. HOUSE. COMMITTEE ON THE JUDICIARY. 96TH CONGRESS, 2ND SESSION. 1980. Telecommunications Act of 1980: Adverse Report together with Additional and Supplemental Views to Accompany House of Representatives Bill 6121, House Report no. 1252, pt. 2, 96th Congress, 2nd Session, 1980. Washington, DC: Government Printing Office; 1980. 44p.

U. S. CONGRESS. SENATE. COMMITTEE ON COMMERCE, SCIENCE, AND TRANSPORTATION. SUBCOMMITTEE ON COMMUNICATIONS. 96TH CONGRESS, 1ST SESSION. 1979. Hearings on Amendments to the Communications Act of 1934, S. 611 and S. 622, before the Subcommittee on Communications of the Committee on Commerce, Science, and Transportation, 96th Congress, 1st Session, 1979. Washington, DC: Government Printing Office; 1979. 4 volumes. LC: 79-604095.

U. S. DEPARTMENT OF COMMERCE. INDUSTRY AND TRADE ADMINISTRATION. 1980. 1980 U. S. Industrial Outlook for 200 Industries with Projections for 1984. Washington, DC: Government Printing Office; 1980 January. 517p. GPO: 003-008-00181-5.

U. S. DOMESTIC COUNCIL. COMMITTEE ON THE RIGHT OF PRIVACY. 1976. National Information Policy: Report to the President of the United States. Washington, DC: National Commission on Libraries and Information Science; 1976. 233p. (Committee Chaired by Nelson A. Rockefeller). Available from: Government Printing Office, Washington, DC.

U. S. EXECUTIVE OFFICE OF THE PRESIDDENT. 1979. Executive Order no. 12046, 3 C.F.R. 158 (1979).

U. S. FEDERAL COMMUNICATIONS COMMISSION (FCC). 1959. In re Allocation of Frequencies in the Bands Above 890 Mc. 27 F. C. C. 359 (1959).

U. S. FEDERAL COMMUNICATIONS COMMISSION (FCC). 1966. In re Regulatory and Policy Problems Presented by the Interdependence of Computer and Communication Services and Facilities. 7 F.C.C.2d 11 (1966).

U. S. FEDERAL COMMUNICATIONS COMMISSION (FCC). 1968. In re Use of the Carterfone Device in Message Toll Telephone Service. 13 F.C.C. 2d 420 (1968).

U. S. FEDERAL COMMUNICATIONS COMMISSION (FCC). 1970. In re Establishment of Policies and to Provide Specialized Common Carrier Services in the Domestic Public Point-to-Point Microwave Radio Service and Proposed Amendments to Parts 21, 43, and 61 of the Commission's Rules. 24 F.C.C. 2d 318 (1970).

U. S. FEDERAL COMMUNICATIONS COMMISSION (FCC). 1971a. In re

Establishment of Policies and to Provide Specialized Common Carrier Services in the Domestic Public Point-to-Point Microwave Radio Service and Proposed Amendments to Parts 21, 43, and 61 of the Commission's Rules. 29 F.C.C. 2d 870 (1971).

U. S. FEDERAL COMMUNICATIONS COMMISSION (FCC). 1971b. In re Regulatory and Policy Problems Presented by the Interdependence of Computer and Communication Services and Facilities. 28 F.C.C. 2d 267 (1971).

U. S. FEDERAL COMMUNICATIONS COMMISSION (FCC). 1972a. In re Establishment of Domestic Communications-Satellite Facilities by Non-Governmental Entities. 35 F.C.C. 2d 844 (1972).

U. S. FEDERAL COMMUNICATIONS COMMISSION (FCC). 1972b. In re Proposals for New or Revised Classes of Interstate and Foreign Message Toll Telephone Service (MTS) and Wide Area Telephone Service (WATS). 35 F.C.C. 2d 539 (1972).

U. S. FEDERAL COMMUNICATIONS COMMISSION (FCC). 1973. In re Proposals for New or Revised Classes of Interstate and Foreign Message Toll Telephone Service (MTS) and Wide Area Telephone Service (WATS). 40 F.C.C. 2d 315 (1973).

U. S. FEDERAL COMMUNICATIONS COMMISSION (FCC). 1974a. In re Bell System Tariff Offerings of Local Distribution Facilities for Use by Other Common Carriers. 46 F.C.C. 2d 413 (1974).

U. S. FEDERAL COMMUNICATIONS COMMISSION (FCC). 1974b. In re Economic Implications and Interrelationships Arising from Policies and Practices Relating to Customer Interconnection, Jurisdictional Separations and Rate-Structures. 46 F.C.C. 2d 214 (1974).

U. S. FEDERAL COMMUNICATIONS COMMISSION (FCC). 1975. In re Proposals for New or Revised Classes of Interstate and Foreign Message Toll Telephone Service (MTS) and Wide Area Telephone Service (WATS). 56 F.C.C. 2d 593 (1975).

U. S. FEDERAL COMMUNICATIONS COMMISSION (FCC). 1976a. In re Amendment of Section 64.702 of the Commission's Rules and Regulations (Second Computer Inquiry). 61 F.C.C. 2d 103 (1976).

U. S. FEDERAL COMMUNICATIONS COMMISSION (FCC). 1976b. In re Economic Implications and Interrelationships Arising from Policies and Practices Relating to Customer Interconnection, Jurisdictional Separations and Rate-Structures. 61 F.C.C. 2d 766 (1976).

U. S. FEDERAL COMMUNICATIONS COMMISSION (FCC). 1976c. In re MCI Telecommunications Corp. 60 F.C.C. 2d 25 (1976).

U. S. FEDERAL COMMUNICATIONS COMMISSION (FCC). 1976d. In re Proposals for New or Revised Classes of Interstate and Foreign Message Toll Telephone Service (MTS) and Wide Area Telephone Service (WATS). 58 F.C.C. 2d 736 (1976).

U. S. FEDERAL COMMUNICATIONS COMMISSION (FCC). 1976e. In re Regulatory Policies Concerning Resale and Shared Use of Common Carrier Services and Facilities. 60 F.C.C. 2d 261 (1976).

U. S. FEDERAL COMMUNICATIONS COMMISSION (FCC). 1976f. Report by the Federal Communications Commission on Domestic Telecommunications Policies. Washington, DC: FCC; 1976 September 27. (Various pagings). Available from: Federal Communications Commission, 1919 M St., NW, Washington, DC 20554.

U. S. FEDERAL COMMUNICATIONS COMMISSION (FCC). 1978. In re MTS and WATS Market Structure. 67 F.C.C. 2d 757 (1978).

U. S. FEDERAL COMMUNICATIONS COMMISSION (FCC). 1979a. Allocating Spectrum for, and to Establish Other Rules and Policies Pertaining to, the Use of Radio in Digital Termination Systems for the Provision of Common Carrier Digital Telecommunications Services. 44 Fed. Reg. 51,257 (1979).

U. S. FEDERAL COMMUNICATIONS COMMISSION (FCC). 1979b. In re Petitions Seeking Amendment of Part 68 of the Commission's Rules Concerning Connection of Telephone Equipment... 72 F.C.C. 2d 330 (1979).

U. S. FEDERAL COMMUNICATIONS COMMISSION (FCC). 1979c. In re Policy and Rules Concerning Rates for Competitive Common Carrier Services and Facilities Authorizations therefor. 77 F.C.C. 2d 308 (1979).

U. S. FEDERAL COMMUNICATIONS COMMISSION (FCC). 1979d. Statistics of Communications Common Carriers. Washington, DC: Government Printing Office; 1979 December 31. 219p. GPO: 004-000-00371-3.

U. S. FEDERAL COMMUNICATIONS COMMISSION (FCC). 1980a. In re Amendment of Part 31 (Uniform System of Accounts for Class A and Class B Telephone Companies) So As to Permit Depreciable Property to Be Placed in Groups Comprised of Units with Expected Equal Life for Depreciation under the Straight-Line Method. 83 F.C.C. 2d 267 (1980).

U. S. FEDERAL COMMUNICATIONS COMMISSION (FCC). 1980b. In re Amendment of Part 67 of the Commission's Rules and Establishment of a Joint Board. 78 F.C.C. 2d 837 (1980).

U. S. FEDERAL COMMUNICATIONS COMMISSION (FCC). 1980c. In re Amendment of Part 67 of the Commission's Rules and Establishment of a Joint Board. 82 F.C.C. 2d 157 (1980).

U. S. FEDERAL COMMUNICATIONS COMMISSION (FCC). 1980d. In re Amendment of Section 64.702 of the Commission's Rules and Regulations (Second Computer Inquiry). 77 F.C.C. 2d 384 (1980).

U. S. FEDERAL COMMUNICATIONS COMMISSION (FCC). 1980e. In re Amendment of Section 64.702 of the Commission's Rules and Regulations (Second Computer Inquiry).____F.C.C. 2d____(1980); 46 Fed. Reg. 5984 (1981); 49 Rad. Reg. 2d 1107 (1980).

U. S. FEDERAL COMMUNICATIONS COMMISSION (FCC). 1980f. In re An Inquiry into the Use of the Bands 825-845 mHz and 870-890 mHz for Cellular Communications Systems; and Amendment of Parts 2 and 22 of Commission's Rules Relative to Cellular Communications Systems. 78 F.C.C. 2d 984 (1980).

U. S. FEDERAL COMMUNICATIONS COMMISSION (FCC). 1980g. In re Digital Communications Protocols. 83 F.C.C. 2d 318 (1980).

U. S. FEDERAL COMMUNICATIONS COMMISSION (FCC). 1980h. In re Economic Implications and Interrelationships Arising from Policies and Practices Relating to Customer Interconnection, Jurisdictional Separations and Rate-Structures. 75 F.C.C. 2d 506 (1980).

U. S. FEDERAL COMMUNICATIONS COMMISSION (FCC). 1980i. In re MTS and WATS Market Structure. 77 F.C.C. 2d 224 (1980).

U. S. FEDERAL COMMUNICATIONS COMMISSION (FCC). 1980j. In re MTS and WATS Market Structure. 81 F.C.C. 2d 177 (1980).

U. S. FEDERAL COMMUNICATIONS COMMISSION (FCC). 1980k. In re

Petitions Seeking Amendment of Part 68 of the Commission's Rules Concerning Connection of Telephone Equipment. . . 76 F.C.C. 2d 246 (1980).

U. S. FEDERAL COMMUNICATIONS COMMISSION (FCC). 1980l. Regulatory Policies Concerning Resale and Shared Use of Common Carrier Domestic Public Switched Network Services. 45 Fed. Reg. 83,580 (1980).

U. S. FEDERAL COMMUNICATIONS COMMISSION (FCC). FEDERAL/STATE-LOCAL ADVISORY COMMITTEE ON CABLE TELEVISION REGULATIONS STEERING COMMITTEE. 1973. The Final Report of the FCC Cable Television Advisory Committee on Federal/State-Local Regulatory Relationships. Washington, DC: FCC; 1973 September. 248p. NTIS: PB 223-147.

U. S. GENERAL ACCOUNTING OFFICE (GAO). 1969. Review of Status of Development Toward Establishment of a Unified National Communications System: Report to the Congress by the Comptroller General of the United States. Washington, DC: GAO; 1976 July 14. 53p. (B-166655).

U. S. GENERAL ACCOUNTING OFFICE (GAO). 1971. Benefits from Centralized Management of Leased Communications Services. Washington, DC: GAO; 1971 December 22. 39p. (B-169857).

U. S. GENERAL ACCOUNTING OFFICE (GAO). 1975. Improved Planning—A Must before a Department-Wide Automatic Data Processing System is Acquired for the Department of Agriculture. Washington, DC: GAO; 1975 June 3. 39p. (LCD-75-108).

U. S. GENERAL ACCOUNTING OFFICE (GAO). 1977a. Better Management of Defense Communications Would Reduce Costs. Washington, DC: GAO; 1977 December 14. 36p. (LCD-77-106).

U. S. GENERAL ACCOUNTING OFFICE (GAO). 1977b. Responsibilities, Actions, and Coordination of Federal Agencies in International Telecommunications Services. Washington, DC: GAO; 1977 September 29. 81p. (CED-77-132).

U. S. GENERAL ACCOUNTING OFFICE (GAO). 1977c. Safeguarding Taxpayer Information—An Evaluation of the Proposed Computerized Tax Administration System. Washington, DC: GAO; 1977 January 17. 44p. (LCD-76-115).

U. S. GENERAL ACCOUNTING OFFICE (GAO). 1977d. Vulnerabilities of Telecommunications Systems to Unauthorized Use. Washington, DC: GAO; 1977 March 31. 29p. (LCD-77-102).

U. S. GENERAL ACCOUNTING OFFICE (GAO). 1978a. Challenges of Protecting Personal Information in an Expanding Federal Computer Network Environment. Washington, DC: GAO; 1978 April 28. 48p. (LCD-76-102).

U. S. GENERAL ACCOUNTING OFFICE (GAO). 1978b. The Federal Information Processing Standards Program: Many Potential Benefits, Little Progress, and Many Problems. Washington, DC: GAO; 1978 April 19. 57p. (FGMSD-78-23).

U. S. GENERAL ACCOUNTING OFFICE (GAO). 1978c. Greater Coordination and a More Effective Policy Needed for International Telecommunications Facilities. Washington, DC: GAO; 1978 March 31. 75p. (CED-78-87).

U. S. GENERAL ACCOUNTING OFFICE (GAO). 1979a. Developing a Domestic Common Carrier Telecommunications Policy: What Are the

48   EDWARD K. ZIMMERMAN AND KARL BRIMMER

Issues? Washington, DC: GAO; 1979 January 24. 42p.
U. S. GENERAL ACCOUNTING OFFICE (GAO). 1979b. Economic and
Operational Benefits in Local Telephone Services Can be Achieved
through Government-Wide Coordinations. Washington, DC: GAO; 1979
November 14. 33p. (LCD-80-9).
U. S. GENERAL ACCOUNTING OFFICE (GAO). 1979c. Organizing the
Federal Communications Commission for Greater Management and
Regulatory Effectiveness. Washington, DC: GAO; 1979 July 30. 143p.
(CED-79-107).
U. S. GENERAL ACCOUNTING OFFICE (GAO). 1979d. Outlook Dim
for Revised Accounting System Needed for Changing Telephone Industry.
Washington, DC: GAO; 1979 November. 65p. (FGMSD-80-9).
U. S. GENERAL ACCOUNTING OFFICE (GAO). 1980a. Increasing Use
of Data Telecommunications Calls for Stronger Protection and Improved
Economies. Washington, DC: GAO; 1980 November 12. 69p. (LCD-
81-1).
U. S. GENERAL ACCOUNTING OFFICE (GAO). 1980b. Reduced Com-
munications Cost through Centralized Management of Multiplex Systems.
Washington, DC: GAO; 1980 May 14. (LDC-80-53).
U. S. GENERAL ACCOUNTING OFFICE (GAO). FINANCIAL AND
GENERAL MANAGEMENT DIVISION. ADP GROUP. 1980. [ADP
Related Documents]. Washington, DC: GAO; 1980 October 15. 75p.
U. S. NATIONAL TELECOMMUNICATIONS AND INFORMATION
ADMINISTRATION (NTIA). 1979. Common Carrier Legislation Com-
ments and Recommendations. Washington, DC: NTIA; 1979. 72p.
Available from: NTIA Office of Policy Analysis and Development, 1800
G St. NW, Washington, DC.
U. S. OFFICE OF MANAGEMENT AND BUDGET. 1978. Federal Data
Processing Policies and Regulations: An Annotated Bibliography of
Laws, Policies, Regulations and Other Documents Pertaining to the Man-
agement of Federal Data Processing and Related Telecommunications
Activities. Springfield, VA: National Technical Information Service
(NTIS); 1978 December. 44p. NTIS: PB 2901-83.
U. S. PRIVACY PROTECTION STUDY COMMISSION. 1977. Personal
Privacy in an Information Society. Washington, DC: Government Print-
ing Office; 1977 July. 654p. (GPO Catalog no. Y3.P93/5:1/1977).
UNITED STATES INDEPENDENT TELEPHONE ASSOCIATION. v. MCI
TELECOMMUNICATIONS CORPORATION. 1978. 434 U.S. 1040
(1978) (Cert. denied).
UNITED STATES INDEPENDENT TELEPHONE ASSOCIATION v. MCI
TELECOMMUNICATIONS CORPORATION. 1979. 439 U.S. 980
(1979) (Cert. denied).
UNITED STATES v. AMERICAN TELEPHONE AND TELEGRAPH COM-
PANY. 1974. No. 74-1698 (D.D.C., filed Nov. 20, 1974).
UNITED STATES v. WESTERN ELECTRIC COMPANY. 1956. (1956)
Trade Cas. (CCH) ¶ 68,246 (D.N.J. Jan. 24, 1956); (Consent Decree).
VAN TREES, HARRY L., ed. 1979. Satellite Communications. New
York, NY: IEEE Press; 1979. 665p. (Selected Reprint Series). ISBN:
0-87942-121-5 and 0-87942-122-3 pbk; LC: 78-65704.
VERVEER, PHILLIP L. 1980. Computer Communications Inquiry II.
In Waters, Maureen L., ed. Communications Networks 80: Proceed-
ings of the Communications Network Conference; 1980 January 28–

30; Washington, DC. Newton, MA: International Information Technology Institute; 1980. 71-73. Available from International Information Technology Institute, 60 Austin St., Newton, MA 02160.
VERMA, PRAMODE K., ed. 1976. Proceedings of the International Council for Computer Communication (ICCC), 3rd International Conference on Computer Communication; 1976 August 3-6; Toronto, Canada. Washington, DC: ICCC; 1976. LC: 76-19189.
VIGILANTE, FRANK S. 1980. The Digital Network Becomes Reality. In: Electronic Industries Association. Telecommunications: Trends and Directions: An Electronic Industries Association Communications Division Seminar Program; 1980 May 27-29; Hyannis, MA. Washington, DC: Electronic Industries Association; 1980. 69-72
VON ALVEN, WILLIAM H. 1980. Part 68: A 'Living' Document. Telephony. 1980 September 22; 199(12): 50-62. ISSN: 0040-2656.
WADE, GLEN, ed. 1978. Packet Communications Networks. Proceedings of the IEEE. 1978 November; 66(11): 285p. (Special Issue Guest Editors: Robert C. Kahn, Keith Uncapher, Harry Van Trees). ISSN: 0018-9219.
WAGNER, DOUGLAS J. 1980. The Future of Local Rates. Phone Call. 1980 October; 19(10): 14-19, 26.
WATERS, MAUREEN L., ed. 1980. Communication Networks 80: Proceedings of the Communication Networks Conference; 1980 January 28-30; Washington, DC. Newton, MA: International Information Technology Institute; 1980. 305p. Available from: International Technology Institute, 60 Austin St., Newton, MA 02160.
WILEY, RICHARD E. 1979. How to Help Formulate a Viable National Telecommunications Policy. Communications News. 1979 November; 16(11): 70-71. ISSN: 0010-3632.
WILK, CHARLES K., ed. 1978. Selected Foreign National Data Protection Laws and Bills. Washington, DC: U. S. Department of Commerce; 1978. 201p. (Office of Telecommunications Special Publication no. 78-19).
ZIMMERMAN, EDWARD K. 1980. The Prospects for Public Information Networking in the 80's. Communications News. 1980 April; 17(4): 50-52. ISSN: 0010-3632.
ZIMMERMAN, EDWARD K. 1981a. Going Public with Electronic Message Systems: Incentives and Barriers. Government Data Systems. 1981 January/February; 10(1): 12-15.
ZIMMERMAN, EDWARD K. 1981b. Implications of Local, State, and Federal Government Use of Electronic Mail and Message Services. In: Vezza, Albert; Kahn, Robert, eds. Technical and Policy Issues in Electronic Mail and Message Systems: Proceedings of the American Federation of Information Processing Societies (AFIPS) Workshop on Technical and Policy Issues in Electronic Mail and Message Systems; 1980 December 11-12; Washington, DC. [1981]. (To be published in 1981). Available from AFIPS, 1815 N. Lynn St., Suite 805, Box 9660, Arlington, VA 22209.

II

Basic Techniques
and Tools

This section contains five chapters—two related to hardware and equipment and three that relate to software, systems, and techniques. The chapter entitled "Data Entry/Display Devices for Interactive Information Retrieval" by Howard Turtle, W. David Penniman, and Thomas Hickey, all of OCLC Online Computer Library Center, Inc., provides a balanced review of the data entry/display technologies incorporated in interactive terminals. The scientific foundations of data entry and display and related research and professional activities are surveyed. Since interactive terminals use relatively few data entry and display techniques, the presentation focuses on the component technologies rather than on specific terminal devices. The major component technologies are identified and described for both entry devices (tactile, optical, and speech) and display devices (hard-copy, CRT, flat panel, and speech). For each component, current work is summarized, future trends are identified, and the human factors associated with the use of the technology are surveyed. The range of available terminal configurations is presented in the form of a matrix showing which data entry and display technologies are commonly used together and which data entry technologies are commonly combined in a single terminal configuration. Future interactive terminal developments are projected.

Philip W. Williams and Gerry Goldsmith of UMIST, Manchester, England, review the use of small computers for information retrieval. In their chapter, entitled "Information Retrieval on Mini- and Microcomputers," the different types of microcomputer are surveyed, and a classification is suggested to distinguish the characteristics of various microcomputers and their area of applications. References are given to evaluations in the literature of the more popular types of microcomputer that might be used for information retrieval applications.

The development of in-house information retrieval systems on minicomputers is reviewed with reference to systems for personal file handling, systems designed for bibliographic collections of specialized information units, and systems where information retrieval has been integrated with other functions. Commercially available software packages are discussed, including CAIRS, MILOR, STATUS, and FACTFINDER (FACTMATCHER). The wide variety of projects being developed on microcomputers is reviewed, and information retrieval systems such as STAR, PRIMATE, and REFLES are discussed. The use of a microcomputer as an intelligent terminal to online systems has been noted by several authors. Its use as an aid to the search is discussed, and its use for carrying out research in information retrieval techniques and for improving the interface to online information systems are also presented. Information on the USERKIT and OL'SAM devices are included, and details are given of research work at Aston University, Drexel University, the University of Illinois, and the University of Manchester Institute of Science and Technology.

David Becker of IIT Research Institute addresses the topic of "Automated Language Processing." In recent years, two main factors have led to major changes in automated language processing (ALP): 1) the development of new cost-effective computer hardware leading to applications in word processing, character recognition, high performance printing, speech applications, and others; and 2) an emerging consensus for a model of computer-based knowledge manipulation that supports sophisticated natural language processing (NLP). This model has led to a number of high performance, practical question-answering systems that perform in such areas as medical diagnosis, analysis of electrical circuits, and travel scheduling. Becker notes that the main factor limiting more widespread use of these knowledge-based methods is the development of a more comprehensive collection of knowledge representations and functions to manipulate them that would enable such systems to handle a more general range of topics. He describes two ways in which these kinds of knowledge techniques can be applied to automating all the logical functions currently accomplished by search specialists in performing information retrieval: 1) the development of "subject expert" programs that are capable of inference in limited domains, and 2) the development of programs that act like ideal librarians in relying on rules of information science and background knowledge to perform the retrievals. Becker reviews publications relevant to these approaches.

Marcia J. Bates, formerly of the University of Washington, has analyzed the literature relevant to "Search Techniques." Search techniques are methods, heuristics, tactics, strategies, or plans, that may be used by people in searching in manual or online information systems. Bates points out that the term "search strategy" has various meanings in the papers she reviewed for her chapter. She defines and distinguishes search mechanics, search formulation, search strategy, and search profile. Coverage is international and chronologically broad, with emphasis on the five-year period 1976–1980. Topics include machine enhancement of human searching, physical search, psychology of searching, research with implications for search techniques, and search heuristics. Bates concludes that research is needed for comparing and testing search strategies in both the online and manual environments; research is needed on the process of browsing and on the psychological processes involved in searching; above all, there is a need to develop theory on the nature of the search process.

Donald T. Hawkins of Bell Laboratories reviews the developments of the past two years in "Online Information Retrieval Systems." He covers bibliographic databases and to a lesser extent nonbibliographic databases. His discussion of the user interface treats intermediary vs. end-user searching, the development of the search strategy, the quality of the database, and the interview between the end user and the searcher. Search management, including equipment, costs, and statistics, continues to be a popular topic in the literature of online retrieval systems and services. New online ordering systems have considerably decreased problems associated with document delivery and interlibrary loans. Online systems in Europe are in a period of rapid growth. There, the establishment of Euronet-DIANE and the International Packet Switched Service has stimulated online retrieval by lowering communications costs. Economic and policy issues, applications, and professional aspects of online searching are also addressed.

2

Data Entry/Display Devices for Interactive Information Retrieval

HOWARD TURTLE
OCLC Online Computer Library Center, Inc.

W. DAVID PENNIMAN
OCLC Online Computer Library Center, Inc.

THOMAS B. HICKEY[1]
OCLC Online Computer Library Center, Inc.

INTRODUCTION

Over the next three years we can expect a 20% compound annual increase in the number of cathode ray tube (CRT) display terminals in use (BENNETT). The commensurate expansion of all types of devices for interfacing people with computer systems will offer new design challenges and product opportunities. This chapter examines progress in the development of effective interface devices and outlines current directions in development efforts. It deals with "personal use" data entry/display devices for interactive information retrieval. (A personal use device is one that might be found at a work station designed to support an individual who is communicating with one or more computer-based information systems.) The chapter excludes data entry/display devices that are normally part of a large, shared computing facility (e.g., card readers, line printers) as well as personal use devices whose function is peripheral to data entry/display (e.g., microcomputers, floppy disks, modems) and devices whose primary function is not general-purpose information retrieval (e.g., point-of-sale terminals, automatic teller machines). The chapter organization is shown in Table 1.

[1] The authors thank Paul Philbin, Rebecca Purdy, and the staff of the OCLC Corporate Library for their outstanding support in assembling and organizing the materials for this chapter.

TABLE 1
Data Entry/Display Devices
for Interactive Information Retrieval

Data Entry Devices		
Tactile	**Optical**	**Other**
Keyboards	Bar code	Speech
Touch-	Optical character	Devices for
sensitive	recognition	the physically
displays	Light pens	impaired
Other		

Display Devices			
Hard-Copy	**Transient-Image**		**Other**
Std. paper	CRT	Flat Panel	Audio
Electrostatic	Standard	Plasma	Devices for
	Graphics	Light emitting	the physically
	Viewdata	diode	impaired
Electro-		Liquid crystal	
sensitive		display	
Thermal		Electroluminescent	
		Other	

Although the chapter focuses on recent work on entry/display devices, it provides historical coverage from the 1960s. Table 2 identifies previous *ARIST* chapters that had major portions devoted to entry/display devices. Other reviews of these devices include *LIBRARY COMPUTER EQUIPMENT REVIEW*, outdated pieces by MCLAUGHLIN and CIOLFI, and a review of bibliographic terminals by MALINCONICO.

SCIENCE OF DATA ENTRY/DISPLAY

Scientific Foundations and Related Research Areas

Important scientific research that contributes to the design and development of data entry/display devices comes from such diverse areas as electronics, optics, psychophysics, and ergonomics. As new devices are developed, additional areas will join the list. However, research will probably emphasize improvements to existing displays (SOBEL, 1977a) and data entry

techniques, despite exploratory work in such areas as speech understanding.

Fundamental models are being investigated that will allow us to improve
the effectiveness of existing devices (MILLER; MORTON ET AL.). The user
interface is felt to need improvement (BRENNER ET AL.; JAMES), and psychological aspects are receiving as much attention as physical devices. The
role of human factors in the design of display devices has been evaluated
(BOOTH & FARRELL; CAKIR ET AL.), and the impact of device selection
on such aspects as decision effectiveness is also being evaluated (KOZAR &
DICKSON; SCHINDLER). While the traditional sciences of electronics,
optics, magnetics, etc. are still receiving considerable attention (SOBEL,
1977a), the key to market success for entry/display devices may lie with the
"softer" sciences (*DATAPRO AUTOMATED OFFICE MANAGEMENT*).
Such factors as eyestrain are now being evaluated with greater attention to
the psychological aspects involved (STEWART), and texts on display devices
devote much of their contents to human factors (BYLANDER; GROVER).

TABLE 2
Past *ARIST* Coverage in Related Areas

Volume/Year	Chapters
15/1980	Chapter 2: Information Technology and Communications Chapter 4: Library Automation: Data Processing and Processing for Data
13/1978	Chapter 4: On-line Systems—Techniques and Services
12/1977	Chapter 6: Computer Communication Networks
11/1976	Chapter 5: On-line Systems—Techniques and Services Chapter 6: Computer Technology—An Update Chapter 7: Library Automation
10/1975	Chapter 5: Communications Technology Chapter 6: Library Automation Chapter 8: The Computer and Publishing
9/1974	Chapter 6: Library and Information Networks
8/1973	Chapter 6: The User Interface in Interactive Systems
7/1972	Chapter 5: The User Interface in Interactive Systems
5/1970	Chapter 11: Management Information Systems
3/1968	Chapter 7: Man–Computer Communication
2/1967	Chapter 7: Hardware Developments and Product Announcements
1/1966	Chapter 8: New Hardware Developments

Related Professional Societies

Professional groups that typically attract individuals working in areas related to data entry/display devices include: Electronic Industries Association, Ergonomics Society, Human Factors Society, Institute of Electrical and Electronics Engineers, Institution of Electrical Engineers, Optical Society of America, Society for Information Display, and the Society of Photo-Optical Instrumentation Engineers.

Standards

Various organizations develop standards related to entry/display devices. Table 3 identifies three basic types of standards, the organizations concerned with them, and examples of each type of standard. For additional information on standards activities, see the references in the table.

DATA ENTRY TECHNOLOGY

This section reviews the current technology through which a human can supply an interactive information retrieval system with data. The scope is restricted to information retrieval systems, but the comments apply equally well to interactive systems in general.

Ordinarily the user supplies an interactive system with data rather than information, but this distinction is becoming fuzzy. Many of the more recent data entry technologies involve a substantial transformation of the raw input to generate a semantically meaningful form. The representation of human speech produced by a speech-understanding system to interpret a database query may not be information, but it is at least a highly refined form of data.

The earliest forms of data entry used toggle switches through which an operator manually entered each bit of information required for the operation of a program. Although this method was truly interactive, it was less than "user friendly" and disappeared with the first commercial computers. (It has reappeared in the past decade with the emergence of low-cost personal or hobby computers.)

Early improvements provided the user with a larger array of switches for automatically translating data to the appropriate binary equivalent. Machine-oriented translations using an implied correspondence between a single switch and a binary value (16 keys for all possible representations of 4 bits) quickly evolved to more human-oriented translations, in which each key corresponds to an individual letter or function. Simple translations of switch settings have been quite effective. Few interactive users think that when they depress the key marked "A" on their terminal that they are setting a switch corresponding to a binary value.

Various methods of keyboard data entry have dominated the industry for the past 30 years and are only now giving way to technologies that can "read" or "listen to" information provided by a human user. Conceptually,

TABLE 3
Standards Information for Data Entry/Display Devices

	Communication Standards	Character Set Standards	Ergonomic Standards
Organizations	American National Standards Institute (ANSI)	American Library Association (ALA)	International Research Organization for Newspaper Technology (IFRA)
	Electronic Industries Association (EIA)	American National Standards Institute (ANSI)	National Institute for Occupational Safety and Health (NIOSH)
	International Telephone and Telegraph Consultative Committee (CCITT)		Institution of Electrical Engineers (IEE)
			Occupational Safety and Health Administration (OSHA)
	Institute of Electrical and Electronics Engineers (IEEE)		National Bureau of Standards (NBS)
			International Standards Organization (ISO)
Examples of Standards	ANSI X3.28	ALA character set	ANSI X4.14 Keyboards
	EIA RS-232C, RS-422, RS-423, RS-170, RS-343A (Display Monitors)	American Standard Code for Information Interchange (ASCII) character set	BS 2481 Typewriter Keyboard
	CCITT V.24	Extended Binary Coded Decimal Interchange Code (EBCDIC)	
References	MALINCONICO; MCNAMARA; WEISSBERGER	MALINCONICO; MCNAMARA	HANES; HART; MOSS ET AL.; RUPP; YANCHINSKI

at least, these newer technologies simply provide a more elaborate translation from switch settings to their binary equivalents.

For this chapter, the input devices now used for interactive information retrieval fall into three categories: 1) those that convert tactile information (e.g., pressing keys, touching a display screen) into machine-readable form; 2) those that convert optical information (printed characters or codes) into machine-readable form; and 3) "other" new or little-used data entry technologies, such as speech-recognition and special-purpose devices for the physically impaired.

Tactile Data Entry Devices

By far the most common input devices used in interactive information retrieval translate touch information into machine-readable form. These devices include the familiar typewriter-like keyboard and its variants, special-purpose displays that allow the user to "touch" what he wants, and those with which the user manipulates a hand-operated device to draw on a special tablet or to select information displayed on a screen.

Keyboards. Keyboards were used widely in the office environment long before interactive computer systems emerged in the 1960s, and their design and use have been studied at length (ALDEN ET AL.). Current keyboards can be distinguished by four characteristics: 1) number of keys, 2) key layout, 3) key coding, and 4) the switch technology used.

Number of keys. Commercially available keyboards have as few as 12 keys for applications requiring only numeric input (Touchtone or numeric pad) and as many as 220 keys for applications involving large alphabets such as Kanji (3,200 characters). A typical English language keyboard will contain as few as 52 keys for a simple typewriter arrangement and may contain well over 100 when special-function keys, control keys, and a separate numeric pad are included. Special keyboards designed to accommodate full alphanumeric input using one hand (12 keys) are available but not widely used (*COMPUTER DESIGN*).

Key layout. The physical arrangement of the keys can markedly affect user performance (ALDEN ET AL.), but no single layout has become an industry standard. HANES presents guidelines for the layout of keyboards for U.S. and international use, while BROWN focuses on Japanese keyboards.

Two common layouts exist for numeric keyboards. Touchtone layouts label keys from upper left to lower right; adding-machine layouts label keys from lower left to upper right. The most common alphabetical arrangement is the typewriter or "qwerty" configuration, but several variations exist (*COMPUTER DESIGN*; HANES).

Key coding. Key color, shape, and marking are commonly used to highlight frequently used keys or key groups. The coding scheme can have a marked effect on user performance. New methods for marking or legending keys are being developed for applications in which a single keyboard is used to represent multiple character sets. These methods range from multiply legended keys, keyboard overlays, and interchangeable keycaps for conventional keyboards to hybrid approaches, in which the keyboard is integrated with a computer-generated display that can be radically altered at will (KNOWLTON; *MACHINE DESIGN*).

Switch technology. Each key position on a keyboard is fundamentally a switch. The technology used to fabricate the switch affects user performance, expected keyboard life, and the range of environments in which it can be used. KEY TRONIC CORPORATION briefly reviews the switch technologies used in conventional keyboards.

Current trends. Keyboards will continue to be the predominant input device used in interactive information retrieval at least through the 1980s. Advances in keyboard fabrication allow mass production at extremely low cost ($25-$100). In the past most terminal manufacturers relied on custom keyboards, but the next decade will see more standardization and mass production. The next decade will also see a proliferation of new keyboards that represent multiple languages, multiple character sets, or multiple sets of function keys on a single keyboard. The human factors involved in the use of these devices are poorly understood, and much additional work will be required before they reach widespread commercial application.

Touch-sensitive displays. Touch-sensitive displays allow an interactive user to enter information by touching a special-purpose display to select from a machine-generated set of options. Their effective use requires careful structuring of the displayed information (SHAW). Touch-sensitive displays are widely used in computer-aided instruction (CAI), information retrieval (FOX & PALAY), and industrial control applications (MCEWING). The use of touch-sensitive displays as relegendable keyboards is becoming more common (CROOK).

The touch sensor is logically and physically independent of the display and may be viewed as a transparent grid positioned in front of the display. This grid may be a transparent sheet or an array of detectors positioned around the edge of the display. Four techniques are used for commercial displays: 1) an array of infrared light beams that are blocked when an object is brought near the screen; 2) an array of wires carrying high frequency signals embedded in a glass or plastic sheet, in which the change in frequency on an orthogonal pair of wires caused by the contact of a human finger determines the position; 3) an acoustic wave technique similar to sonar; and 4) a multiple-layer technique, in which the human touch brings a conductive plastic sheet into contact with a resistive substrate, generating a voltage that determines the position of contact. Any of these sensing techniques could be used with (or without) any type of display, but most commercially available units use CRT (CROOK) or plasma panel (*MACHINE DESIGN*) devices. SHAW describes representative commercial devices.

Other tactile data entry devices. A number of input devices have been developed in the past decade that are not yet widely used for interactive information retrieval but could be. This section describes some of them. RITCHIE & TURNER and CARD ET AL. (1978) provide more detailed reviews.

Joysticks. With a joystick, a tiltable "stick," the user can move the cursor on a TV or CRT screen by changing the stick's inclination. Joysticks were first used with graphics displays and TV games but have also been used as a low-cost alternative to light pens or touch-sensitive displays in experimental applications ranging from menu-driven information retrieval to text editing.

Mice. A "mouse" performs the same function as a joystick; it allows the user to change the cursor position on a screen. Rather than positioning a stick, the user positions the cursor by moving a small device mounted on wheels across a flat surface such as a table.

Digitizing tablets. A digitizing tablet provides a flat surface, in which an embedded array of closely spaced wires detects the position of a special wand or stylus when touched. It functions much like a touch-sensitive display except that it is usually opaque and thus cannot be mounted over a display. It also reads the position of a special stylus rather than a human finger and provides very high resolution (typically 0.01 inch). Digitizing tablets have long been used in engineering and graphics applications (MACHOVER ET AL.), but greater speed and lower cost (less than $1,000 for an 8½ X 11-inch surface) have led to their use in areas such as signature verification and the recognition of handwritten text and drawings (TURNER & RITCHIE).

Optical Data Entry Devices

Optical input devices convert visible information (e.g., printed codes or text, the contents of a CRT display) into a form that is directly usable by the machine. They are used to avoid manual keyboard entry or to enter information that is difficult to describe (such as a precise location on a CRT screen). Optical input devices have only recently come into common use in interactive information retrieval. Most of the current optical technologies were first used in areas such as inventory control, artificial intelligence (AI), and graphics (RITCHIE & TURNER). Three of these technologies are now used in interactive information retrieval: 1) bar code readers, 2) optical character readers, and 3) light pens.

Bar code readers. Bar code readers ("wands") are devices that "read" a label printed with a pattern of light and dark stripes ("bars") of varying widths. The pattern is converted to a sequence of characters, which is transmitted directly to the computer. In typical applications, bar code readers are connected directly to the user's terminal. Input text then appears to have come directly from the keyboard.

Several different methods for encoding information in the pattern are used. Some represent only numeric information and a few special characters; others represent a full set of alphabetical, numerical, and special characters. Common coding schemes include UPC (Universal Product Code, familiar to most retail shoppers), CODABAR, and Code 39 (U.S. NATIONAL LIBRARY OF MEDICINE).

Several techniques are used to "read" the code. The techniques are distinquished primarily by the form of light used (visible, infrared, or laser), the type of electronics used in the decoding (discrete logic or microprocessor), and the physical structure of the decoding unit (a hand-held wand that is passed over the label or a stationary unit over which the label is passed).

Bar code readers are used in library circulation control systems (MARKUSON; SIMPSON). Information about individual patrons or books can be retrieved by scanning a bar code label on a library card or book. Bar code readers are easy to use and offer significant improvements over manual entry in speed and lower error rates. Their primary disadvantages are the requirement for a preprinted label that cannot be read by humans and an error rate that, although it is lower than for manual entry, is still high.

Optical character readers. Optical character readers are similar to bar code readers but read strings of character information that have been printed in a special font. The label information can be read by a human, but the error rate is much higher than with bar code readers. U.S. NATIONAL LIBRARY OF MEDICINE provides a thorough review of current bar code and optical character recognition (OCR) technology.

Light pens. Light pens are hand-held devices that allow a user to transmit information automatically by pointing to a location on a CRT screen. The light pen responds to the wavelength of light emitted by the specific phosphors used on the screen. When the light pen is placed near the screen, its detector is triggered by the electron beam that paints the characters on the screen. Special circuitry determines where the electron beam is positioned and converts this information into a form usable by the machine (MACHOVER ET AL.).

Light pens were initially developed for graphics terminals but are finding use in interactive systems in which the user points the light pen at the appropriate response in a displayed list. They are similar to touch-sensitive displays in function but offer much higher resolution.

Other Data Entry Devices

Speech recognition. Much effort has been expended over the past decade to develop devices that can recognize and "understand" human speech (REDDY). Until recently, high equipment costs, limited vocabulary, poor performance with multiple speakers, and an inability to recognize a continuous stream of speech have limited the applications in which speech recognition could be justified (SIMMONS). One representative system has a vocabulary of 250 words, can recognize words spoken by a known speaker at 200 words per minute, and costs about $17,000 (MANUEL). Prototype systems for retrieving and entering inventory and financial information are being tested. If expected cost reductions and performance improvements materialize, speech recognition will become common in simple telephone retrieval applications by 1985.

Speech-understanding systems, which involve both recognition and the correct semantic interpretation of continuous speech, are still experimental. ERMAN ET AL. provide an excellent review of the current research.

Devices for the physically impaired. The development of data entry devices for the disabled has been spurred in recent years by the falling costs of hardware (VANDERHEIDEN), federal legislation designed to improve education and employment opportunities for the handicapped (BLASZCZYK), and the realization that many jobs in the information industry are well suited to handicapped and homebound individuals (GIANNINI). Access to information retrieval services is not the primary focus of current research, but many of the techniques that allow the handicapped to interact with their environment through a computer are directly applicable. Current data entry devices range from commercially available braille keyboards to experimental work stations for use by quadriplegics (SCHNEIDER ET AL.).

DISPLAY TECHNOLOGY

Display technology is evolving rapidly, and new product announcements appear almost daily. Display devices fall into two general categories: hard-copy and transient-image. Although it is generally accepted that the type of display can have a marked effect on user performance, little empirical data are available to support this thesis. KOZAR & DICKSON suggest that hard-copy devices can improve decision effectiveness in some applications. PENNIMAN & DOMINICK and TURTLE describe current research that can provide information about user performance with different display types. This section describes the basic methods used to form character images, reviews current hard-copy and transient-image display technology, and reviews new or little-used display techniques.

Methods of Character Representation

The information displayed at an interactive terminal consists of graphics and text. Except for special information systems that rely heavily on graphics (e.g., cartography), display is generally limited to text characters. Although usually discussed separately, the basic methods of character formation apply to both hard-copy and transient-image devices. JONES describes methods of character formation on CRTs, and WIESELMAN gives an excellent review of the common methods of hard-copy character formation. He distinguishes printers on the basis of three characteristics: 1) matrix vs. fully formed, 2) serial vs. line, and 3) impact vs. non-impact.

Matrix representations normally use an array of dots (dot matrix), although electronic displays often use bars or segments. BYLANDER and DILLOW present possible segment and dot matrix geometries, including the common representation of alphanumerics in a 5×7 dot matrix. Dot matrix printers offer lower cost and higher print rates than fully formed character printers (WIESELMAN). As the number of dots available for character formation increases, dot matrix printers approach the quality of fully formed characters. The decreasing costs of semiconductor memory and the availability of microprocessors for terminal control are resulting in dot matrix printers that are general purpose raster devices with tremendous flexibility. A raster device views a page or screen as a huge dot matrix containing between 3,000 and 90,000 dots per square inch and allows the display of graphics, bold face headings, unusual symbols, and special character fonts (WINNER).

Fully formed characters use the familiar typewriter technology, in which a plastic or metal slug cast as an entire character is brought into contact with ribbon and paper. Fully formed characters are most often used for high quality and offline printing. WIESELMAN gives a lucid review of impact techniques for both fully formed and dot matrix printing.

Hard-Copy Devices

Hard-copy devices can be distinguished by the type of paper used—either plain paper onto which ink or toner is applied or special papers that are sensitive to heat, light, or electrical charge. Plain paper hard-copy printers use one of three processes: 1) impact, in which a ribbon is forced into contact with the paper; 2) Xerography, which uses copier technology to bind a toner to the paper; or 3) inkjet, in which electrically charged droplets of ink are shot at the paper. All of these processes can produce very high quality output. Impact printing is the most mature, although price and performance continue to improve (ADKISSON; HURWITZ; WIESELMAN). Xerography has only recently been an option for an individual work station. It can produce very high speeds (two pages per second) with high quality and offers the promise of integration with office copiers. Inkjet is commonly used in high speed printers but remains too expensive for interactive terminal use.

Special-paper hard-copy devices invariably use a dot matrix or raster print mechanism. The special paper allows an image to be formed without the impact of a ribbon, offering quieter operation and higher speed than impact printing but increased operation and maintenance costs. Three special-paper processes are used: thermal, electrosensitive, and electrostatic. In the most common process, thermal, the image is formed on a chemically treated, heat-sensitive paper by a print head containing heated wires. Electrosensitive printers use paper with a thin metallic coating that is burned away by an applied voltage. Electrostatic printers use a special dielectric paper that retains a charge long enough to pick up a liquid toner. Electrostatic printing is similar to Xerography except that no intermediate drum is used to collect toner. It is the only special-paper process used for high quality output. Wieselman has excellent descriptions and diagrams of these devices.

Color hard-copy technology is summarized by HIRSHON. Color cameras with integral CRT screens are available and offer excellent prints. Color impact printers require at least three ribbon colors for forming color combinations. Xerography can produce color, but costs are prohibitive (about $28,000). Good color can also be produced with multiple inkjets. None of these techniques is widely used for information retrieval, and all cost considerably more than conventional black-and-white processes for comparable speed and quality.

Transient-Image Displays

For many interactive information retrieval applications, no hard-copy record of the terminal session is required. For these applications, transient-image devices offer several advantages: 1) higher speed, 2) lower purchase and operating costs, 3) reduced noise, 4) lower maintenance costs, and 5) longer life (SNIGIER, 1977). Transient displays currently dominate the terminal market.

By far the most common transient display device in use is the familiar CRT. Although several newer technologies have been developed (CHANG; WESTON) to overcome inherent CRT disadvantages (CRTs are bulky, heavy, fragile, and require relatively high voltages), none of these "flat panel" displays seems likely to supplant the CRT in the foreseeable future except in special applications.

CRTs. The CRT is one of the oldest technologies still used in the computer industry; early units designed for oscilloscopes predate the transistor. Continued improvements over the past 40 years have led to their widespread use in radar, TV, instrument displays, and computer terminals. Although CRT technology is relatively mature, major improvements in electron guns, phosphors, drive circuitry, and fabrication techniques have resulted in devices that bear little physical resemblance to their predecessors.

All CRTs operate by directing a stream of electrons against a phosphorescent layer onto a transparent sheet. The electron beam is steered or deflected by controlling a magnetic or electrostatic field through which it passes to selectively illuminate portions of the screen. Two methods are used to position the electron beam. Raster scan CRTs treat the display as an array of points (pixels) and scan the entire array, row by row, selectively illuminating individual points. Random scan (also known as vector, direct scan, or beam deflection) CRTs scan only those points on the screen that are to be illuminated. All TV and most terminal displays are raster scan CRTs. Random scan CRTs are used only in high-resolution devices (BUN).

The human factors involved in the design of CRTs are reasonably well understood. MARTIN reviews the physiological factors considered in the design of CRT displays and concludes that although modern CRTs are well matched to human vision, major improvements are possible. UMBERS examines the human factors of CRT use in process control applications; MOSS ET AL. review possible health hazards associated with CRT radiation.

For this review, current CRT displays are divided into three groups: 1) those of moderate resolution used in standard interactive terminals, 2) those of high resolution used for graphics applications, and 3) those of low resolution used for TV/viewdata applications.

Standard CRT displays. WARREN and DATAPRO RESEARCH CORPORATION (1980a; 1980b) review commercially available display terminals. WHIELDON describes the features commonly found in modern display terminals. HOUSE & SHANKLE and CRAWFORD give guidelines for selecting a display terminal for a given application.

A "standard" terminal display is a moderate-resolution (600–800 scan lines per screen), monochrome, raster scan CRT that measures 12-15 inches diagonally and uses green or grey phosphors. It displays 20-25 lines of 80 characters each and supports both upper- and lowercase characters using a 5 × 7 to 8 × 10 dot matrix. The display itself costs $70–$150, and when packaged with a keyboard and associated circuitry, it will cost $600–$3,000. Costs depend primarily on the "intelligence" of the associated circuitry.

The market for such displays is strong. It is estimated that two and a half to three million CRT-based terminals are currently in use and that this number will increase annually by 18-20% (WELLS; WHIELDON). Since these figures do not include the substantial demand generated by the home entertainment market, it is not surprising that display technology is under active development in the United States, Japan, and Western Europe. Five trends are evident in the current market:

- Cost reductions. Improvements in fabrication techniques both for CRTs and semiconductor drive components coupled with the increased use of very large-scale integration (VLSI) in control circuits will continue to reduce costs (WARREN). These cost reductions have resulted in cheaper terminals, but the physical display unit is no longer the dominant factor in terminal costs. Further display cost reductions will not significantly affect the cost of the end product.
- Color. Color displays in interactive terminals are becoming increasingly widespread. The development of high quality color displays for the home entertainment market is eroding the once significant cost advantage of monochrome displays (MANUEL).
- Larger screens. Improvements in drive circuitry to compensate for edge distortion at high deflection angles will allow larger screens (30-40 inch) (WARREN). Projection CRTs (which project the CRT image onto an intermediate screen) currently allow large screens (6 feet) but have relatively poor resolution (CHANG).
- Improved resolution. The amount of information that can be legibly displayed (the display resolution) depends on the bandwidth of the display (the speed with which the electron beam can be positioned) and the persistence of the phosphors (the length of time they will luminesce after excitation). Display bandwidth has been steadily increasing, and new phosphors are being developed (MARTIN). Terminals that can display 30–48 lines of 132 characters are available, and the trend toward displays of higher resolution will continue (BASSAK).
- Increased intelligence. Low-cost microprocessor technology has resulted in terminals that do more than simply transmit characters entered by the user and display characters received from the computer. In 1976 roughly 85% of all terminals were "dumb," but by 1981 it is estimated that over half of all installed terminals will incorporate microprocessor control (WELLS).

Graphics displays. The ability to display graphics as well as text is becoming common (MYERS, 1979). MYERS (1980) reviews the visual factors to be considered in graphics design, focusing on high-resolution color displays.

Interactive graphics displays are and will remain the domain of the CRT. New graphics terminals provide color in addition to several levels of grey (QUILLIAM; SNIGIER, 1980). The increasing demand for color will tend to increase CRT dominance (TANNAS & GOEDE). Low-cost CRTs support graphics by providing characters for vertical, horizontal, and diagonal lines and corner connectors, which can be used to draw a limited range of figures such as bar graphs.

This section is concerned, however, with full graphics in which each point (pixel) on the screen of a raster display can be manipulated. In a conventional display each character position is typically an 8 X 10 array of points (pixels), each of whose points is either "on" or "off." Each character to be displayed corresponds to a particular pattern of the 80 points in the 8 X 10 character array. To store the information that can be displayed on a conventional 80 X 25 screen, 2,000 characters of memory are required to completely specify the configuration of the 160,000 pixels on the entire screen. Thus, conventional displays use the fact that only a few of the possible configurations of the 8 X 10 array are required to represent characters.

In contrast, graphics displays allow each pixel to be specified individually. If we assume that the screen has the same resolution as the conventional screen just described, then ten times as much storage (20,000 characters) is required to represent the entire screen. The extra storage allows the display of any desired configuration of points rather than only those configurations corresponding to characters. Many graphics terminals allow each point to be specified as completely on, completely off, or somewhere in between. To specify each point's intensity or grey scale value, two to eight times as much information is needed. Allowing each point to have both color and intensity values results in even larger information requirements. Color graphics resolution is normally limited to 512 X 512 although resolutions of 4096 X 4096 are available (DATAPRO RESEARCH CORPORATION, 1979). These higher resolutions are the result of improved screens and decreasing costs of the storage needed to support such displays.

Graphics terminals are rapidly turning into graphics "computers" (ADAMS & WALLIS), which can apply complex operations to sections of the display and display memory. Many of the displays offer pan and zoom capability so that portions of the display's internal image can be selected for presentation.

TV/viewdata displays. There is a strong and growing interest in the development of home and consumer information systems (BASSAK; CARNE) that will use the home TV set as the display device. The TV set can be custom built to incorporate the required data entry and communications equipment, or a separate device can be clipped to the antenna leads of a standard TV.

Two basic approaches have been described: 1) teletext, in which information is carried on unused portions of a broadcast TV signal, and 2) viewdata, which uses a standard telephone and modem (CARNE). Viewdata systems are currently preferred because they lend themselves more easily to interactive use.

IEEE TRANSACTIONS ON CONSUMER ELECTRONICS presents 25 papers describing teletext and viewdata systems. Speculation on the future of viewdata applications abounds (CARNE; MARTINO), but little information exists to indicate which services will prove feasible and attractive to users. VIEWDATA/VIDEOTEX REPORT cites over 35 viewdata experiments in various stages of planning and execution. Their results will provide some information about potential use; however, lack of experience and uncertainty about the effect on existing communications facilities, regulatory issues, and international standards (BROTMAN; CICIORA; HOLMES) make current projections unreliable.

Flat panel displays. Much research is being done to replace CRTs with flat panel displays (WINNER). Flat panels promise compact, portable displays, but as WESTON points out, when the number of characters exceeds 200, the CRT display is unsurpassed in terms of cost and image quality. Current research focuses on displays with full graphics capabilities suitable for TV (HAYASHI ET AL.; SOBEL, 1977a; UCHIIKE & FUKUSHIMA) and on improved small displays (DAVIES ET AL.; HEFTMAN; JENNINGS; KING; MCDERMOTT).

The major alternatives to CRTs are plasma panels, light emitting diodes (LEDs), liquid crystal (LC) displays, and electroluminescent (EL) displays. Less proven technologies include displays made up of colored microscopic particles and film. Of these CRT alternatives, only the plasma panel is widely used in terminals (ALLAN).

BYLANDER offers a lengthy technical review of electronic displays, including a short section on CRTs. AICHROTH and ALLAN provide shorter and less technical reviews of CRT alternatives. HAYASHI ET AL., KOJIMA, and UCHIIKE & FUKUSHIMA discuss recent trends in flat panel research in Japan. DILLOW contrasts the tradeoffs between display cost and application suitability. STEYER & GOEDE outline future display requirements (100-140 points per inch with grey scale and color capability) and the challenges they pose. The human eye's extreme sensitivity to edge discontinuities remains a major problem for flat panel displays, as does the need to address the hundreds of thousands of pixels needed for competitive displays. TANNAS & GOEDE review the alternatives to CRTs and are pessimistic about their future. ANDREWS notes that if research on CRTs with higher deflection angles is successful, the CRT will continue to be the dominant display.

Plasma panels. The plasma panels used as terminals are AC (alternating current) plasma panels, a type of gas discharge display. The light is produced by the electrical stimulation of a light-emitting gas, normally neon with small amounts of other gases, such as argon. PLESHKO gives an overview of the present technology, and WINNER reviews the current research in AC and DC (direct current) plasma panel technology. Research on TV applications, including color, is reported in HAYASHI ET AL. and UCHIIKE & FUKUSHIMA. The plasma panel's major advantages are the inherent memory of the screen and its transparency, which makes it suitable for rear projection.

LED displays. LEDs are most often used for small, single-line displays. The standard color is red, although other colors are possible (JENNINGS). The light is produced by a semiconductor diode that emits light when forward-biased (the polarity and magnitude of the applied voltage support the flow of current). Its advantages include low cost, simple drive circuitry (BYLANDER), and proven longevity (HEFTMAN). Although AICHROTH reports arrays of 50 LEDs per inch and KOJIMA describes arrays of moderate size, the application to general information retrieval seems limited to small hand-held devices.

70   HOWARD TURTLE, DAVID PENNIMAN AND THOMAS HICKEY

LC displays. LC displays (LCDs) compete directly with LED displays and have an edge in alphanumeric applications (DAVIES ET AL.; DEWEY ET AL.). The operation of LCDs is fundamentally different from most electronic displays. LCDs do not generate light but depend on reflected light, as does a printed page. This property makes them more useful than LEDs under high ambient light conditions; LCDs are the only transient image displays that are useful under very bright light. Liquid crystals are organic compounds whose light transmission properties change when their molecular alignment is altered by an electric field. Their main advantage is low power consumption. Low switching speeds (MORTON ET AL.; STEYER & GOEDE) are an impediment for TV applications, but low power consumption may make them the display of choice for hand-held devices. LCDs are being considered by the French for videophone applications (*ELECTRONICS*).

EL displays. EL displays, previously dismissed as impractical (AICHROTH), are now becoming available (ALLAN; DEJACKMO; WINNER). They are fundamentally similar to LEDs, but because of differences in fabrication techniques and applications, they are discussed separately in the literature. RANBY & SMITH give a good review of EL displays and cite low efficiency as their main disadvantage. STEYER & GOEDE feel that uniformity is also a problem. MILLER & SCHLAM review the application of thin-film EL displays. Application of this technology to information retrieval in the future is unknown.

Other flat panel displays. Other flat panel display technologies exist, but they are experimental. One of the best developed is a large screen display with light supplied by laser (SHOHAT). Displays using microscopic balls, which are colored on one side, are being developed (LEE; SHERIDON & BERKOVITZ; WINNER) as are electrophoretic displays, which use magnetic particles suspended in a densely colored liquid with which they interact (JENNINGS). The advantages of the particle displays are their inherent memory and low power requirements. Much work is needed before any of these systems will be commercially feasible.

Other Display Devices

Audio. Audio response is rapidly becoming a viable alternative to the conventional text display. Synthesized speech in toys, notably Speak and Spell by Texas Instruments, Inc. (BASSAK), has resulted in the widespread availability of comparatively inexpensive integrated circuits that can be used for speech output. MIKI ET AL. suggest an alternative approach—building a synthesizer from high speed microprocessors. WITTEN & ABBESS give a complete listing of a program that accepts a phonetic representation of speech and controls a voice synthesizer with a microcomputer.

One current application of voice synthesis is an automated telephone information service (WITTEN & MADAMS). It can give the time, play games, and provide information about electronic components. Witten and Madams describe the present state of speech synthesis as mediocre but claim that experience shows that users quickly and permanently adjust to the strange "accent." Another major application of voice synthesis provides speech for those who are blind and nonverbal.

Devices for the physically impaired. Microcomputers have had a major impact on the support that can be provided to the handicapped (AYLOR ET AL.). Unfortunately, many handicapped persons have unique problems that are not amenable to standard solutions, and the resulting custom designs are notoriously difficult to maintain (VANDERHEIDEN).

Retrieval terminals for the blind use either tactile output (e.g., braille terminals) or voice synthesis. CRT-based terminals with oversized characters (1 to 1½ inches) are available for the partially sighted (WHIELDON). Speaking terminals can help the nonverbal person in communication, although alternatives exist, such as the "newscaster" portable displays (NEWELL & BRUMFIT).

Articles describing computer applications for the handicapped are available in *COMPUTER*. RAHIMI discusses terminals for the nonverbal that use voice synthesis as their primary output. ROWELL ET AL. are developing a system dubbed UNICOM (Universal Communicator) for a similar population. This unit, which is undergoing clinical trials, concentrates on text and text editing as its primary mode of communication.

CURRENT DEVICES

This chapter has reviewed the underlying data entry/display technologies used in current terminals; this section reviews the ways in which the component technologies are combined in commercial terminals. Several services publish periodic reviews of commercially available terminals (DATAPRO RESEARCH CORPORATION, 1979; 1980a; 1980b), which may be consulted for information about specific devices and manufacturers.

Table 4 consists of a matrix containing a row for each input technology and a column for each display technology and again for each input technology. Marked entries indicate which input and output technologies are commonly used together and which input devices are usually combined in terminals that allow more than one form of input. Multiple output technologies are not shown. Except for a printer used with a CRT, terminals that incorporate multiple output devices are uncommon, although some do exist (e.g., single-line LED display with hard copy). Note that the input/input matrix contains entries only above the diagonal.

The pervasive use of alphanumeric keyboards and numeric pads is clearly evident—they are the only input technology commonly used with all output technologies and have been used in conjunction with virtually all other input technologies. Except for speech recognition, all of the other input technologies are most often used to supplement keyboard input.

The widespread use of the standard CRT is also clearly evident—it is the only output technology used with all input technologies. There are two reasons for this. First, many of the input technologies shown were designed

TABLE 4
Common Co-occurrence of Data Entry/Display Technologies

Numeric keypad	Touch-sensitive display	Mouse/joystick	Graphics tablet	Bar code reader	OCR	Light pen	Speech recognition		Standard paper hard-copy	Special paper hard-copy	TV	Standard CRT	Graphics CRT	Plasma panel	Speech synthesis
								Input/Input / **Input/Output**							
X	X	X	X	X	X	X	X	Full keyboard	X	X	X	X	X	X	X
X	X	X	X	X	X			Numeric keypad	X	X	X	X	X	X	X
								Touch-sensitive display				X		X	
		X						Mouse/joystick				X	X	X	
							X	Graphics tablet				X	X		
								Bar code reader				X			
								OCR				X			
								Light pen				X	X		
								Speech recognition				X			X

for screen-oriented displays, thus favoring CRTs over hard copy. Second, most CRTs come equipped with a "printer port." Printer ports were designed to allow attachment of a hard-copy printer but are often bidirectional and allow a second input device to be connected directly to the terminal.

Two final notes regarding the information in Table 4 are in order. First, it indicates common usage. For example, there is no technical reason why both bar code and OCR readers cannot be used in a single terminal configuration, but no current application exists. Second, the fact that two technologies are used together does not imply that they can be purchased in an assembled package. Many of the configurations require equipment from more than one supplier.

FUTURE TRENDS

The development of new terminal devices is driven by two primary factors: the available component technology and the special needs of anticipated applications. Although these two factors are discussed separately, they are not truly distinct. New applications are driven, or at least enabled, by emerging component technology. At the same time, the development of new components is strongly influenced by the anticipation of markets generated by new or expanding applications. The next decade will bring new terminals developed for specific applications and will also bring marked improvements in performance and costs resulting from improvements in state-of-the-art hardware and software.

Technology Trends

Terminal devices used for interactive information retrieval draw almost exclusively on commercially available components. Terminal manufacturers rarely attempt to develop new technology, and even "custom" terminals are simply a new or special packaging of commercially available components. Improvements in terminal devices, then, can be expected to mirror developments in the computer industry at large:

- The low end of the terminal price range will continue to drop. HUTCHISON estimates that an intelligent home terminal will cost $300 by 1990.
- At any given cost, new terminals will offer improved displays and more intelligence.
- Increasingly powerful terminals will become available at the high end of the price range. Many terminal work stations are more powerful than the minicomputers of even five years ago.

Over the next decade these developments will be fueled by annual cost reductions of: 40% for memory components, 25% for logic components, and 10% for communications (HUTCHISON).

Terminals using keyboard input with CRT or hard-copy displays will continue to predominate during the next decade. New devices will present variations and improvements on the same basic work station. The following technology-driven changes can be foreseen.

- The resolution of both hard-copy and transient-image displays will improve markedly. STEYER & GOEDE contend that the trend is toward supporting the type of information possible on a conventionally printed page. This implies resolutions of more than 100 dots per inch with improved grey scale and color.
- Widespread use of graphics and custom type fonts will be encouraged by the increased use of raster scan/dot matrix devices in both transient-image and hard-copy displays (BOCHNER; CRAIG).
- Current intelligent terminals will be supplanted by increasingly powerful machines incorporating large amounts of memory, mass storage, and high speed communications capability. Today's terminals will evolve to stand-alone work stations, capable of a great deal of independent processing.

- Work stations within an organization will be connected to each other and to multiple mainframes by high speed local networks, permitting access to shared peripherals and integration with other office equipment.
- Touch-sensitive screens will become common in public use terminals. Optical input technology will not become common except in special applications. Voice recognition will become common for centralized systems accessed over telephone lines and in devices designed for the handicapped but will not find widespread home or business use in the next five to ten years.
- The number of terminals in use will grow at an annual rate of 18–20% (WELLS; WHIELDON). Terminals already outnumber typewriters in many offices, and substantial penetration of the home market can be expected by 1985.
- Flat panel display technologies will be widely used in small hand-held terminals. Hand-held personal computers are already available for less than $250, but they have small displays (24 characters) and no communications facilities. Hand-held terminals supporting 80 X 10 displays and communications over the switched telephone network are likely to appear within two to four years. By 1990, these terminals will offer improved displays and large storage and may use broadcast communications to eliminate the need for direct telephone connection.

Application Trends

Several applications are expected to influence terminal development in the 1980s:

- Low-cost viewdata terminals for home use are expected to become as common as video games, reaching 30% of U.S. homes by 1992 (MARTINO). This market is relatively new and difficult to predict, but early experiments indicate that the potential is large.
- Electronic mail (MARILL) is now being used on a relatively small scale. As postage costs rise and communications costs fall, terminals with local editing, mass storage, and improved communications to support electronic mail will become increasingly popular. Telecommunication currently handles 60% of all U.S. communications traffic and should grow to 75% by the year 2000 (MARTINO).
- If teleconferencing (JOHANSEN ET AL.; PALME) develops in the way its proponents envision, then graphics, video, and audio will join text as standard retrieval media.
- Word-processing terminals will demand displays with very large information capacities (on the order of 160 X 160 characters to allow simultaneous display of several text pages) and

high-resolution graphics. The ability to interact with and to display information from multiple sources simultaneously will be common. Current word-processing equipment will be integrated with other communication and information retrieval services.

The accuracy of these predictions can be determined only with time. It is common, however, to overestimate what may be accomplished in three to five years while underestimating what can happen over a decade.

CONCLUSION

Interactive information retrieval has existed for only 15 years. During this period terminals have evolved from noisy, 10-character-per-second, hard-copy devices with limited character sets and clumsy keyboards to the currently popular high speed (30–2000 characters per second), high-resolution CRTs using various easy-to-handle input devices.

Although terminals will continue to evolve, the important performance improvements will not be achieved through faster, lower-cost hardware but through greater appreciation of the human factors that are not well understood. For other devices, the human factors research has been inherited. It is not clear, for example, that the results of studies of typewriter keyboard use by skilled typists can be applied directly to keyboard use in interactive information retrieval. Studies that focus on individual devices are necessary, but they do not often address the context in which the devices are used. Initial research is being done to address the broader issue of task performance, but much more will be required if we are to succeed in making information services readily available to the public.

The terminal devices of the future are likely to play a larger role in improved interactive systems. They will become the individual's personal search intermediary, providing uniform access to a wide variety of information services, using different command languages and different machines in geographically distributed locations. Terminal devices already do more than simply accept and display data. Terminals of the next decade may well provide a personal gateway to all of the communication and information services required by an individual user.

BIBLIOGRAPHY

ADAMS, J.; WALLIS, R. 1977. New Concepts in Display Technology. Computer. 1977 August; 10(8): 61–69. ISSN: 0018-9162.

ADKISSON, JAMES W. 1980. Benefits and Limitations of Wire Matrix Printer Technology. Computer Design. 1980 February; 19(2): 160–165.

AICHROTH, J. W. 1977. Flat Panel Displays Offer Graphics Alternatives. Computer Design. 1977 October; 16(10): 101–106.

ALDEN, DAVID G.; DANIELS, RICHARD W.; KANARICK, ARNOLD F.
1972. Keyboard Design and Operation: A Review of the Major Issues.
Human Factors. 1972 August; 14(4): 275–293. ISSN: 0018-7208.
ALLAN, R. 1980. Display Technologies Offer Rich Lode for Designers.
Electronics. 1980 March 13; 53(6): 127–138. ISSN: 0013-5070.
ANDREWS, BOB. 1980. Contemporary Displays—A Review of Opto-
electronics Technology. Electronics and Power. 1980 June; 26(6):
465–467. ISSN: 0013-5127.
AYLOR, J. H.; JOHNSON, B. W.; RAMEY, R. L. 1981. The Impact of
Microcomputers on Devices to Aid the Handicapped. Computer. 1981
January; 14(1): 35–39. ISSN: 0018-9162.
BASSAK, GIL. 1980. Consumer. Electronics. 1980 October 23; 53(22):
214–218. ISSN: 0013-5070.
BENNETT, J. L. 1979. The Commercial Impact of Usability in Interactive
Systems. In: Man/Computer Communications: Volume 2, Invited
Papers. Berkshire, England: Infotech International, Ltd.; 1979. 1–17.
ISBN: 0-855395-70-2.
BLASZCZYK, HENRY J. 1981. Computing and the Handicapped: The
Challenge in Education. Computer. 1981 January; 14(1): 15–17.
ISSN: 0018-9162.
BOCHNER, PETER. 1980. Impact Vendors See OEM Sales Soaring. Com-
puter Business News. 1980 October: 1, 4.
BOOTH, JOHN M.; FARRELL, RICHARD J. 1979. Overview of Human
Engineering Considerations for Electro-Optical Displays. In: Parsons,
John E., ed. Advances in Display Technology: Proceedings of the
Society of Photo-Optical Instrumentation Engineers; 1979 August 29–
30; San Diego, CA. Bellingham, WA: Society of Photo-Optical Instru-
mentation Engineers; 1979. 199: 78–108. ISBN: 0-892522-27-5.
BRENNER, L. P.; HUSTON-MIYAMOTO, M.; SELF, D. A.; SELF, P. C.;
SMITH, L. C. 1980. User-Computer Interface Designs for Information
Systems: A Review. Library Research. 1980-81 Spring; 2(1): 63–73.
ISSN: 0164-0763.
BROTMAN, STUART N. 1980. Teletext and Viewdata—Technical,
Economic and Legal Aspects. Telecommunications Policy. 1980 June;
4(2): 154–155. ISSN: 0308-5961.
BROWN, CHARLES R. 1975. Human Factors Problems in the Design and
Evaluation of Key-Entry Devices for the Japanese Language. In:
Chapanis, A., ed. Ethnic Variables in Human Factors Engineering.
Baltimore, MD: The Johns Hopkins University Press; 1975. 207–224.
BUN, JEAN. 1980. Comparative Evaluation of High-Resolution Color
CRTs. In: Winner, Lewis, ed. Society for Information Display (SID)
International Symposium Digest of Technical Papers: Volume 11; 1980
April 29–May 1; San Diego, CA. Los Angeles, CA: SID; 1980. 166–
167. LC: 75-642555.
BYLANDER, E. G. 1979. Electronic Displays. New York, NY: McGraw-
Hill, Inc.; 1979. 175p. ISBN: 0-07-009510-8.
CAKIR, A.; HART, D. J.; STEWART, T. F. M. 1980. Visual Display Ter-
minals. Chichester, England: John Wiley & Sons; 1980. 334p.
CARD, STUART K.; ENGLISH, W. K.; BURR, B. J. 1978. Evaluation of
Mouse, Rate-Controlled Isometric Joystick, and Text Keys for Text
Selection on a CRT. Ergonomics. 1978 August; 21(8): 601–613. ISSN:
0014-0139.

DATA ENTRY/DISPLAY DEVICES 77

CARD, STUART K.; MORAN, THOMAS P.; NEWELL, ALLEN. 1980. The Keystroke Level Model for User Performance Time with Interactive Systems. Communications of the ACM. 1980 July; 23(7): 396-410. ISSN: 0001-0782.

CARNE, E. B. 1979. The Wired Household. IEEE Spectrum. 1979 October; 16(10): 61-66. ISSN: 0018-9235.

CHANG, I. F. 1980. Recent Advances in Display Technologies. Proceedings of the Society for Information Display. 1980; 21(2): 45-54. ISSN: 0036-1496.

CICIORA, WALTER S. 1980. Consumer Information Display Systems. In: Winner, Lewis, ed. Society for Information Display (SID) International Symposium Digest of Technical Papers: Volume 11; 1980 April 29–May 1; San Diego, CA. Los Angeles, CA: SID; 1980. 18-19. LC: 75-642555.

CIOLFI, PHILLIP K. 1973. Communications Terminals. Modern Data. 1973 April; 6(4): 44-57. ISSN: 0026-7678.

COMPUTER. 1981. Computing and the Handicapped. Computer. 1981 January; 14(1): 115p. (Entire issue on title topic). ISSN: 0018-9162.

COMPUTER DESIGN. 1978. Typing Keyboard Provides 128 ASCII Characters Using One Hand. Computer Design. 1978 April; 17(4): 48, 52.

CRAIG, PETER. 1980. Matrix Printers. Digital Design. 1980 December; 10(12): 50.

CRAWFORD, WALT. 1980. CRT Terminal Checklist. Journal of Library Automation. 1980 March; 13(1): 36-44. ISSN: 0022-2240.

CROOK, K. 1976. CRT Touch Panels Provide Maximum Flexibility in Computer Interaction. Control Engineering. 1976 July; 23: 33-34. ISSN: 0010-8049.

DATAPRO AUTOMATED OFFICE MANAGEMENT. 1980. Ergonomics: The Gymnastics of System Design. Datapro Automated Office Management. 1980 September; 4(9): 1-2. Available from: Datapro Research Corporation, Delran, NJ 08075.

DATAPRO RESEARCH CORPORATION. 1979. All About Graphics Display Devices. In: Datapro Research Corporation. Datapro 70: The EDP Buyer's Bible. Delran, NJ: Datapro; 1979 October. Volume 2: 92a-92w. Available from: Datapro Research Corporation, Delran, NJ 08075.

DATAPRO RESEARCH CORPORATION. 1980a. All About Alphanumeric Display Terminals. In: Datapro Research Corporation. Datapro 70: The EDP Buyer's Bible. Delran, NJ: Datapro; 1980 June. Volume 2. Available from: Datapro Research Corporation, Delran, NJ 08075.

DATAPRO RESEARCH CORPORATION. 1980b. All About Teleprinter Terminals. In: Datapro Research Corporation. Datapro 70: The EDP Buyer's Bible. Delran, NJ: Datapro; 1980 September. Volume 2. Available from: Datapro Research Corporation, Delran, NJ 08075.

DAVIES, D.; FISCHER, W.; FORCE, G.; HARRISON, K.; LU, S. 1980. Practical Liquid Crystal Display Forms Forty Characters. Electronics. 1980 January 3; 53(1): 151-156. ISSN: 0013-5070.

DEJACKMO, M. 1980. Major Challenge to CRTs from Flat-Panel Displays. Mini-Micro Systems. 1980 November; 13(11): 113-114.

DEWEY, ANTHONY G.; JACOBS, JOHN T.; HUTH, BERNARD G.; SINCERBOX, GLENN T.; SPROKEL, GERARD J.; JULIANA, ANTHONY; KOEPCKE, RICHARD W. 1977. A 2000-Character Thermally-Addressed

Liquid Crystal Projection Display. In: Winner, Lewis, ed. Digest of Technical Papers of the Society for Information Display International Symposium (SID); 1977 April 19–21; Boston, MA. Los Angeles, CA: SID; 1977. 108–109.

DILLOW, J. W. 1977. Ergonomics versus Economics in Display Systems. Span. 1977 May–June; 13(3): 5–9.

ELECTRONICS. 1977. French Lab Produces Tiny LCD for Videophone Applications. Electronics. 1977 December 22; 50(26): 55–56. ISSN: 0013-5070.

ERMAN, LEE D.; HAYES-ROTH, FREDERICK; LESSER, VICTOR R.; REDDY, D. RAJ. 1980. The Hearsay-II Speech Understanding System: Integrating Knowledge to Resolve Uncertainty. Computing Surveys. 1980 June; 12(2): 213–253. ISSN: 0010-4892.

FOX, M. S.; PALAY, A. J. 1979. The BROWSE System: An Introduction. In: Tally, Roy D.; Dueltgen, Ronald R., eds. Information Choices and Policies: Proceedings of the American Society for Information Science 42nd Annual Conference: Volume 16; 1979 October 14–18; Minneapolis, MN. White Plains, NY: Knowledge Industry Publications, Inc.; 1979. 183–193. ISSN: 0044-7870; ISBN: 0-914236-47-4; LC: 64-8303.

GENNETTEN, E. W. 1979. An Overview of Military Tactical Display Terminals. Computer Design. 1979 May; 18(5): 191–200.

GIANNINI, MARGARET J. 1981. Computing and the Handicapped: A Promising Alliance. Computer. 1981 January; 14(1): 12–13. ISSN: 0018-9162.

GROVER, DERRICK, ed. 1976. Visual Display Units and Their Application. Surrey, England: IPC Science & Technology Press, Ltd.; 1976. 207p. ISBN: 0-902852-65-5.

HANES, LEWIS F. 1975. Human Factors in International Keyboard Arrangement. In: Chapanis, A., ed. Ethnic Variables in Human Factors Engineering. Baltimore, MD: The Johns Hopkins University Press; 1975. 189–206.

HART, DAVID J. 1976. The Human Aspects of Working with Visual Display Terminals. 1976 February. 30p. (International Research Association for Newspaper Technology (IFRA) Research Report no. 76/02). Available from: IFRA, Washingtonplatz 1-61, Darmstadt, West Germany.

HAYASHI, KOZO; YOKOZAWA, MINORI; KOIKE, JUNRO; SAKAI, TETSUO; MATSUZAKI, HIDEOMI; KANEKO, RYUICHI; KOJIMA, TAKEHIRO; OHISHI, IWAD. 1979. Gas-Discharge Panels for Color TV Display. 1979 March. 46p. (NHK Technical Monograph no. 28).

HEFTMAN, G. 1979. Focus On Alphanumeric Displays: Bright Future for Colorful, Intelligent Rivals. Electronic Design. 1979 September 13; 27(19): 163–168.

HIRSHON, B. 1980. Guide to Color Hard-Copy. Digital Design. 1980 September; 10(9): 46–56.

HOLMES, EDITH. 1980. Why the U.S. Isn't Rushing on Videotex Standards. Business Week. 1980 November 17; (2663): 148, 152. ISSN: 0007-7135.

HOUSE, WILLIAM C.; SHANKLE, JAMES E. 1979. A User-Oriented Approach Assists Terminal Selection in Educational Institutions. Journal of Educational Data Processing. 1979; 16(2): 9–14. ISSN: 0022-0647.

HURWITZ, JUDITH. 1980. Dot Matrix Line Printers Securing a Niche. Mini-Micro Systems. 1980 March; 13(3): 58, 60, 67, 68.

HUTCHISON, W. G. 1979. Computer Technology to 1990. Computer Data. 1979 May; 23-25.
IEEE TRANSACTIONS ON CONSUMER ELECTRONICS. 1979. Consumer Text Display Systems (Teletext and Viewdata). IEEE Transactions on Consumer Electronics. 1979 July; CE-25(3): 235-429. (Entire issue on title topic). ISSN: 0098-3063.
JAMES, E. B. 1980. The User Interface. The Computer Journal. 1980 February; 23(1): 25-28. ISSN: 0010-4620.
JENNINGS, BRIAN. 1977. Displays. Electronic Engineering. 1977 February; 49: 69, 71, 73, 75, 77, 79. ISSN: 0013-4902.
JOHANSEN, R.; VALLEE, J.; SPANGLER, K. 1978. Electronic Meetings: Utopian Dreams & Complex Realities. The Futurist. 1978 October; 12(4): 313-319. ISSN: 0016-3317.
JONES, IORWERTH. 1976. The Technology of Visual Display Units. In: Grover, Derrick, ed. Visual Display Units and Their Application. Berkshire, England: IPC Science & Technology Press, Ltd.; 1976. 40-62. ISBN: 0-902852-65-5.
KEY TRONIC CORPORATION. 1980. Keyboards. Digital Design. 1980 December; 10(12): 64, 94.
KING, T. 1978. Displays? Engineering. 1978 December; 218: 1328-1329. ISSN: 0013-7782.
KNOWLTON, K. C. 1977. Computer Displays Optically Superimposed on Input Devices. The Bell System Technical Journal. 1977 March; 56(3): 367-383. ISSN: 0005-8580.
KOJIMA, TAKEHIRO. 1980. Recent Flat Panel Display Developments in Japan. In: Winner, Lewis, ed. Society for Information Display (SID) International Symposium Digest of Technical Papers: Volume 11; 1980 April 29-May 1; San Diego, CA. Los Angeles, CA: SID; 1980. 22-23. LC: 75-642555.
KOZAR, K. A.; DICKSON, G. W. 1978. An Experimental Study of the Effects of Data Display Media on Decision Effectiveness. International Journal of Man-Machine Studies. 1978; 10: 495-505. ISSN: 0020-7373.
LEE, LAWRENCE L. 1977. Matrix-Addressed Magnetic Particles Displays. In: Winner, Lewis, ed. Digest of Technical Papers of the Society for Information Display (SID) International Symposium; 1977 April 19-21; Boston, MA. Los Angeles, CA: SID; 1977. 112-113.
LIBRARY COMPUTER EQUIPMENT REVIEW. 1979. Display Terminals: A Review of Features & Functions. Library Computer Equipment Review. 1979 July-December; 1(2): 68-79. ISSN: 0191-1295.
MACHINE DESIGN. 1977. Man Touches Display Panel to Communicate with Machine. Machine Design. 1977 April; 49: 8-10. ISSN: 0024-9114.
MACHOVER, C.; NEIGHBORS, M.; STUART, C. 1977. Graphics Displays: Factors in Systems Design. IEEE Spectrum. 1977 October; 14(10): 22-27. ISSN: 0018-9235.
MALINCONICO, S. MICHAEL. 1978. Bibliographic Terminals, Development Status—United States—1977. Libri: International Library Review. 1978; 28(2): 87-108. ISSN: 0024-2667.
MANUEL, TOM. 1980. Computers and Peripherals. Electronics. 1980 October 23; 53(22): 192-196, 201-202. ISSN: 0013-5070.
MARKUSON, BARBARA EVANS. 1978. Granting Amnesty and Other

80   HOWARD TURTLE, DAVID PENNIMAN AND THOMAS HICKEY

Fascinating Aspects of Automated Circulation. American Libraries. 1978 April; 9(4): 205–222. ISSN: 0002-9769.

MARILL, THOMAS. 1979. Readers' Forum: Time to Retire the Telephone? Datamation. 1979 August; 25(9): 185–188. ISSN: 0011-6963.

MARTIN, ANDRE. 1977. The CRT/Observer Interface. Electro-Optical Systems Design. 1977 June; 9(6): 35–41. ISSN: 0146-8162.

MARTINO, JOSEPH P. 1979. Telecommunications in the Year 2000. The Futurist. 1979 April; 13(2): 95–101. ISSN: 0016-3317.

MCDERMOTT, JIM. 1977. Focus on Readouts. Electronic Design. 1977 December 6; 25(25): 56–64.

MCEWING, R. W. 1977. Touch Displays in Industrial Computer Systems. In: Proceedings of the International Conference on Displays for Man-Machine Systems; 1977 April 4–7; Lancaster, England. London, England: Institution of Electrical Engineers; 1977. 24–27. ISBN: 0-852961-73-1.

MCLAUGHLIN, RICHARD A. 1973. Alphanumeric Display Terminal Survey. Datamation. 1973 November; 19(11): 71–92. ISSN: 0011-6963.

MCNAMARA, JOHN E. 1977. Technical Aspects of Data Communication. Bedford, MA: Digital Equipment Corporation, 1977. 387p. ISBN: 0-932376-01-0; LC: 77-93590.

MIKI, N.; NOMURA, T.; NAGAI, N. 1978. Speech Synthesizer Terminal Using a Microprocessor. In: Proceedings of the International Conference on Cybernetics and Society; 1978 November 3–7; Tokyo-Kyoto, Japan. New York, NY: IEEE Press; 1978. 1289–1293. (IEEE Catalog no. 78 CH1306-0 SCM). LC: 75-28733.

MILLER, LAWRENCE H. 1979. A Resource for Investigating Human Interaction with Computers. In: Boutmy, E. J.; Danthine, A., eds. Teleinformatics 79; 1979 June 11–13; Paris, France. Amsterdam, The Netherlands: North-Holland Publishing Co.; 1979. 195–200. ISBN: 0-444853-49-9.

MILLER, M. ROBERT; SCHLAM, ELLIOT. 1979. Electroluminescent Display Technology. In: Parsons, John E., ed. Advances in Display Technology: Proceedings of the Society of Photo-Optical Instrumentation Engineers; 1979 August 29–30; San Diego, CA. Bellingham, WA: Society of Photo-Optical Instrumentation Engineers; 1979. 199: 71–75. ISBN: 0-892522-27-5.

MORTON, J.; BARNARD, P.; HAMMOND, N.; LONG, J. B. 1979. Interacting with the Computer: A Framework. In: Boutmy, E. J.; Danthine, A., eds. Teleinformatics 79; 1979 June 11–13; Paris, France. Amsterdam, The Netherlands: North-Holland Publishing Co.; 1979. 201–208. ISBN: 0-444853-49-9.

MOSS, C. EUGENE; MURRAY, WILLIAM E.; PARR, WORDIE H.; MESSITE, JACQUELINE; KARCHES, GERALD J. 1977. A Report on Electromagnetic Radiation Surveys of Video Display Terminals. Cincinnati, OH: National Institute for Occupational Safety and Health, Division of Biomedical and Behavioral Science; 1977 December. 20p. (DHEW (NIOSH) Publication no. 78-129). Available from: Superintendent of Documents, U.S. Government Printing Office, Washington, DC 20402.

MYERS, WARE. 1979. Interactive Graphics: Flying High. Computer. 1979 July; 12(7): 8–17. ISSN: 0018-9162.

MYERS, WARE. 1980. Computer Graphics: A Two Way Street. Computer. 1980 July; 13(7): 49–58. ISSN: 0018-9162.

NEWELL, A. F.; BRUMFIT, P. J. 1979. Experiments Concerned with Reading "Newscaster"-Style Displays. International Journal of Man-Machine Studies. 1979; 11: 287-300. ISSN: 0020-7373.

PALME, JACOB. 1979. A Human-Computer Interface for Non-Computer Specialists. Stockholm, Sweden: Swedish National Defense Research Institute; 1979 March. 10p. (FDA report C 10128-M3 (E5,H9)).

PENNIMAN, W. D.; DOMINICK, W. D. 1980. Monitoring and Evaluation of On-Line Information System Usage. Information Processing & Management. 1980 January; 16(1): 17-35.

PLESHKO, PETER. 1980. AC Plasma Display Device Technology: An Overview. Proceedings of the Society for Information Display. 1980; 21(2): 93-100. ISSN: 0036-1496.

QUILLIAM, H. 1979. Graphics Terminals Have a Colourful Future. Communications International. 1979 November; 6(11): 26, 28, 30.

RAHIMI, M. A. 1981. Intelligent Prosthetic Devices. Computer. 1981 January; 14(1): 19-24. ISSN: 0018-9162.

RANBY, P. W.; SMITH, D. W. 1980. Electroluminescent Panel Devices. Proceedings of the IEE, Part A: Physical Science, Measurement and Instrumentation, Management and Education Reviews. 1980 April; 127(3): 196-201. ISSN: 0413-702X.

REDDY, D. RAJ, ed. 1975. Speech Recognition: Invited Papers Presented at the Institute of Electrical and Electronics Engineers Symposium; 1974; Carnegie-Mellon University, Pittsburgh, PA. New York, NY: Academic Press; 1975. 542p. ISBN: 0-12-584550-2; LC: 75-30648.

RITCHIE, G. J.; TURNER, J. A. 1975. Input Devices for Interactive Graphics. International Journal of Man-Machine Studies. 1975; 7: 639-680. ISSN: 0020-7373.

ROWELL, D.; DALRYMPLE, G. F.; OLSEN, J. 1978. UNICOM: A Universal Communication and Control System for the Non-Verbal Motor Impaired. ACM SIGCAPH Newsletter. 1978 October; 24: 56-59.

RUPP, BRUCE A. 1980. Visual Display Standards Activity. In: Winner, Lewis, ed. Society for Information Display (SID) International Symposium Digest of Technical Papers: Volume 11; 1980 April 29-May 1; San Diego, CA. Los Angeles, CA: SID; 1980. 187. LC: 75-642555.

SCHINDLER, RICHARD A. 1979. Physical Measures of Image Quality and Their Relationship to Performance. In: Parsons, John E., ed. Advances in Display Technology: Proceedings of the Society of Photo-Optical Instrumentation Engineers; 1979 August 29-30; San Diego, CA. Bellingham, WA: Society of Photo-Optical Instrumentation Engineers; 1979. 199: 117-125. ISBN: 0-892522-27-5.

SCHNEIDER, WOLFGER; SCHMEISSER, GERHARD; SEAMONE, WOODROW. 1981. A Computer-Aided Robotic Arm/Worktable for the High-Level Quadriplegic. Computer. 1981 January; 14(1): 41-47. ISSN: 0018-9162.

SHAW, L. C. 1980. Why Touch Sensing? Datamation. 1980 August; 26(8): 138-141. ISSN: 0011-6963.

SHERIDON, NICHOLAS K.; BERKOVITZ, MICHAEL A. 1977. The Gyricon—A Twisting Ball Display. In: Winner, Lewis, ed. Digest of Technical Papers of the Society for Information Display (SID) International Symposium; 1977 April 19-21; Boston, MA. Los Angeles, CA: SID; 1977. 114-115.

SHOHAT, M. 1979. Computer Peripherals. Military Electronics/Countermeasures. 1979 September; 5(9): 56, 58, 62, 64.

82   HOWARD TURTLE, DAVID PENNIMAN AND THOMAS HICKEY

SIMMONS, E. JOSEPH. 1979. Speech Recognition Technology. Computer Design. 1979 June; 18(6): 95-101.

SIMPSON, GEORGE A. 1978. Automated Circulation Systems in Public Libraries. McLean, VA: The Mitre Corporation, 1978 June. 46p. (Mitre Report no: MTR-7769, revision 1).

SNIGIER, PAUL. 1977. Computer Terminals—Dumb, Smart or Intelligent, They Form the Key Man-Computer Interface. Electronic Design News. 1977 May 5; 22(9): 42-52. ISSN: 0012-7515.

SNIGIER, PAUL. 1980. Graphic Display Devices. Digital Design. 1980 April; 10(4): 39-44.

SOBEL, ALAN. 1977a. Current Display Research—A Survey. In: Technical Digest [of the] International Electron Devices Meeting; 1977 December 5-7; Washington, DC. New York, NY: Institute of Electrical and Electronics Engineers; 1977. 64-68. LC: 78-20188; OCLC: 4010637.

SOBEL, ALAN. 1977b. Gas-Discharge Displays: The State of the Art. Proceedings of the Society for Information Display. 1977 First Quarter; 18(1): 51-63. ISSN: 0036-1496.

STEWART, T. F. M. 1979. Eyestrain and Visual Display Units: A Review. Displays. 1979 April; 1(1): 25-32. ISSN: 0141-9382.

STEYER, T. R.; GOEDE, WALTER F. 1979. Challenges of Advanced Display Technology Development. In: Parsons, John E., ed. Advances in Display Technology: Proceedings of the Society of Photo-Optical Instrumentation Engineers; 1979 August 29-30; San Diego, CA. Bellingham, WA: Society of Photo-Optical Instrumentation Engineers; 1979. 199: 48-52. ISBN: 0-892522-27-5.

TANNAS, LAWRENCE E.; GOEDE, WALTER F. 1978. Flat Panel Displays: A Critique. IEEE Spectrum. 1978 July; 15(7): 26-32. ISSN: 0018-9235.

TURNER, J. A.; RITCHIE, G. J. 1977. Fast Computer Graphic Data Entry: A New Zero-Crossing Delay Technique. In: Proceedings of the International Conference on Displays for Man-Machine Systems; 1977 April 4-7; Lancaster, England. London, England: Institution of Electrical Engineers; 1977. 24-27. ISBN: 0-852961-73-1.

TURTLE, HOWARD. 1980. Evaluating Human/Computer Interaction in a Controlled Environment. In: Benenfield, Alan R.; Kazlauskas, Edward John, eds. Communicating Information: Proceedings of the American Society for Information Science 43rd Annual Meeting: Volume 17; 1980 October 5-10; Anaheim, CA. White Plains, NY: Knowledge Industry Publications; 1980. 320-322. ISSN: 0044-7870; ISBN: 0-914236-73-3; LC: 74-12932.

U.S. NATIONAL LIBRARY OF MEDICINE. LISTER HILL NATIONAL CENTER FOR BIOMEDICAL COMMUNICATIONS. 1978. Machine Readable Identification Systems for Library Materials. Washington, DC; 1978. 95p. (Lister Hill Contract report CR 7801).

UCHIIKE, H.; FUKUSHIMA, Y. 1977. Plasma Displays. In: Proceedings of the International Conference on Phenomena in Ionized Gasses: Volume 3, 1977. 361-381.

UMBERS, I. G. 1978. Facing Up to CRT Communication. Process Engineering. 1978 April: 75-79.

VANDERHEIDEN, GREGG C. 1981. Practical Application of Microcomputers to Aid the Handicapped. Computer. 1981 January; 14(1): 54-61. ISSN: 0018-9162.

VIEWDATA/VIDEOTEX REPORT. 1980. Box Score. Viewdata/Video-
tex Report. 1980 December; 1(12): 7-8. (Monthly newsletter published
by LINK Resources Corporation, 215 Park Avenue South, New York,
NY 10003).
WARREN, CARL. 1980. Computers and Peripherals. Electronic Design
News. 1980 July 20; 25(14): 152-164. ISSN: 0012-7515.
WEISSBERGER, ALAN J. 1978. Here's A Data-Comm Channel Saver:
Design A Serial Communications Interface in LSI. Electronic Design.
1979 June 7; 27(12): 98-104.
WELLS, LARRY J. 1978. The Market for CRT's. Telecommunications.
1978 April; 12(4): 67-68.
WESTON, G. F. 1978. Alphanumeric Display. Proceedings of the IEE,
IEE Reviews. 1978 November; 125(11R): 1077-1099. ISSN: 0020-
3270.
WHIELDON, D. 1979. What's New in Displays? Computer Decisions.
1979 September; 11(9): 14, 16, 20, 22. ISSN: 0010-4558.
WIESELMAN, IRVING L. 1979. Trends in Computer Printer Technology.
Computer Design. 1979 January; 18(1): 107-115.
WINNER, LEWIS, ed. 1980. Society for Information Display (SID) Inter-
national Symposium Digest of Technical Papers: Volume 11; 1980 April
29-May 1; San Diego, CA. Los Angeles, CA: SID; 1980. 254p. LC:
75-642555.
WITTEN, I. H.; ABBESS, J. 1979. A Microcomputer-Based Speech Syn-
thesis-by-Rule System. International Journal of Man-Machine Studies.
1979 November; 11: 585-620. ISSN: 0020-7373.
WITTEN, IAN H.; MADAMS, PETER H. C. 1977. The Telephone Enquiry
Service: A Man-Machine System Using Synthetic Speech. International
Journal of Man-Machine Studies. 1977; 9: 449-464. ISSN: 0020-7373.
YANCHINSKI, STEPHANIE. 1978. Newspapers Cast Worried Eye at TV
Screens. New Scientist. 1978 February 16; 77: 413.

3 Information Retrieval on Mini- and Microcomputers

PHILIP W. WILLIAMS
University of Manchester Institute
of Science and Technology

GERRY GOLDSMITH
University of Manchester Institute
of Science and Technology

INTRODUCTION

Survey of Small Computers

The cost of computers has been falling by a factor of 10 every four years (NOYCE), making them more affordable to those who work with information. When reliable minicomputers became available about ten years ago, organizations with large resources devoted to information gathering could purchase their own computer facilities. Until then some information work could be done by sharing a large computer facility with the rest of the organization but the advent of minicomputer facilities for $100,000 to $200,000 made dedicated use for information functions possible. However, at that price only a few large organizations could afford to develop systems, and computing for local information purposes was slow to spread.

Now significant processing power can be obtained for as little as $800, and a microcomputer system with disk storage and printer can be purchased for $3,500. (All prices quoted are approximate because they change rapidly.) These prices are within the reach of many information units and libraries, which are investigating seriously such an investment.

Micro- and minicomputers can be divided approximately into classes with a rough correlation between price and features.

Microprocessor kits. These can cost as little as $100 and can use a TV screen for display and a nonstandard keyboard for input. Examples are the Nascom (BORLAND) and the Cambridge MK14 (TOOP). In this form they are of interest only to a user who has electronic knowledge and are outside the scope of this paper.

Miniature microcomputers. A few small systems coming onto the market are engineered for the non-expert. The Sinclair ZX80 is priced around $200 and has a BASIC interpreter, a keyboard, and a limited display and can link to a domestic TV set, a cassette tape recorder, and some other peripherals (MCCALLUM; TEBBUTT, 1980a). The Newbury Newbrain has various models from $200 to $400 that have similar facilities, with the additional feature of an internal battery, so that they can be independent of the power source from several minutes to a few hours. Both Sharp and Radio Shack have produced a cheap microcomputer for the public (MILLER). The Radio Shack version sells for $250.

Personal computers. Several computers have been introduced to appeal to those with limited computer knowledge. They usually have a full typewriter-style keyboard, a computer chip that is so small that it is dwarfed by the other keyboard electronics, a video screen, and (in the cheapest form) a cassette tape recorder for storing information in a permanent form between uses. The smallest has 4,000 characters of storage available to the user, and the largest has about 48,000. Many of these are widely available and have been tested and reviewed in the consumer microcomputing journals. Surveys have been done of the TRS-80 (DENNIS, 1978a; FYLSTRA, 1978a; WITHERS), the Apple (HELMERS; SPIELMAN), the Commodore PET (CALVER & TEBBUTT; FYLSTRA, 1978b; *PRACTICAL COMPUTING*, 1978), the Texas Instruments TI99 (*PRACTICAL COMPUTING*, 1980; TSENG) and the Intertec Superbrain (WATT), and there is a general survey by FOX. the cheapest versions range between $6000 and $1,500, but the addition of storage on a dual floppy disk unit, which allows rapid access to any piece of information, will add about $1,100. A reasonable printer costs between $600 and $1,500.

Professional microcomputers. Some microcomputers are especially suitable for those who wish to modify the unit or to add extra equipment. Computer manufacturers such as Ohio Scientific, North Star (HEALEY ET AL.; SEGAL), and Cromemco (EISENBACH, 1979a) provide good information on the structure of their units. These computers are provided with slots for easy connection of equipment or addition of new facilities. In contrast, personal computers have all their equipment provided by the manufacturer; information on how to attach other equipment is often not available, and the construction of the computer would make this difficult. For most librarians a system with ready-made programs or equipment that can be used directly on the machine is desirable so that the need to tailor the machine personally is obviated. These machines usually cost from $3,500 to $10,000.

Small minicomputers. A number of machines in the price range $10,000 to $25,000 are essentially the beginning of the minicomputer range. They have a data unit of 16 bits, which means that each data unit can store two characters instead of one; more importantly the range of numbers that can be stored in one data unit is 64,000 instead of 256 in the 8-bit machine, making them more powerful than 8-bit units. They usually have 8-inch disks, allowing more storage than the 5-inch floppies, and they are more reliable. Their printers are more robust and expensive and can take substantial use. They can also be configured so that several users (four to 16) can use the machines simultaneously, particularly if the activity is data entry or file editing. Typical minicomputers in this class are the LSI 11 from Digital Equipment Corp. (DEC) and the Alpha Microsystems machine.

Microprocessor development systems. Some systems have been specifically designed for the development of programs that will be stored in read-only memory (ROM) and for testing and modification before a final version is produced. These are typically used by electronics engineers who design the components to fit into other machines. Although they could be used for ordinary computing, they would not be the natural choice for most users. The price range is $7,000 to $10,000.

Minicomputers. The cost of the larger minicomputers, from $25,000 to $200,000, is determined largely by their amount of disk storage and their complexity of operation. If many users need simultaneous access or if there will be significant access to the machine by telecommunications links or if several million characters have to be stored, then the cost will exceed the $25,000 to $200,000 range.

The librarian or information worker is likely to choose either a personal computer or a small minicomputer. The latter is recommended because vendors give more support for this type of machine and the equipment is more robust. More programs for microcomputers will be developed as users gain experience, but there will be an important difference between the personal computer situation and the historical development of the minicomputer. The low price of personal computers will make it difficult for software to be developed at a price that seems acceptable to the users. The costs of the programs will be very high in comparison with the purchase price of the computer—e.g., a ratio of 10 to 1 by 1985 is estimated. Thus, specialized programs will either be very expensive or they will be obtained informally with no support. There will be cheap programs with wide market appeal, such as word processing packages and small business accounting systems, and one must consider carefully how much information work can be done with these standard systems.

Useful information can be found in computer journals such as *Best of the Computer Faires, Byte, Computers and People, Creative Computing, Dr. Dobbs Journal of Computer Calisthenics and Orthodontia, Info World, Personal Computers, Personal Computer World, Practical Computing,* and *Small Business Computers.*

Difficulties to Consider

The microcomputer revolution is occurring quite differently from the way that mainframe computers were introduced, and there are important differences between the new possibilities for microcomputers and the earlier growth of minicomputer applications. Mainframe computers were introduced in specialized departments with high budgets, and the sale of the machines generated enough money to provide good support services for customers. The introduction of minicomputers changed the picture somewhat because the minicomputer does not need a special environment and its prices are low enough for purchase by individual sections rather than a whole organization. However, these machines still needed people with knowledge of computer practice to run them, and the prices have allowed some support from the manufacturers.

In the case of microcomputers the cost is low enough to allow many information units and even individuals to purchase them. However, these prices do not include a sufficient margin for the sellers to offer supporting service, and many are sold in retail shops. The paper by WALSH on the development of attitudes to computing applications shows the sequence of mistakes that are typical of those who are introducing computers for the first time. The many people who are starting to use small computers should learn from this experience.

Among the problems that need to be understood are programming costs, reliability, choice of supplier, and computer housekeeping methods. The true cost of creating new programs for personal use should be properly evaluated. It is usually cheaper to buy programs than to employ staff to build them.

Problems of reliability in both the components and the programs for small microcomputers still exist. The disk systems for two of the most popular microcomputer systems had programming errors that caused loss of data and programs. One author (GENTRY) describes the faults in the TRS-80 system, which were rectified in the NEWDOS improvement. *PRACTICAL COMPUTING* (1979a) described some faults found by the reviewers of existing disk systems. They state that the documentation for the Commodore PET system was very difficult to use until recently and was incorrect in some places, and there were serious faults in the TRS-80 and PET operating systems for a considerable time.

The choice of supplier is important. Support from the supplier in using the machine is necessary, and service and advice on new developments are also essential. Since microcomputer businesses are new and often small, the situation is unstable and some companies go out of business. It is just as important to assess the supplier as to judge the equipment.

In computing departments certain practices have been developed over many years to preserve the investment in programs and data. The amount of data, the cost of creating data, and even more important the cost of losing data become progressively more significant over a long period. The ease of programming often encourages new users to obtain their own facilities without the training in computer housekeeping methods that are essential to safeguard the information and programs that are established.

If a small microcomputer is purchased, the user should expect to need more knowledge of computing methods and should be prepared to learn about computer housekeeping. Those who do not wish to do this should purchase a small minicomputer and use programs that have been proven successful.

MINICOMPUTERS IN INFORMATION RETRIEVAL

Library Systems

The use of minicomputers for administrative purposes in libraries is not included in this chapter, but some of the significant contributions to this topic are mentioned to set the context for the library applications that have an aspect of information retrieval. The use of minicomputers in libraries was reviewed by PEARSON in the 1975 *ARIST*, and library automation was reviewed in *ARIST* by GROSCH in 1976 and by REED & VROOMAN in 1979. A book by GROSCH (1979) titled *Minicomputers in Libraries 1979-80*, which gives a comprehensive discussion of the topic, also includes a directory of installed systems and the results of a questionnaire on their use. Another useful source of information on minicomputer systems is the Proceedings of the Conference on Library and Bibliographic Applications of Minicomputers held in Australia (MIDDLETON).

The early computerized library systems depended in most cases on existing mainframe and bureau services, which did not give libraries full control over their operations. In many situations the libraries had little influence over their computer time—i.e., when it was available, how much was available, and its cost. Often the systems were not designed for library needs, and many institutions were slow to adopt online processing, which is appropriate for library activities. The advent of minicomputer facilities at a price that was within the budget of some libraries enabled the development of systems specifically dedicated to libraries and designed for their use.

However, the growth of these library systems was retarded by the belief that centralized data processing was the most cost-effective method. There is also a risk involved in mounting the effort needed for a new system. To develop a new system using a minicomputer controlled by the library demands staff who are willing and able to develop expertise in a new technical skill and are enthusiastic for system changes (WAINWRIGHT). Lack of suitable software on minicomputers, particularly for library work, was a problem in the 1970s because the software development for minicomputers lagged far behind that of the hardware.

The difficulties with minicomputers are now easing as more software for library applications becomes available. Traditionally, libraries have developed single application systems for a specific task—e.g., acquisitions or circulation control. Often a library was able to computerize only the most urgent function because it did not have the resources to computerize all applications at once. When single applications are developed separately, it is not easy to combine them into a coordinated system. The outputs from one system may be required for another, but the data format may be different or more information may be needed for the next system. Too often the problems are recognized only after attempts are made to add new systems.

GROSCH (1979) considers this situation and concludes that an integrated system is more complex to develop and therefore more costly but is probably worth the investment. With a well-designed database, extra applications can be added and data relationships can be changed with minimal reprogramming. Database management systems (DBMSs) were reviewed by HUFFENBERGER in *ARIST* (1979), and their application in libraries is discussed by GROSCH (1977; 1978).

In-house Information Retrieval Systems

Personal file-handling systems. The early information retrieval systems developed on minicomputers were intended for personal indexes and files to replace the diverse pieces of information collected from various sources, which were previously recorded on ordinary cards, edge-notched cards, or in notebooks or possibly not recorded at all. During the late 1960s and early 1970s, there were several small computer systems designed to store and retrieve records of this type. These systems are reviewed by LEGGATE ET AL. (1976; 1977) and include FAMULUS, SCRAPBOOK, SHOEBOX, and AUTONOTE.

LEGGATE ET AL. (1976) also describe the development and use of an experimental online personal file-handling system, the USERFILE project. It was developed at Oxford University on a PDP 11/20 minicomputer with 12K central processing unit, a 2.4-megabyte disk pack, and tapes. Two terminals were linked to the computer, and all staff and students in two chemistry departments were given the opportunity to use the system during 1974–1975. Results of a questionnaire indicated a demand and a need for such a system.

A similar system, called General Retrieval of Information (GRIP), was developed at Hoechst Pharmaceutical Research Laboratories in 1975 in response to user requests for computer storage and retrieval of bibliographic records in personal files (PARKER & THORPE). GRIP was implemented on a Hewlett Packard 2100S.

Both systems were designed to handle files containing up to about 4,000 records. They both use unformatted records—i.e., the user can enter any text up to the maximum length (500 characters on GRIP, 1,722 on USER-FILE)—to simplify data entry, which is the main problem in encouraging use of such a system. Individuals can use identifiers within their text to organize their file. Unformatted records were used to allow a wide variety of entered data and to allow different types of data to be mixed within a file. Two disadvantages of the system are that it is not possible to identify and search on a particular field (e.g., author or title) or to print selected fields.

Searching is done by serial string matching in both systems, i.e., the whole file is searched for the given character string. This method is slow—a problem when dealing with large files.

Most large information retrieval systems use inverted files with multiple indexes rather than serial searching in order to give fast searching speeds, a factor that becomes progressively more important as file size increases. A personal file system that uses this method is the Interactive Retrieval of Information System (IRIS), developed by TOLIVER. Like GRIP and USERFILE a flexible structure allows the user to enter data in various formats, but tags are used to identify fields, and the user specifies the fields that will be used for the indexes. The search language emulates DIALOG.

Specialized information systems. In 1976, STERNER & BREIDENSTEIN reported the development of a small information retrieval system on a Wang 2200B minicomputer at the Denver Wildlife Research Center. It was designed as a scientific reprint reference system and is based on a modified version of the Uniterm Coordinate Index System (UCIS). It does not have the flexibility of a system such as IRIS, with its inverted file system; keyword codes must be assigned to each article, and these codes are used for retrieval. Because the programs are written in Advanced BASIC, the system is adaptable to other computers.

Another computerized collection of references is the Hail Bibliography (CLARK & WILDHAGEN), which was developed on a Wang 2200T for the Atmospheric Sciences section of the Illinois Water Survey and was also written in BASIC. Records consist of citation number, author, title, reference, year, language, subject code, and geographic location code. Searching can be done on most of these fields, but the field must be specified before the search is performed. Boolean operators can be used to a limited extent on the keyword-in-title search, and truncation is allowed.

The same computer (a Wang 2200T) has also been used for a system called WASTELINE (SINGER ET AL.). The references in this system are concerned with food waste and its utilization, and in 1975 about 100,000 references were being handled each year. Because traditional office filing methods could not adequately store and retrieve these references, a minicomputer was selected. WASTELINE uses an inverted file with a thesaurus that indicates related, narrower, and broader terms in the system. Before beginning a search one can ask for the number of references under each thesaurus term. Search logic is then built up one keyword at a time with a Boolean operator. WASTELINE has now been superseded by FIRST (Food Information Retrieval by Selected Term), which will handle tens of thousands of references. Microfiche will be used as a secondary storage medium, and reference numbers in the inverted files will refer to microfiche frames.

A system that is different in structure is the Minicomputer Operated Retrieval (Partially Heuristic) System (MORPHS), developed by the Malaysian Rubber Producers Research Association and first reported by BELL & JONES (1976). It replaced a feature card system to eliminate the tedious tasks of drilling and repetitive filing. A Varian 620L, which was being used for other purposes, was selected. This is a minicomputer with 12K core, and this small storage limits the keyword length to eight characters. To improve the performance of this keyword system, automatic root finding and a feature allowing the role of a word to be specified were introduced. Plural forms are converted to singular ones, and index entries are reduced to their root forms by a stemming algorithm, which operates correctly 90% of the time (BELL & JONES, 1979). Role indicators are used to replace suffixes and affixes. Thus, either the root may be searched (e.g., MIX) or the derived forms (MIX-role A, meaning MIXING, or MIX-role D, meaning MIXED). Compound expressions and concepts can also be handled. These techniques are described in detail by BELL & JONES (1976).

The developments of this system, which allow more complex search strategies, are discussed by BELL & JONES (1980). They state that simplicity for the searcher is achieved only by increasing the system's complexity, and they believe that public information systems should be much more approachable by the ordinary scientist or user (BELL & JONES, 1978).

The AMP Inc. Information Center has developed a minicomputer system to store and to retrieve all their internal technical documents collected from various operating divisions (BIRULA ET AL.). When reported in 1978 there were 8,000 documents, and 600 new ones were being added each month. The system was designed to cope with many different types of present and future documents. All words (except those on a stop list) appear in the inverted files, so that all terms in a document are searchable. For document display the user can select a standard format (short or long) or choose the specific data elements to be displayed.

The AMP system incorporates three levels of dialog to cater to a wide range of users. The first level displays questions with multiple-choice responses to guide the casual user through the search process; the second allows the user to control the search but provides some assistance; the third dialog reduces all system responses to a minimum.

Integrated systems. A minicomputer in an information center is not limited to information retrieval, and some of the systems mentioned have shared the computer with other tasks. In this case a more effective system is possible if an integrated approach can be adopted although this requires careful planning at the design stage.

An investigation into the design and implementation of an integrated minicomputer-based system is described by KEREN ET AL. The Development of Minicomputer Applications in an Environment of Scientific and Technological Information Centers (DOMESTIC) provides for database creation and management, information storage and retrieval, reference and referral services, library management tasks, information center administration, and information networking. In 1978 DOMESTIC was in the pilot system design phase as a joint venture of Kayser-Threde (Germany) and the National Center of Scientific and Technological Information (Israel).

The information storage and retrieval component, described briefly by Keren et al., includes a thesaurus and a subject index file. Standard Boolean operators and commands can be used in any order or multiplicity, and it is also possible to search for terms in a particular order or proximity range. Either a multi- or partial-file search can be done.

The integrated approach has been applied to the design of the minicomputer-based system of the International Development Research Center (IDRC), which allows the same variety of tasks as DOMESTIC. The IDRC system is different in that it has been designed to conform to the relational model of databases. This concept is described briefly by DANELIUK in her comprehensive paper on the IDRC system (for further reading see MARTIN).

In a relational system a simple structure is adopted for the files at the expense of storage space and retrieval speed. Inverted files, used by most of the information retrieval systems discussed here, are used widely because they give fast access to data. Although relational theory does not provide for non-relational access, IDRC decided to add a facility for inverted files. The system manager can specify the fields from which keys are to be extracted for inversion.

DANELIUK describes the background of the IDRC system and its development and functions, stressing the importance of the definition of data and of their relationship to other data. The system includes a fully interactive user language and a multilingual thesaurus based on a list of economic and social development terms published in many languages by the Organization for Economic Cooperation and Development (OECD). The IDRC user can search in French, English, or Spanish, and the search terms are automatically translated into the other languages and linked by the operator "*OR*" for searching.

Software packages. Only a few commercially available packages specifically designed for information retrieval on minicomputers have been reported. Most were developed by an organization for its in-house use and have subsequently become commercially available. They vary greatly in scope, approach, and file organization.

The systems discussed here are mainly free-text systems (defined by LANCASTER as a "retrieval system that operates on words occurring in titles, abstracts or text"). ASHFORD (1980a) describes and compares the characteristics of DBMSs and free-text systems. He also reports the results of a study of the potential users and application areas for free-text systems in Britain (ASHFORD, 1980b).

Despite their variation, these systems seem to have two common aims: flexibility and portability (BOURDAIS; TESKEY). The user can choose from various data-entry formats and indexing techniques to match his particular requirements. The programs are written in high-level languages, FORTRAN being the most frequently used, so that the package can be mounted on several different computers.

One package that is used for many different applications is STATUS, which was developed by the U.K. Atomic Energy Authority at Harwell. It was originally designed for the storage and retrieval of statutes and other legal data, but STATUS now handles technical abstracts, research data, catalogs, data on hazardous chemicals, and many other types of information. It is mounted on both mainframes and minicomputers, and ASHFORD (1980a) discusses a selection of users, with applications and type of computer. TESKEY describes the system and its facilities and advanced features, with examples from the Harwell Automated Loans system (HAL). The application of STATUS to the library records of the Building Research Establishment is described by NEVILLE, and HAL is briefly covered in *VINE* (1980).

A similar type of system is a product of MINICOMPUTER SYSTEMS, LIMITED (MCS) and is called FACTFINDER (or FACTMATCHER). It incorporates database management, information retrieval, and text editing in a single system and, like STATUS, is being used for various applications.

In both STATUS and FACTFINDER all words in the text are indexed (except for stop words, which can be specified by the user). If the user chooses to format the records, searching can be restricted to a particular field (e.g., author). Both systems allow proximity searching and truncation of terms. STATUS also has a powerful "macro" facility. (A "macro" is a mnemonic for a set of previously chosen commands.)

The Computer Assisted Information Retrieval System (CAIRS) grew out of the need to computerize the information services of the Leatherhead Food Research Association, which collects a wide range of scientific and technical information (SAUNDERS & CLINE). The selection, design criteria, and operation of CAIRS are described by SAUNDERS. The software was originally written in assembly language, the majority of the program development being done by Libra Information Systems (LIS), but it has since been refined and rewritten in a higher-level language, RTL2.

At Leatherhead, CAIRS has been running since 1974 on a Texas Instruments minicomputer, and the database now holds around 75,000 documents directly accessible online via display terminals. The facilities provided are described by SAUNDERS & CLINE, and an in-house search service of this type is compared both practically and economically with online searching of external databases.

STATUS and CAIRS both offer a choice of natural language indexing or a thesaurus. CAIRS provides three methods of indexing: 1) automatic indexing, where terms in the title and abstract (if present) are indexed; 2) semiautomatic indexing where the keywords are tagged on entry; and 3) manual indexing, where the user enters a list of keywords for each reference. Restriction of a search to a particular field is done by serial searching.

Two multilingual systems (in addition to the IDRC system) are MILOR and the Vrije Universitaet Brussels Information System (VUBIS). VUBIS, reported by GROSCH (1979), is an interactive cataloging input and inquiry system, a joint development of the Free University of Brussels and Interactive Systems N.V.S.A., also of Brussels. Keywords are assigned within the Universal Decimal Classification scheme (UDC), and searching is done on these keywords or directly by UDC. At the Free University French, Flemish, and English are used although Interactive Systems is planning to make other languages available.

MILOR, described by BOURDAIS, also allows a choice of three languages during searching and for indexing. This system has been developed and is marketed by GIXI, a French company of the CISI group. MILOR is designed to be flexible, although it is aimed particularly at specialized information centers. One user is the Intergovernmental Bureau for Informatics (IBI) in Italy, which uses the trilingual facility and collects and analyzes international publications on the social, political, and economic aspects of informatics.

Unlike STATUS and CAIRS, MILOR does not provide natural language indexing. Two structures are possible: a lexicon of preferential terms with their synonyms or a thesaurus with generic term, specific term, related term, and synonym relationships. Terms are linked in the different languages although this is not always true for synonyms. The record structure is defined by the user and can contain up to 25 categories or fields.

INMAGIC is a package developed by Warner-Eddison Associates, available for use on Digital Equipment Corp. minicomputers. Similar to the other systems described here, it enables the user to define the structure of his databases, to enter and to update them, and to search them online, using Boolean commands. There is no restriction on the length of records, fields or subfields, and any field can be indexed. Print formats are designed by the user, and output can be sorted into various sequences.

Two systems have been developed by Lipman Management Resources (LMR). These are the Adaptive Management System for Special Libraries and Information Bureaux (ADLIB), reported by GROSCH (1979), and the Adaptive Information Management System (ADMIN). The latter provides software of more general applicability. ASHFORD (1980a) compares the two systems as an example of the different approaches that are practical in the minicomputer field.

A rather different system is SCRAPBOOK (TRIAD COMPUTING SYSTEMS), a text-handling system developed at the National Physical Laboratory in the U.K. It provides facilities for fast and efficient drafting, maintenance, examination, and printing of textual documents. Cross-references can be included in the text and followed up when required, but this system was not designed to provide the same facilities for retrieval as the others.

Hardware solutions. Most of the systems described rely on inverted file indexes for fast data retrieval. These indexes can be very large—i.e., 50–150% of the bibliographic file. The alternative, serial searching of text, is normally slow, but with sophisticated hardware techniques, it is possible to scan text extremely quickly and at low cost.

The Associative File Processor (AFP) system has been developed for this purpose. BIRD explains how it works and gives its advantages. It is designed to carry out the basic retrieval process in a special-purpose parallel processor rather than by programming techniques. This hardware executes the term-matching function and releases the central processing unit for other work. It can process 40 to 70 complex queries simultaneously.

Research at Herriot Watt University (Scotland) is also concerned with associative processing of text. Special hardware has been built, and data-compression techniques based on frequency analysis quadruple searching speed, overall operation being 500 times faster than with conventional software methods.

Other Applications

Minicomputers as intelligent terminals. MONSEN (1977) explored the effects that minicomputers can have on the online retrieval environment. He described the normal terminal environment, including the costs of equipment and searching, and compared it with the minicomputer environment. Here the higher transmission speeds are used to keep costs down and to make it more economical to display references online. More important is the storage of these references and the ability to delete irrelevant material and to reformat data for printing. Monsen found a higher level of acceptance of the final search product by the end user (MONSEN, 1978). Monsen cited other uses for a minicomputer in this area, such as automatic searching, storage of searches and search aids, and an interface for the unskilled user.

Training. Training for information retrieval was reviewed in *ARIST* by WANGER in 1979, and two systems on minicomputers are of interest here. One is TRAINER, which was initially developed as a research project (CARUSO & GRIFFITHS). According to CARUSO, tape copies of the programs have been distributed to more than 20 institutions in four countries. The system provides online instruction and practice in using the large-scale commercial systems such as DIALOG and ORBIT.

The second system is described by LUNDEEN. The minicomputer at the University of Hawaii is programmed to provide an introduction to bibliographic databases, Boolean logic, and online searching. Databases are set up, and students can learn to enter bibliographic records into the files. The low cost of operating such a system rather than a commercial system makes it an attractive proposition for initial training.

MICROCOMPUTERS IN INFORMATION RETRIEVAL

Because the low cost of microcomputers has now brought them within the reach of many small organizations or individuals, they are being used in new applications areas. There is a powerful psychological appeal in having a computer system that is under one's direct control. Past difficulties in trying to obtain congenial systems from central data processing departments provide another strong incentive for library and information units to establish their own systems.

The main problem is the lack of suitable software packages for information retrieval. As the cost of microcomputers decreases, the cost of writing the systems to use on the machines becomes more conspicuous. Many library and information units cannot afford custom-built software (which now costs several times the cost of the computing equipment). The alternative of having internal staff write the programs may hide the costs involved, but it introduces all the problems of learning the new discipline of programming (VICKERY & BROOKS).

Since microcomputers are now widely available, much software is being produced, often by information practitioners or personal computer users rather than by computer professionals. Many projects are being developed by research workers in information science and by librarians, but their quality is uncertain because many of them are unpublished and they have not been used widely. The wide variety of microcomputer applications in information handling includes word processing, storage and retrieval of data in personal files or reference files, and the use of the microcomputer as a terminal for increased effectiveness of online searching (GRIFFITHS; PRATT, 1980a; WINFIELD).

Microcomputers in Libraries

Nearly all microcomputers offer word processing facilities, and these can be used for entry, updating, and printing of such material as serials lists, bibliographies, and guides to local reference sources (PRATT, 1980a). A microcomputer is also suitable for handling in-house reference files containing data relevant to the library, such as telephone numbers and addresses, indexes to reference tools, and sources of answers for infrequently requested information. A system for storing and retrieving such data is Reference Librarian Enhancement System (REFLES) (BIVINS & PALMER, 1979; 1980), described below. ANDREWS ET AL. discuss in-house reference files and look at some system alternatives—microcomputers, minicomputers, and private database services.

Cataloging is practicable on a microcomputer only for a small collection, but other functions such as circulation, borrower-checking, and order processing can be implemented (P. W. WILLIAMS, 1979b). HYMAN (1980) examines the use of the large business microcomputers, with hard disk storage, for cataloging and information retrieval systems. He discusses the storage capacity in terms of numbers of records, the problems of data validation and indexing, limitations on searching, and the formatting and sorting of output.

A circulation system used at the Oakridge, OR, public library is described by CHRISTIAN. Items that are checked out are recorded on the system, along with the borrowers' file, acquisitions, and department expenditures. The computer can search for an item by due date, borrower number, author, title, or Dewey decimal number and answer questions regarding the number of books a person has borrowed and other relevant details. A microcomputer was found to be a practical solution for small libraries such as this (Oakridge has 1,000 volumes and an annual circulation of about 17,000).

Online searching of the commercial databases can also be done via the microcomputer, and retrieved records can be stored locally and integrated with local citations to produce bibliographies, or they can be compared with the local collection (PRATT, 1980b). Some suggestions have been made for local networking to allow libraries in the same area to share reference files and use electronic messaging. BORGMAN & KORFHAGE have discussed the possibility of a network of personal computers linked to the library for accessing information.

CORTEX software (NOERR) for intelligent terminals is being developed by the British Library for local processing in libraries. It is designed to facilitate cataloging and data creation and will be extended to provide enhanced facilities for online searching.

In-house Information Retrieval Systems

Most research and information workers accumulate a collection of reports, papers, bibliographic references, leaflets, and catalogs. These items remain potential, not actual, sources of information unless their contents are accessible (CAWKELL, 1980b). A microcomputer system can be used to index, store, and retrieve this type of information as it is needed.

One such system is the Personal Retrieval of Information by Microcomputer and Telecommunications Ensemble (PRIMATE), developed by CAWKELL (1980b) at the Institute for Scientific Information (ISI). PRIMATE records are completely unformatted, as in some of the personal file-handling minicomputer systems (e.g., USERFILE and GRIP). Unformatted records make the system flexible and allow the user to enter data in different formats. More importantly they relieve the user of indexing, which, as Cawkell notes, is often a major nuisance in a busy office or research unit. In PRIMATE the record itself is the index because string searching is used and a hit is a record that contains the search term anywhere in its text.

Unfortunately, searching on a particular field (e.g., author or title) is not normally possible, and sorting is a problem. False drops can occur when the search string is located by chance although this can usually be tolerated in a relatively small system of this nature. It is the ease of input and the speed and convenience of locating material that are important to the user.

In addition to the management, storage, and retrieval of information, system design has been extended to office tasks, such as text processing, sorting, ordering, and printing of particular records (e.g., addresses). Communications with another PRIMATE machine and facilities for accessing databases on remote computers are also planned.

REFLES was designed to handle in-house files in the reference department of a library and was developed at the University of California, Los Angeles. The prototype system REFLES1, described by BIVINS & PALMER (1979), has been modified to provide a more generalized software package, REFLES2, which will be available commercially. REFLES, like PRIMATE, is designed to accept data in any format but differs in that it uses a thesaurus. When a record is entered into the system, the user must assign it a unique main descriptor and up to three cross-references. These thesaurus terms or their corresponding numerical codes are then used for searching. Facilities are provided for displaying and editing thesaurus terms.

A comprehensive information retrieval system has been developed by CUADRA ASSOCIATES; the System To Automate Records (STAR) is available for purchase or lease as a software package and as an integrated system. It operates on the Alpha Microsystems microcomputer, which is a 16-bit word machine, almost a minicomputer. A typical system is stated as having 128K bytes of memory, two cathode ray tube (CRT) terminals, ten million bytes of hard disk storage, and a high quality printer. The system can be extended to support many additional terminals.

STAR is aimed at technical information centers, special libraries, small businesses, law firms, and publishers and has many of the features normally associated with minicomputer systems. These include a choice of controlled or uncontrolled vocabulary, the sorting of records on any field, and the storing of searches for selective dissemination of information (SDI) and multi-database searching. The user defines his own database, field specifications, error checking, data entry screens, and output formats. When searching, full Boolean operators with nested parentheses to any level can be used with fixed- and variable-length truncation and numeric ranging.

Both PRIMATE and STAR recognize the need for software to do general office tasks as well as information storage and retrieval. On the Alpha microcomputer more specialized software for library support or other applications could also be added.

Interactive programs for data entry and editing are a necessary feature of all the systems mentioned, so that the user need not have any prior knowledge of computers. STAR, for example, provides "menus" and form filling on the screen.

The U. K. Clinical Research Center is developing a bibliographic data entry and retrieval system for the Biomedical Engineering Current Awareness Notification (BECAN). The BECAN database consists of 31,000 indexed references dating from 1962, with 2,500 additions each year. These are stored on 8-inch floppy disks, and author, subject, and country indexes are held. The Center hopes to offer the programs on a wider basis as a package for individual researchers (PROJECT FAIR).

Microcomputers are also being used for simulating searches to familiarize students with command languages and host systems and to teach search formulation. One system that was created both for teaching purposes and for storing personal bibliographic files on a PET microcomputer is described by VICKERY & BROOKS. At the College of Librarianship in Wales, a new project is developing a teaching package for online searching, and a previous project has implemented programs for teaching the principles of coding input strings for producing printed index entries. Aslib is developing a system to introduce information retrieval to school children, using a simplified subset of the Euronet common command language (CCL) to retrieve records stored on floppy disk.

Microcomputers as Intelligent Terminals

Many microcomputers now have communications facilities and can serve as terminals to larger systems or can communicate with other microcomputers. They can be programmed to emulate any standard terminal, and software for this is becoming more widely available. A microcomputer can also be programmed to access teletext and viewdata services and electronic mail systems (CAWKELL, 1980a).

The Source offers the first home computer consumer information network (GRIFFITHS). Via Telenet people can dial up UPI (United Press International) articles from the past seven years, computer programs, airline information, and video games. Electronic mail can be sent to other terminals, and for 75 cents, the computer message can become a Mailgram deposited at O'Hare International Airport. With word processing facilities a microcomputer can be used to prepare reports and to dispatch them to other systems via telecommunications.

Online searching. Microcomputers also play an important part in online searching. First, they can be programmed to handle the dial-up procedures, communications protocol, and log-on procedures for various host systems. Then the user simply specifies which system he wishes to access. This makes the job of connecting to a system easy and eliminates the need for the user to learn many different procedures. It also speeds up the log-on process. P. W. WILLIAMS (1979a) describes how search preparation offline, before connecting to the host computer, substantially reduces online time and thus saves on search costs. This is acceptable as long as normal online interaction is freely allowed at any point. Williams points out that reduced costs per search need not reduce the revenue to the online vendor because more people will use the systems and many existing users on a fixed budget will carry out more searches.

The preparation of a search offline also means that the searcher can check for typing and syntax errors before transmitting the search. When online, the searcher can devote full concentration to the search output and react intelligently to the information received. Williams describes two approaches to the provision of such facilities. Either a purpose-built microcomputer box containing the appropriate software can be connected to the user's terminal, or a full microcomputer system can be used. With the box the user does not need any programming knowledge, and the programs cannot be inadvertently damaged. A device of this type, the USERKIT, which can be operated with about a dozen simple commands, is available commercially (P. W. WILLIAMS, 1980a).

STEFFENSON & KING also recommend the offline preparation of a search. They use an intelligent terminal with attached cassette tape unit to record the search. This method is also useful for local SDI searches; the limits on accession numbers, dates of publication, or update codes are edited as required. Standard sets of terms representing concepts that are used frequently can also be recorded on tape and incorporated into a search. Unfortunately, with cassette tapes, items from various places on the tape cannot be recalled rapidly while online, but tapes are cheaper than microcomputers.

In 1979, HULEATT reported the use of a cassette unit for improving search output. All data received at the terminal were recorded on cassette (and printed if required), and later the search results were edited, reformatted, and tidied up. For final printing the name of the database, the requestor, and other details such as total cost can be shown.

These facilities can be incorporated into a microcomputer system. The interactive selection of relevant references for printing and the sorting of references into a particular order are possible. Retrieved records can be incorporated into a personal database (G. K. THOMPSON).

The ability to store retrieved data for offline manipulation is demonstrated by STERNBERGER. An Apple computer with 48K bytes of memory, an acoustic modem, a microprinter, and a disk drive is used to access the Dow Jones news retrieval database. The Portfolio Evaluator package (developed jointly by Dow Jones and Apple) allows the user to store about six different portfolios, to retrieve the latest data from the remote database, and to do offline calculations on this data. For example, the value of the portfolio and gains and losses can be calculated and displayed.

BUTLER describes the use of an Apple microcomputer as an intelligent terminal and the development of an interface to the DIALOG system that provides a simple, rapid search of the Magazine Index or the National Newspaper Index databases. With the growth of nonbibliographic databases, this type of facility is very useful. Personal computers with this type of system make data access available to a wide range of users.

Many of the facilities described here are available on the Information Broker's Terminal System (IBTS), a fully integrated hardware and software package developed by Fred Bellomy (THE INFOMART). The facilities include offline preparation and storage of searches with fast transmission, automatic responses to certain host messages, the logging of searches, storage and editing of output, and the ability to access locally stored information regarding host systems and databases. The hardware includes a Tektronic graphics terminal with 32K bytes of memory, a Digital Microsystems computer with 64K bytes of memory, two floppy disk drives, and a printer (a hard disk is also available).

The user interface. The conflicting aims when designing the interface for large online information systems are summed up by GOLDSTEIN & FORD as: 1) optimization of the interface for the end user—i.e., making it user oriented; and 2) optimization of a single interface for a large, heterogeneous user population. Because this is an intractable problem, various alternatives are presented. A minicomputer or large microcomputer could provide user interfaces for a number of local users, or an intelligent terminal could provide an interface suited to the particular user of that terminal or even a variety of interfaces at different levels.

Various projects under development are concerned with the user interface. One is the Online Search Assistance Machine (OL'SAM) developed by the Franklin Institute Research Laboratory and based on Individualized Instruction for Data Access (IIDA) (MEADOW & EPSTEIN). OL'SAM is designed to simplify access to bibliographic databases and to improve the cost-benefit ratio of searching for both the new searcher and the skilled intermediary. All access and log-on protocols are managed automatically, and syntax errors are detected before transmission. An additional aid for the novice is the monitoring of strategy patterns to suggest more productive strategies (FRANKLIN INSTITUTE RESEARCH LABORATORY).

OL'SAM can also multiplex two users on the same network line who are working independently on the same database on the same host. This saves costs and is useful in the learning situation. Searches can be stored and edited locally as they can with the USERKIT.

The different command languages have always presented a problem to the searcher who wishes to access various host systems. Either a CCL is required or an interface that translates from one language to another. A European CCL has been developed and is available on some systems (NEGUS). Version 1 of OL'SAM released in December 1980, accesses three search systems: Lockheed, System Development Corp. (SDC), and the National Library of Medicine (NLM), and provides a single DIALOG-type of language, with additional prompts and help for searching.

The multiplicity of databases and search systems, with their various access protocols, command languages, responses and output formats, is a great problem. It is difficult for searchers to maintain expertise in many different systems and files, and the need for intermediaries increases. WILLIAMS & PREECE believe that standardization is unlikely and that the alternative is a distributed transparent system in which the user would not see the complexities of the component systems. The research program at the University of Illinois is intended to specify the design of a total transparent information retrieval system (TTIRS), to indicate relevant research projects, and to develop and test its components. Some examples of "transparency aids" are given by M. E. WILLIAMS.

A prototype mini-transparent system called the Searcher's Workbench (TSW) has been implemented on an Alpha Microsystems computer (PREECE & WILLIAMS). It is designed for the novice and is menu driven. A touch panel is used for all input except search terms, and a single command language is provided. The microcomputer maps user queries onto the format required by the host system, and as the user moves from one system to another, a knowledge base describing the capabilities of each real-world system and database is used to modify the model search system. TSW accesses two hosts and five databases, and access is also provided to two transparency aids, Battelle's Vocabulary Switching System and the database selector at the University of Illinois.

Testing retrieval techniques. JAMIESON (1978), of the University of Aston, feels that only very simple search techniques have been implemented on the large commercial systems in order to maintain a viable, fast, efficient system for many users. Sophisticated techniques have generally been used in laboratory situations with small test collections. Jamieson suggests the use of a microcomputer as an intelligent terminal to the commercial online systems to allow various retrieval techniques to be economically implemented and tested on a "real-life" collection of documents.

However, as JAMIESON (1979a) notes, not all retrieval techniques can be implemented in this way. The host system's files are normally organized to cope with ordinary Boolean searching, and information such as the distribution of terms within documents, which is necessary for certain techniques, is not stored. However some strategies can be implemented—e.g., term weighting and generation of ranked output, the use of relevance information, user-friendly dialog, and post-retrieval clustering (JAMIESON, 1979a; 1979b). Details of these techniques and the way in which they are implemented at the University of Aston, in particular the relevance weighting technique, are in JAMIESON & ODDY.

Microcomputers and videotex. This area was reviewed by CAWKELL (1980a) in *ARIST*, and here the discussion is confined to recent developments that are relevant. A selection of papers on videotex can be found in the proceedings of the 4th International Online Meeting [*ONLINE REVIEW*].

An important application of viewdata is the downloading of software from a database to a microcomputer, called "telesoftware." Local and national networks for the distribution of educational software are discussed by ASTON. BROWN describes the development of a viewdata telesoftware system for education by the Council for Educational Technology in the U.K. This enables sections of the Prestel database, both information and programs, to be stored locally on disk for use when required.

In-house viewdata systems are being mounted on minicomputers—e.g., the system at the London Stock Exchange (HAYTER) and a package called COMPUTEX, which has many additional features (JOAN DE SMITH). A microcomputer can be used as an intelligent terminal to access private and public viewdata systems. One such system is the SPARROW (INFORMATION SERVICES AND EQUIPMENT), which is designed to provide advanced editing facilities for entering data and the power to retrieve and to manipulate data from Prestel and other viewdata systems.

In the future we may see the microcomputer being used as a multifunction terminal to access viewdata and teletext systems, online retrieval systems such as DIALOG, electronic mail systems, and many more.

CONCLUSIONS

The low cost of microcomputers means that many libraries can realistically consider their purchase and use them for internal or external information retrieval. Although some minicomputers and their programs have proved their worth, the new systems on recently marketed microcomputers have not been in use long enough for definitive judgements to be made. The information worker should take great care to evaluate the microcomputer itself, the facilities provided in its program, the robustness of the program when used by unskilled operators, and the stability of the supplier. The knowledge required to operate the systems successfully will diminish as systems are developed further, but present purchasers should be prepared to learn some details of computer operation.

BIBLIOGRAPHY

ANDREWS, KAREN L.; ARMSTRONG, JUNE; BENENFELD, ALAN R. 1980. Microcomputers, Minicomputers, or Private Database Services in Reference Work: Some Decision Factors. In: Benenfeld, A. R.; Kazlauskas, E. J., eds. Communicating Information: Proceedings of the American Society for Information Science 43rd Annual Meeting; 1980 October 5-10; Anaheim, CA. White Plains, NY: Knowledge Industry Publications, Inc.; 1980. 310-313. ISBN: 0-914236-73-3.

ASHFORD, JOHN H. 1976. Software Cost: Making It or Buying It. Program (England). 1976 January; 10(1): 1-6. ISSN: 0033-0337.

ASHFORD, JOHN H. 1980a. Information Management Packages on Minicomputers. Journal of Information Science (England). 1980; (2): 23-28. ISSN: 0165-5515.

ASHFORD, JOHN H. 1980b. Report of a Study of the Potential Users and Application Areas for Free Text Information Storage and Retrieval Systems in Britain, 1979-81. Program (England). 1980 January; 14(1): 14-23. ISSN: 0033-0337.

ASHFORD, JOHN H.; MATKIN, DEREK I. 1979. The Future for Free Text Systems. Computer Bulletin. 1979 September: 18-21. ISSN: 0010-4531.

ASTON, MIKE. 1980. Distributing Computer Aided Learning Software. In: Proceedings of the 4th International Online Information Meeting; 1980 December 9-11; London, England. Oxford, England and New Jersey: Learned Information; 1980. 227-234. ISBN: 0-904933-28-8.

BARKER, P. G. 1978. BINSYS—A Personal Information Retrieval System. Journal of Informatics (England). 1978 April; 2(1): 34-50.

BECKMAN, M.; PORTER, L.; BLACK, J. 1978. Integrated Online Access. In: Brenner, E. H., ed. The Information Age in Perspective: Proceedings of the American Society for Information Science 41st Annual Meeting; 1978 November 13-17; New York, NY. White Plains, NY: Knowledge Industry Publications, Inc.; 1978. 28-32. ISBN: 0-914236-229; ISSN: 0044-7870.

BELL, COLIN L. M.; JONES, KEVIN P. 1976. A Minicomputer Retrieval System with Automatic Root Finding and Roling Facilities. Program (England). 1976 January; 10(1): 14-27. ISSN: 0033-0337.

BELL, COLIN L. M.; JONES, KEVIN P. 1978. Towards a New Philosophy for Information Retrieval. Journal of Informatics (England). 1978 April; 2(1): 52-55. (Paper given at the British Computer Society Information Retrieval Specialist Group Research Colloquium, 1978 3-4 April; Leeds, England).

BELL, COLIN L. M.; JONES, KEVIN P. 1979. Towards Everyday Language Information Retrieval Systems via Minicomputers. Journal of the

American Society for Information Science. 1979 November; 30(6): 334-339. ISSN: 0002-8231.
BELL, COLIN L. M.; JONES, KEVIN P. 1980. The Development of a Highly Interactive Searching Technique for MORPHS—Minicomputer Operated Retrieval (Partially Heuristic) System. Information Processing and Management. 1980; 16(1): 37-47. ISSN: 0306-4573.
BIRD, R. M. 1979. The Associative File Processor, a Special Purpose Hardware System for Test Search and Retrieval. In: Proceedings of the Institution of Electrical and Electronic Engineers (IEEE) National Aerospace and Electronics Conference NAECON; 1979 May 15-17; Dayton, OH. New York, NY: IEEE; 1979. 443-449. Available from: IEEE.
BIRULA, KAY; GRAHAM, WILLIAM; GUDES, EHUD. 1978. An Inhouse Online Information Retrieval System Using a Minicomputer. In: Brenner, E. H., ed. The Information Age in Perspective: Proceedings of the American Society for Information Science 41st Annual Meeting; 1978 November 13-17; New York, NY. White Plains, NY: Knowledge Industry Publications, Inc.; 1978. 32-34. ISBN: 0-914236-229; ISSN: 0044-7870.
BIVINS, KATHLEEN T.; PALMER, ROGER C. 1979. REFLES (Reference Librarian Enhancement System). In: Proceedings of the American Society for Information Science 42nd Annual Meeting; 1979; Minneapolis, MN. White Plains, NY: Knowledge Industry Publications, Inc.; 1979. 58-65. ISBN: 0-914236-474; ISSN: 0044-7870.
BIVINS, KATHLEEN T.; PALMER, ROGER C. 1980. REFLES: An Individual Microcomputer System for Fact Retrieval. Online Review (England). 1980 December; 4(4): 357-365. ISSN: 0309-314X.
BORGMAN, CHRISTINE L.; KORFHAGE, ROBERT R. 1978. The Public Library Interface to Personal Computer Systems. In: Brenner, E. H., ed. The Information Age in Perspective: Proceedings of the American Society for Information Science 41st Annual Meeting; 1978 November 13-17; New York, NY. White Plains, NY: Knowledge Industry Publications, Inc.; 1978. 41-43. ISBN: 0-914236-229; ISSN: 0044-7870.
BORLAND, K. S. 1978. Yours to Command. Personal Computer World (England). 1978 January; 1(1): 20-23.
BOURDAIS, ALAIN. 1979. MILOR, La Recherche Retrospective sur Mini-Ordinateurs [MILOR, Retrospective Search on Minicomputers]. Documentaliste (France). 1979 May-June; 16(3): 106-111. (Abstract in English; text in French).
BROWN, MIKE. 1980. Prestel and Education—A Viewdata Telesoftware System for Education. In: Proceedings of the 4th International Online Information Meeting; 1980 December 9-11; London, England. Oxford, England and Medford, NJ: Learned Information; 1980. 115-118. ISBN: 0-904933-28-8.
BUTLER, BRETT. 1979. Beyond the Library—U.S. Online Trends. In: Proceedings of the 3rd International Online Information Meeting; 1979 December 4-6; London, England. Oxford, England and New Jersey Learned Information; 1979. 385-392. ISBN: 0-904933-21-0.
CALVER, P.; TEBBUTT, D. 1980. CBM 8032. Personal Computer World. 1980 September; 3(9): 84-85.
CARUSO, ELAINE. 1981. TRAINER. Online. 1981 January; 5(1): 36-38. ISSN: 0146-5422.

CARUSO, ELAINE; GRIFFITHS, JOHN. 1977. A Trainer for Online Systems. Online. 1977 October; 1(4): 28–34. ISSN: 0146-5422.
CAWKELL, ANTHONY E. 1980a. Information Technology and Communications. In: Williams, M. E., ed. Annual Review of Information Science and Technology: Volume 15. White Plains, NY: Knowledge Industry Publications, Inc.; 1980. 37–65.
CAWKELL, ANTHONY E. 1980b. Personal Microcomputer Systems for Office Use. In: Proceedings of the 4th International Online Information Meeting; 1980 December 9–11; London, England. Oxford, England and Medford, NJ: Learned Information; 1980. 377–385. ISBN: 0-904933-28-8.
CHRISTIAN, DEBORAH. 1980. The Microcomputer at Oakridge, Oregon. Library Journal. 1980 July; 1470–1471. ISSN: 0000-0027.
CLARK, MARCIA E.; WILDHAGEN, ERIC C. 1979. An Information Storage and Retrieval System using a Minicomputer. Bulletin of the American Meteorological Society. 1979 January; 60(1): 28–31.
COLL, J. 1978. Pet 2001 Review. Personal Computer World. 1978 February; 1(2).
CRAVEN, TIMOTHY C. 1980. Microcomputer-Generated Graphic Displays as an Aid in String Indexing. Journal of the American Society for Information Science. 1980 March; 31(2): 123–124. ISSN: 0002-8231.
CUADRA ASSOCIATES. 1980. Cuadra Associates Announces a New STAR in the Information World. Santa Monica, CA; 1980. 1p. (Pamphlet). Available from: Cuadra Associates, Inc.; 1523 Sixth Street, Suite 12, Santa Monica, CA 90406.
DANELIUK, FAYE A. 1978. The IDRC's Minicomputer-Based Bibliographic Information System. In: The Application of Inexpensive Minicomputers to Information Work; 1978 April 17–18; Delft, The Netherlands. Neuilly-sur-Seine, France: AGARD; 1978. 4.1–4.9. (AGARD Lecture Series no. 92).
DENNIS, MIKE. 1978a. Good Value for Money. Personal Computer World. 1978 September; 1(9).
DENNIS, MIKE. 1978b. PCW Review—Research Machines 380Z. Personal Computer World. 1978 February; 1(2): 47–53.
DUBOIS, J. E.; BONNET, J. C.; LEMAGNEY, A.; LACROIX, O. 1977. Pluridata: The DARC Data Bank System. In: Proceedings of the 1st International Online Information Meeting; 1977; London, England. Oxford, England and Medford, NJ: Learned Information; 1977. 169–172. ISBN: 0-904933-10-5.
EISENBACH, S. 1979a. The Cromemco System 3. Personal Computer World. 1979 October; 2(10): 38–42.
EISENBACH, S. 1979b. The Micromation Z-Plus. Personal Computer World. 1979 December; 2(12): 42–47.
EVANS, C. D. 1979. The Versatile Terminal. In: Proceedings of the 3rd International Online Information Meeting; 1979 December 4–6; London, England. Oxford, England and Medford, NJ. Learned Information; 1979. 109–122. ISBN: 0-904933-21-0.
FOSDICK, HOWARD. 1980. The Microcomputer Revolution. Library Journal. 1980 July: 1467–1472. ISSN: 0000-0027.
FOX, T. 1981. Let the Buyer Compare. Interface Age. 1981 January; 6(1): 76–85.

FRANKLIN INSTITUTE RESEARCH LABORATORY. 1980. Online Database Search Assistance Machine. 1980. (Pamphlet). Available from: Franklin Institute Research Laboratory, The Benjamin Franklin Parkway, Philadelphia, PA.

FYLSTRA, D. 1978a. The Radio Shack TRS80. Byte. 1978 April; 3(4): 49-60.

FYLSTRA, D. 1978b. User's Report: The Pet 2001. Byte. 1978 March; 3(3): 114-117.

GENTRY, H. S. 1979. Let's Look at Newdos. Kilobaud. 1979 November; 78-80.

GOLDSTEIN, CHARLES M.; FORD, WILLIAM H. 1978. The User-Cordial Interface. Online Review (England). 1978 September; 2(3): 269-275. ISSN: 0309-314X.

GRIFFITHS, JOSE-MARIE. 1980. Applications of Mini and Micro Computers to Information Handling. In: Benenfeld, A. R.; Kazlauskas, E. J., eds. Communicating Information: Proceedings of the American Society for Information Science 43rd Annual Meeting; 1980 October 5-10; Anaheim, CA. White Plains, NY: Knowledge Industry Publications, Inc.; 1980. 306-309. ISBN: 0-914236-73-3.

GROSCH, AUDREY N. 1976. Library Automation. In: Williams, M. E., ed. Annual Review of Information Science and Technology: Volume 11. White Plains, NY: Knowledge Industry Publications, Inc.; 1976. 225-266. ISBN: 0-87715-212-8.

GROSCH, AUDREY N. 1977. Fourth Generation Systems for Libraries, The Marriage of Data Base Management Systems and Online Minicomputer Hardware. Special Libraries. 1977 July/August: 221-226. ISSN: 0038-6723.

GROSCH, AUDREY N. 1978. Commercial Data Base Management System (DBMS) Software in Larger Minicomputer Configurations. In: The Application of Inexpensive Minicomputers to Information Work; 1978 April 17-18; Delft, The Netherlands. Neuilly-sur-Seine, France: AGARD; 1978. 8.1-8.10. (AGARD Lecture Series no. 92).

GROSCH, AUDREY N. 1979. Minicomputers in Libraries 1979-80. White Plains, NY: Knowledge Industry Publications, Inc.; 1979. 142p. ISBN: 0-914236-19-9.

HAYTER, G. A. 1980. TOPIC: A Private Viewdata System for the Stock Exchange. In: Proceedings of the 4th International Online Information Meeting; 1980 December 9-11; London, England. Oxford, England and Medford, NJ: Learned Information; 1980. 123-128. ISBN: 0-904933-28-8.

HEALEY, M.; WOODWARD, P.; REES, M. 1979. The North Star Horizon. Personal Computer World. 1979 April; 2(4): 23-27.

HELMERS, C. 1978. An Apple to Byte. Byte. 1978 March; 3(3): 18-127.

HUFFENBERGER, M. A. 1979. Data Base Management Systems. In: Williams, M. E., ed. Annual Review of Information Science and Technology: Volume 14. White Plains, NY: Knowledge Industry Publications, Inc.; 1979. 153-190. ISBN: 0-914236-44-X.

HULEATT, RICHARD S. 1979. Finishing the Online Search. Online. 1979 April; 3(2): 24-29. ISSN: 0146-5422.

HYMAN, MIKE. 1978. The Role of Minicomputers in Libraries and Information Units. Aslib Proceedings (England). 1978 October-November; 30(10-11): 373-382. ISSN: 0001-253X.

HYMAN, MIKE. 1980. A Computer for Every Library—A Practical Reality at Last?. In: Proceedings of the 4th International Online Information Meeting; 1980 December 9–11; London, England. Oxford, England and Medford, NJ: Learned Information; 1980. 235–244. ISBN: 0-904933-28-8.
HYMAN, MIKE; WALLIS, ELEANOR. 1976. Mini-Computers and Bibliographic Information Retrieval. London, England: The British Library; 1976. 125p. (Research and Development Report no. 5305 HC). ISBN: 0-85350-144-0.
INFORMATION SERVICES AND EQUIPMENT LIMITED. 1980. The Sparrow Viewdata Editor. London, England; 1980. 4p. (Pamphlet). Available from: Information Services and Equipment, 387, High Road, Willesden, London, England.
JACKOBIAK, F. 1978. Use of an Online Terminal to Build Your Own Files. In: Proceedings of the 2nd International Online Information Meeting; 1980 December 5–7; London, England. Oxford, England and Medford, NJ: Learned Information; 1978. 91–102.
JAMIESON, STEPHEN H. 1978. Machine Architectures Suitable for Information Retrieval Systems. Journal of Informatics (England). 1978 April; 2(1): 56–61.
JAMIESON, STEPHEN H. 1979a. An Intelligent Terminal for Information Retrieval. Journal of Informatics (England). 1979 April; 3(1): 51–56.
JAMIESON, STEPHEN H. 1979b. The Economic Implementation of Experimental Retrieval Techniques on a Very Large Scale Using an Intelligent Terminal. Association for Computing Machinery (ACM) SIGIR Forum. 1979; 14(2): 45–51.
JAMIESON, STEPHEN H.; ODDY, ROBERT N. 1980. Low-Cost Implementation of Experimental Retrieval Techniques for Online Users. In: Proceedings of the 4th International Online Information Meeting; 1980 December 9–11; London, England. Oxford, England and Medford, NJ: Learned Information; 1980. 201–210. ISBN: 0-904933-28-8.
JOAN DE SMITH (SYSTEMS) LIMITED. 1980. COMPUTEX. London, England; 1980. 1p. (Brochure). Available from Joan De Smith, 41, Gloucester Place, London, England.
KAZLAUSKAS, E. J.; HOLT, T. D. 1980. The Application of a Minicomputer to Thesaurus Construction. Journal of the American Society for Information Science. 1980 September; 31(5): 363–368. ISSN: 0002-8231.
KEREN, C.; SEELBACH, H. E.; WALLMAN, P. 1978. Using Minicomputers in Information Work—Project Domestic. Nachrichten für Dokumentation (Germany). 1978 September; 29(4/5): 163–164. ISSN: 0027-7436.
LANCASTER, F. WILFRID. 1978. Towards Paperless Information Systems. New York, NY and London, England: Academic Press; 1978. 179p. (U.K. edition). ISBN: 0-12-436050-5.
LEGGATE, P.; EAGLESTONE, B. M.; JARMAN, R. A.; NORGETT, M. M.; WILLIAMS, A. P. 1976. The Userfile Project—The Development and Use of an Online Personal File Handling System on a PDP 11/20 Mini Computer. London, England: British Library; 1976. (Research and Development Report No. 5317).
LEGGATE, P.; EAGLESTONE, B. M.; JARMAN, R. A.; NORGETT, M. M.; WILLIAMS, A. P. 1977. An Online System for Handling Personal

Databases on a PDP 11/20 Minicomputer. Aslib Proceedings (England). 1977 February; 29(2): 56–66. ISSN: 0001-253X.

LUNDEEN, GERALD. 1977. Introducing the Concepts of On-Line Boolean Searching with a Minicomputer-Based System. In: The Value of Information: Collection of Papers Presented at the American Society for Information Science (ASIS) 6th Mid-Year Meeting; 1977 May 19–21; Syracuse, NY. Washington, DC: ASIS; 1977. 103–106.

MARTIN, JAMES. 1977. Computer Data-Base Organisation. Englewood Cliffs, NJ: Prentice-Hall, Inc.; 1977. 713p. ISBN: 0-13-165423-3.

MCCALLUM, J. C. 1981. The Sinclair Research ZX80. Byte. 1981 January; 6(1): 94–102.

MEADOW, CHARLES T.; EPSTEIN, B. E. 1977. Individualized Instruction for Data Access. In: Proceedings of the 1st International Online Information Meeting; 1977; London, England. Oxford, England and Medford, NJ: Learned Information; 1977. 179–194. ISBN: 0-904933-10-5.

MEADOW, CHARLES T.; TOLIVER, DAVID E.; EDELMANN, JANET V. 1978. A Technique for Machine Assistance to Online Searchers. In: Brenner, E. H., ed. The Information Age in Perspective: Proceedings of the American Society for Information Science 41st Annual Meeting; 1978 November 13–17; New York, NY. White Plains, NY: Knowledge Industry Publications, Inc.; 1978. 222–225. ISBN: 0-914236-229; ISSN: 0044-7870.

MIDDLETON, M. R., ed. 1979. Proceedings of the National Conference on Library and Bibliographic Applications of Minicomputers; 1979 August 22–24; Sydney, Australia. Australia: School of Librarianship, University of New South Wales: 1979. ISBN: 0-909796-15-7.

MILLER, A. R. 1980. Basic in Your Pocket. Interface Age. 1980 December; 5(12): 86–91.

MINICOMPUTER SYSTEMS LIMITED. 1980. FACTFINDER, A Breakthrough in Minicomputer-Based Text File Management. 1980. (Pamphlets). Available from: Minicomputer Systems Ltd., Park House, Park Street, Maidenhead, England and 399, Fairview Park Drive, Elmsford, NY.

MONSEN, GORDON L., JR. 1977. Computer Terminals and Minicomputers in Online Retrieval. Online Review (England). 1977 September; 1(3): 217–229. ISSN: 0309-314X.

MONSEN, GORDON L., JR. 1978. Case Study in Business/Management Information. In: Brenner, E. H., ed. The Information Age in Perspective: Proceedings of the American Society for Information Science 41st Annual Meeting; 1978 November 13–17; New York, NY. White Plains, NY: Knowledge Industry Publications, Inc.; 1978. 233–235. ISBN: 0-914236-229; ISSN: 0044-7870.

NEGUS, ALAN E. 1979. Development of the Euronet-Diane Common Command Language. In: Proceedings of the 3rd International Online Information Meeting; 1979 December 4–6; London, England. Oxford, England and Medford, NJ: Learned Information; 1979. 95–98. ISBN: 0-904933-21-0.

NEVILLE, HUGH. 1979. Back to Nature in Bricket Wood—BRE On-Line Library Records. CIIG Review (England). 1979 Spring; (3): 4–6.

NOERR, PETER. 1980. The British Library Microcomputer Editing System. In: Gilchrist, A., ed. Minis, Micros and Terminals: Proceedings of the

Joint British Computer Society and Institute of Information Scientists Conference; 1980 November; Manchester, England. London, England: Heyden Press; 1980. (To be published).

NOYCE, N. N. 1977. Microelectronics. Scientific American. 1977 September; 2-9. ISSN: 0036-8733.

ONLINE REVIEW. 1980. Proceedings of the 4th International Online Information Meeting; 1980 December 9-11; London, England. Oxford, England and Medford, NJ: Learned Information; 1980. ISBN: 0-904933-28-8.

PARKER, IAN M.; THORPE, P. 1979. GRIP—A Personal Online Indexing System Using a Minicomputer. Program (England). 1979 January; 13(1): 14-22. ISSN: 0033-0337.

PEARSON, K. M., JR. 1975. Minicomputers in the Library. In: Cuadra, C., ed. Annual Review of Information Science and Technology: Volume 10. White Plains, NY: Knowledge Industry Publications, Inc.; 1975. 139-163. ISBN: 0-87715-210-1.

PRACTICAL COMPUTING. 1978. The PET Microcomputer. Practical Computing. 1978 October; 1(2): 21-24.

PRACTICAL COMPUTING. 1979a. Disk Comparisons. Practical Computing. 1979 October; 2(10): 57-59.

PRACTICAL COMPUTING. 1979b. Review of Science of Cambridge MK II. Practical Computing. 1979 May; 2(5): 40-41.

PRACTICAL COMPUTING. 1980. Texas Instruments TI99/4. Practical Computing. 1980 August; 3(8).

PRATT, ALLAN D. 1980a. Microcomputers as Information Dissemination Tools. In: Benenfeld, A. R.; Kazlauskas, E. J., eds. Communicating Information: Proceedings of the American Society for Information Science 43rd Annual Meeting; 1980 October 5-10; Anaheim, CA. White Plains, NY: Knowledge Industry Publications Inc.; 1980. 314-316. ISBN: 0-914236-73-3.

PRATT, ALLAN D. 1980b. The Use of Microcomputers in Libraries. Journal of Library Automation. 1980 March; 13(1): 7-17. ISSN: 0022-2240.

PREECE, SCOTT E.; WILLIAMS, MARTHA E. 1980. Software for the Searcher's Workbench. In: Benenfeld, A. R.; Kazlauskas, E. J., eds. Communicating Information: Proceedings of the American Society for Information Science 43rd Annual Meeting; 1980 October 5-10; Anaheim, CA. White Plains, NY: Knowledge Industry Publications, Inc.; 1980. 403-405. ISBN: 0-914236-73-3.

PROJECT FAIR. 1980. FAIR Medical Engineering Information Service. 6p. (Leaflet). Available from: Project Fair, Clinical Research Centre, Watford Road, Harrow, Middlesex, England.

REED, M. J. P.; VROOMAN, H. T. 1979. Library Automation. In: Williams, M. E., ed. Annual Review of Information Science and Technology: Volume 14. White Plains, NY: Knowledge Industry Publications, Inc.; 1979. 193-216. ISBN: 0-914236-44-X.

ROWLEY, J. E. 1979. Mechanised Inhouse Information Retrieval Systems. London, England: Clive Bingley; 1979. 208p. ISBN: 0-85157-259-6.

SAUNDERS, R. J. D. 1977. An Online Computer Assisted Information Retrieval System Using a Minicomputer (CAIRS). Program (England). 1977 January; 11(1): 16-30. ISSN: 0033-0337.

SAUNDERS, R. J. D.; CLINE, G. N. 1979. The Use and Application of a

Minicomputer-Based, In-House Information Retrieval System. In: Proceedings of the 3rd International Online Information Meeting; 1979 December 4-6; London, England. Oxford, England and Medford, NJ: Learned Information; 1979. 393-405. ISBN: 0-904933-21-0.

SEGAL, H. 1981. Benchmark North Star Horizon. Interface Age. 1981 January; 6(1): 62-64.

SINGER, D. D.; SMART, G. A.; ROSSI, J. M. 1978. The Role of a Mini-Computer in an Information Department to Provide Online In-House Services. In: Proceedings of the 2nd International Online Information Meeting; 1978 December 5-7; London, England. Oxford, England and Medford, NJ: Learned Information; 1978. 83-90. ISBN: 0-904933-156.

SPIELMAN, B. 1979. Contrasting Eurapple with ITT 2020. Practical Computing. 1979 December; 2(12): 62-64.

STEFFENSON, MARTIN B.; KING, KATHRYN L. 1981. Prerecord Your Online Bibliographic Searches for Time and Money Savings. Online. 1981 January; 5(1): 47-49.

STERNBERGER, PAUL. 1980. Using Personal Home Computers to Retrieve Information from Online Databases. In: Proceedings of the 4th International Online Information Meeting; 1980 December 9-11; London, England. Oxford, England and Medford, NJ: Learned Information; 1980. 79-84. ISBN: 0-904933-28-8.

STERNER, RAY T.; BREIDENSTEIN, CHARLES P. 1976. Set of Advanced-BASIC Programs for Literature Storage and Retrieval with Minicomputers. Behaviour Research Methods and Instrumentation. 1976 August; 8(4): 397-398.

TEBBUTT, D. 1980a. Sinclair ZX80. Personal Computer World. 1980 April; 3(4): 55-59.

TEBBUTT, D. 1980b. TI99/4 Home Computer. Personal Computer World. 1980 May; 3(5): 48-51.

TESKEY, F. N. 1980. STATUS and Integrated Information Systems. Journal of Documentation (England). 1980 March; 36(1): 33-41. ISSN: 0022-0418.

THE INFOMART. 1980. The Information Broker's Terminal System (IBTS). 5p. (Leaflet). Available from: The Infomart, P.O. Box 2400, Santa Barbara, CA 93120.

THOMPSON, GEORGE K. 1978. The Use of Microcomputers by Secondary Services and Individual Researchers in the Social Sciences. In: Brenner, E. H., ed. The Information Age in Perspective: Proceedings of the American Society for Information Science 41st Annual Meeting 1978; 1978 November 13-17; New York, NY. White Plains, NY: Knowledge Industry Publications, Inc.; 1978. 341-343. ISBN: 0-914236-229; ISSN: 0044-7870.

TOLIVER, DAVID. 1979. Interactive Retrieval Information Systems. Personal Computing. 1979 November; 3: 38-50.

TOOP, NICK. 1978. A Mighty Micromite. Personal Computer World. 1978 February; 1(2): 10-12.

TRIAD COMPUTING SYSTEMS LIMITED. 1980. Scrapbook Information Handling System. 1980. 7p. (Brochure). Available from: Triad Computing Systems, 42, Kingsway, London, England.

TSENG. 1980. Texas TI99/4 Home Computer. Practical Computing. 1980 August; 3(8): 62-64.
VICKERY, A.; BROOKS, H. 1980. Microcomputer, Liberator or Enslaver. In: Proceedings of the 4th International Online Information Meeting; 1980 December 9-11; London, England. Oxford, England and Medford, NJ: Learned Information; 1980. 387-396. ISBN: 0-904933-28-8.
VINE. 1979. MOLARS: Getting to Grips with a Special Library's Problems. Vine (England). 1979 May; 28: 21-26.
VINE. 1980. Developments at Harwell. Vine (England). 1980 December; 36: 11-12.
WAINWRIGHT, JANE. 1976. Why Use a Minicomputer? Some Factors Affecting Their Selection. Program (England). 1976 January; 10(1): 7-13. ISSN: 0033-0337.
WALSH, M. E. 1978. Where Are We, How Did We Get There and Where Are We Going. Journal of Systems Management. 1978 November; 6-21.
WANGER, JUDITH. 1979. Education and Training for Online Systems. In: Williams, M. E., ed. Annual Review of Information Science and Technology: Volume 14. White Plains, NY: Knowledge Industry Publications, Inc.; 1979. 219-245. ISBN: 0-914236-44-X.
WATT, D. B. 1980. Easy-to-Fix Superbrain Looks Like Good Value for Money. Practical Computing. 1980 April; 3(4): 64-65.
WILLIAMS, MARTHA E. 1980. Research toward a Transparent Information System. Paper presented at: Oak Ridge National Laboratory, 1980 September. 10p. Available from: the author, Information Retrieval Research Laboratory, 5-135 CSL, University of Illinois, Urbana, IL 61801.
WILLIAMS, MARTHA E.; PREECE, SCOTT E. 1980. Elements of a Distributed Transparent Information Retrieval System. In: Benenfeld, A. R.; Kazlauskas, E. J., eds. Communicating Information: Proceedings of the American Society for Information Science 43rd Annual Meeting; 1980 October 5-10; Anaheim, CA. White Plains, NY: Knowledge Industry Publications, Inc.; 1980. ISBN: 0-914236-73-3.
WILLIAMS, PHILIP W. 1979a. Microprocessor Assisted Terminals for Online Information Systems. In: Proceedings of the 3rd International Online Information Meeting; 1979 December 4-6; London, England. Oxford, England and Medford, NJ: Learned Information; 1979. 139-146. ISBN: 0-904933-21-0.
WILLIAMS, PHILIP W. 1979b. The Potential of the Microprocessor in Library and Information Work. Aslib Proceedings (England). 1979 April; 31(4): 202-209. ISSN: 0001-253X.
WILLIAMS, PHILIP W. 1980a. Intelligent Access to Online Systems. In: Proceedings of the 4th International Online Information Meeting; 1980 December 9-11; London, England. Oxford, England and Medford, NJ: Learned Information; 1980. 397-408. ISBN: 0-904933-28-8.
WILLIAMS, PHILIP W. 1980b. New Opportunities from Information Technology. Journal of Information Science (England). 1980; 2: 29-36. ISSN: 0165-5515.
WINFIELD, R. P. 1980. An Informal Survey of Operational Microprocessor-Based Systems, Autumn 1979. Program (England). 1980 July; 14(3): 121-129. ISSN: 0033-0337.
WITHERS, STEPHEN. 1980. TRS80 Model II. Personal Computer World. 1980 June; 3(6): 50-53.

4 Automated Language Processing

DAVID BECKER
IIT Research Institute

INTRODUCTION

This chapter discusses automated language processing (ALP)—i.e., the computer manipulation of non-numeric data (usually English words). ALP includes list processing (LP), in which the data items are analyzed as lists of words or names, and natural language processing (NLP), in which the data items are analyzed as sentences that obey rules of grammar and that convey meaning. LP topics discussed include word processing (WP), dictionary-based automatic spelling correction, and keyword information retrieval (IR). NLP topics discussed include automatic syntax correction, question-answering systems, and machine translation (MT). However, much of the discussion is about computer meaning representations and the possibility that they are crucial to NLP. In addition, a number of hardware advances are discussed that contribute to ALP in general: videodisks, laser printers, voice input to computer, voice output from computer, optical character recognition (OCR), and specialized computers.

Status vs. *ARIST* and Major Reviews

Two previous *ARIST* chapters contain material closely related to this chapter. In Volume 11, DAMERAU reviewed ALP, concentrating mostly on question-answering systems and their components (parsers, meaning representations, and logic evaluation modules). In *ARIST*, Volume 15, SMITH analyzed the conceptual and practical relationships between artificial intelligence (AI) and information processing, focusing on some aspects of how AI research and procedures relate to the tasks of IR. The many recent, relevant publications made it impossible for this review to be exhaustive. About 10% of the relevant citations are given here. Roughly 1,000 citations were seriously considered, and in several of the sections, citation counts are given to indicate the number of publications encountered but not cited. Many additional citations can be found in the reviews cited, in the Bibliography, in the review by Smith, and in other related *ARIST* chapters. "What Can Be Automated?" (ARDEN) is an excellent general review, published since Smith's, that discusses NLP research in the context of other computer-processing problems.

Overview

Since the review by Damerau, ALP has been changed by hardware and software advances. These changes include: 1) the popularization of low-cost home computer systems powerful enough to perform simple ALP activities, such as maintaining bibliographic files or data files (recipes, reports, mailing lists); 2) the development of "talking" and "listening" devices; 3) the enhancement of OCR systems to accept largely unrestricted character fonts; 4) the growing use of WP systems by small businesses; 5) the integration of WP techniques into publishing and database activities; and 6) the development of English language question-answering systems with very high competence in specific technical disciplines (medicine, chemistry, electrical engineering). This list is not exhaustive.

The hardware advances that have contributed to these changes include the sharp decrease in the price/performance ratio for computer hardware, the development of single-chip processors and special-purpose chips, floppy disks, and relatively low-cost large-capacity (nominally 100 Mbyte) disks that have made computer-based ALP economically competitive and have greatly reduced the barriers of capital investment and system reliability. Costs are so low that hardware reliability can be obtained by buying redundant backup modules. New processor architectures are expected to continue these trends [e.g., associative processors (MALLER; SCHUEGRAF), database machines (RAUZINO), multiprocessor architectures (e.g., ROBERTS; SALTON, 1980b), and the LISP (linguistic string processing) machine (SCHOICHET; STEELE & SUSSMAN)].

The rapid growth in the number of computer systems has in turn created the markets (and the incentives) for additional hardware-related developments (speaking and listening devices, etc.). It has also provided the opportunity for many people to become acquainted with NLP ideas and, ultimately, to contribute to NLP developments. This enlarged community includes hobbyist innovators, who now have available to them computer languages that facilitate ALP processing tasks, such as LISP (ALLEN), and small LISP-based research prototype systems (CHARNIAK ET AL.; RIESBECK & CHARNIAK).

The software advances mainly involve language parsing, computer-meaning representation (REPC), logical inference, and database organization. Some systems that use these innovations interact with a person in English on subjects such as medical diagnosis (DAVIS ET AL.), travel reservations (BOBROW ET AL.), and the relative positions of blocks (WINOGRAD, 1972). To accomplish these tasks computer programs that use English language rules (i.e., grammar) and subject-area knowledge (e.g., medicine, geometry, etc.) are required. The subject-area knowledge is necessary for sentence parsing as well as for generating answers. The subject-area knowledge is stored in the computer as REPCs, and the rules to manipulate them are also stored.

The capabilities of current bibliographic IR and WP systems are very different from the capabilities of question-answering systems. For the most part, WP and IR systems do not use REPCs, they don't deal with meaning, they don't check grammar, and they don't identify errors other than invalid spelling.

Most bibliographic IR systems are based either on Boolean combinations of keywords selected by the user or on statistical properties of the keyword distribution in a record collection. Such methods allow large databases to be processed at relatively low cost. Development of question-answering and meaning analysis capabilities for IR and WP awaits the advent of suitable REPCs.

Sources

The basic sources that disseminate the literature on ALP are largely unchanged from those listed by Damerau and by Smith. *Cognitive Science* and *AI Magazine* are new journals that are pertinent to research in NLP.

DATA INPUT/OUTPUT AND FORMATTING

The development of convenient NL input/output (I/O) facilities (between human and computer and between computers) is an area dominated by corporate research and development rather than by academic research. Most of the advances here involve the construction of new hardware. Accordingly, the key sources are trade publications, such as *Datamation, Mini-Micro Systems, Electrical Engineering Times,* and *Computerworld.* This area is technically complex, involving state-of-the-art electronics and materials processing. A few advances that have significant impact on ALP are cited below; technical details are omitted.

Prices for special-font OCR equipment and services have fallen by more than 50% in the past three years, reflecting the general price/performance ratio improvements that are widespread in the computer industry. Also significant are the development and commercial offering of a universal-font character recognition device by Kurzweil Computer Products, Inc. This device was initially developed under funding by the National Science Foundation (NSF). It accepts text of arbitrary fonts (ordinary newspapers, books, etc.) at a transparent window and transforms it into machine-readable data files. In one Kurzweil unit, the machine-readable file is used to drive a voice-generation unit so that the device can "read" to the blind (ROSENBERG).

The technology of voice/speech recognition and generation has entered the marketplace in a variety of products, including Speak and Spell by Texas Instruments, inexpensive speech-generation cards for hobby computers, and many rumored applications (cars that tell drivers about maintenance problems and consumer appliances that tell users when actions are required) (POWELL & THOMPSON; ROBINSON). Several systems seem to "speak" with a slight Swedish accent, while others sound vaguely Texan or Japanese. Voice-controlled telephone dialers now approach practicality (RABINER ET AL.), and HEARSAY-II (a speech-recognition program) is reported to have shown significant progress at recognizing speech consisting of words from a sample vocabulary of 1,000 words (ERDMAN ET AL.).

Another development that is affecting current ALP is laser printers. Some of these printers can be configured to produce camera-ready copy in different type fonts (some fonts can be specified by the user). This development has already changed the way in which many reports are generated, and its impact on the handling of foreign and symbolic languages may be even more significant. In 1980, IBM Corp. and Wang Computer Systems each introduced computer hardware and software systems to handle Chinese ideographs. A related area (too broad to be covered here) is the development of graphics languages that make it more convenient to take advantage of the new print hardware. These languages enable a user to create graphic images [usually for video and/or cathode ray tube (CRT) or line printer] by entering a few commands or by using joysticks (a control device roughly analogous to a steering wheel and used in computer video games). One development in this area is Knuth's graphics language for the specification and design of new type fonts. BERNHARD describes a system that uses the Kurzweil omnifont character recognition scanner to enter text, an ECRM digitizer to enter graphics, programs to compose pages (Composition Software Services), and a Xerox 9700 laser printer for output. Together, these units make up an electronic publishing station.

Another development with significant potential impact for ALP data transfer is the new videodisk technology. A videodisk that can play 30 minutes of a standard TV signal contains 54,000 frames of TV data. In some videodisk systems, these frames can be addressed in about three seconds and displayed independently. If a page of text could be displayed on each frame, 54,000 pages could be stored on one side of one disk (108,000 frames on two sides), at a reproduction cost of about $3.00 and with significant savings for storage and shipment (because of data compression). Although mastering costs are about $4,000 (to convert a videotape to a master videodisk), they are small, on a per-disk basis, for a production run of many disks. Other advantages are the apparent stability of videodisk as an archival medium and its compatibility with computer controllable display sequencing for computer-aided instruction (CAI). Unfortunately, several problems must be solved before videodisk technology can store journal text economically for standard TV, the most serious of which is "resolution." About six times as many image points are on a typical page of text as can be resolved in a standard video frame. Therefore, one page of text would have to be decomposed into about six video frames for it to be legible on a standard TV screen. Naturally, image decomposition involves problems of hardware and format. For example, how do you decompose a video image of one page into six separate images without degrading user comprehension of text? This resolution problem also reduces the estimated text capacity of one disk to about 10,000 pages. Several projects are under way to explore the feasibility of videodisk use for document storage. The IIT Research Institute is developing software reformatting systems to overcome image resolution problems so that camera images of text and electronically generated images of machine-readable files can be conveniently read from standard TV screens using videodisks (SCHIPMA & BECKER).

Pergamon Press has developed Video Patsearch, which provides access to the 700,000 U.S. patents issued since 1971 via video images of patent drawings along with abstracts and other textual material stored on eight videodisks (*MANAGEMENT INFORMATION SYSTEMS WEEK*). Sears has produced a videodisk version of their 236-page spring (1981) catalog, which is being tested in two markets (*BUSINESS WEEK*). Toshiba has announced a videodisk system for document storage and retrieval, estimated to be marketed in 1984, that overcomes the resolution problem by using nonstandard high-resolution video (TOSHIBA AMERICA, INCORPORATED).

WORD PROCESSING

In the past three years more people have had their working methods directly affected by the advent of low-cost WP stations than by any other single ALP innovation. This chapter was prepared on a Digital Equipment Corp. (DEC) PDP 11/34, using the DEC editor, EDI, and a text-formatting program distributed at no cost to members of DECUS, the DEC users group. The use of this rudimentary WP equipment has reduced the time required for the mechanics of manuscript preparation by at least 70%, counting the savings in typographical corrections, rephrasing, and editing. WP is not new. What is new is its availability at irresistible price/performance ratios and in packages that are tailored for specific applications. These applications include convenient interfaces to photocomposition equipment (ADAMS & CLEAVE; BERNHARD) and convenient facilities for generating educational materials (BUNDERSON). WP packages are offered for home computers, and reports on WP capabilities even appear in such journals as *Popular Mechanics* (SHAPIRO) and *Byte* (RUCKDESCHEL). Recent reviews cover the status of software packages that provide WP services on microcomputers (BERNHARD; JONG). To date, WP developments have come mainly from the commercial sector, with little contribution from the academic community.

Typical WP systems have long offered users the capability to edit and to reformat their texts using convenient commands. The major new features of WP are automatic spelling correction and network coordination (sometimes involving shared logic) of locally intelligent WP stations. The automatic spelling correction is usually implemented by hashing into a dictionary that is stored online. Any term that is not in the dictionary is flagged in the text, so that the user may be sure that he has used valid, but not necessarily appropriate, words. In 1980, typical WP commercial dictionaries ranged from 25,000 to 100,000 words, and some supported as many as seven languages (KINNUCAN). Hand-held multilanguage word and phrase translators which used similar techniques of hashed entry into compressed format files were first marketed in 1978 (HECKEL). Some models have voice output.

The growth of shared logic and network systems has been fostered by several factors, including: 1) increased mean time between failure and 2) the ability of individual users of the system to use the data files and other resources of other users. In a network configuration, the WP work force is divided into small groups, and each group has its local microcomputer. That microcomputer handles the bulk of their WP transactions directly, but it also communicates with other microcomputers and usually to a more powerful, central minicomputer or mainframe. This division of processing labor allows the local microcomputer to operate even when other nodes (other local microcomputers or mainframes or work stations) on the system are not working. It also allows the local node to access data stored at other nodes (e.g., mailing lists, personnel files, inventories). This sharing of system resources by different users will be encouraged by the recent adoption of new standards, such as the Ethernet carrier-sensed multiple access/collision detection (CSMA/CD) protocol (produced by DEC, Intel, and Xerox Corp.) and the token passing protocol, two standards which have been accepted by the Institute of Electrical and Electronics Engineers (IEEE) (SHUTT).

Significant progress has been made in the automatic detection and correction of spelling errors in databases (HALL & DOWLING; PETERSON). In searching the literature for this review, I found many misspellings in the bibliographic records. Some were simple one-letter transpositions; others I could not decipher. In recent years, such spelling errors have been usually detected and corrected by extracting all the terms in the database and noting their locations (inverting the file), sorting the list, and counting the frequency with which each term occurs. Because the misspellings generally are found in the low-frequency items, these items were manually screened for errors. ZAMORA presented an alternative to this procedure. Analogous to the WP dictionary look-up procedure, a hashing algorithm for dictionary verification of spelling was developed to correct errors in the *Chemical Abstracts* (CA) database. It is unclear whether, in general, it will prove more efficient to check spelling before or after file inversion. Inverting first entails fewer look-ups for high-frequency terms, but it also means less efficient correction since the record with the error must be accessed.

Since WP systems now check spelling, their next logical capability is to check syntax—i.e., that subjects agree with verbs, that adjectives agree with nouns, and eventually that the meaning of each candidate sentence makes sense. This is the step that has separated research activities from production activities for about 20 years. For a formal language, such as FORTRAN, PL-1, or LISP, it is essential to build a syntax checker that, as a step in compilation, verifies that the statements entered are valid (conform to the specifications of the language). This is possible because the symbols used in, say, FORTRAN, are unambiguous, and syntax checking is a self-contained process within each statement. However, testing whether a computer program "makes sense" is a very difficult problem, known as "proof of correctness," for which much work remains to be done (ARDEN). In contrast, the symbols and structures that make up natural language (NL) sentences are ambiguous. Experience has shown [especially the failure of automatic computer translation of text from one language to another (U.S. NATIONAL RESEARCH COUNCIL)] that the only satisfactory way to resolve the ambiguities inherent in English is by evaluating each possible interpretation of each candidate sentence and selecting the best interpretations (puns may be intentional) by referring to a REPC. This is a difficult computer process because the construction of the REPC invariably involves the incorporation of background information that is not explicitly present in the candidate sentences (the instantiation process) and other problems (discussed below) that are not well understood. For example, when I say that "the book falls," gravity is implied as the agent even though it is not explicitly mentioned. A REPC would identify this as an instance of "gravity" within its model of forces. Despite these problems, machine translators based on simple REPCs can be quite useful, even if they do make mistakes. The situation for machine translators is reviewed by GARFIELD, by HUTCHINS, and by ZACHARY.

Significant progress has been made in checking English syntax and meaning when a REPC is used and the dialog is limited to the subjects handled by that REPC. In 1972, Winograd achieved a significant breakthrough by building a set of computer programs that could communicate in English about the positions of some imaginary geometric solids (e.g., blue spheres, red cubes, orange rectangular prisms) in an imaginary box (WINOGRAD, 1972). Given sentences such as, "Move the red cube on the orange rectangular prism to the top of the blue sphere," and, "Is it now the highest object in the box?," the system generated appropriate English answers. To do this, the system had a REPC of the Blockworld in which the positions of all the blocks were recorded (e.g., a computerized map). The system also had functions that enabled it to read and or update the map. In response to a question, the system generated an answer by: 1) interpreting the question in terms of the system's functions (which involves resolving ambiguities in the question); 2) applying the functions to the map to determine the required data; and 3) generating the English response. When given commands to add blocks or to move blocks, Winograd's system determined if the moves were geometrically possible and responded, appropriately, in English. To extend this work to the range of sentences encountered in WP and IR, it seems appropriate to build systems such as Winograd's but with REPCs and processing modules for contexts beyond that of Blockworld.

COMPUTER MEANING REPRESENTATION (REPC)

This section reviews some ideas on REPCs that are somewhat abstract. The concepts discussed are not necessary for an understanding of the sections that follow.

Because REPCs are a central part of computer problem solving, many REPCs have been constructed quite apart from any consideration of NLP. BRODIE reviews 350 citations pertinent to REPCs. In this section, approximately six contexts in which computational models have been constructed are discussed. The purpose is to indicate by example what constitutes a "context," to give perspective to what fraction of familiar contexts has been represented and, therefore, how many remain to be done. I believe that not until REPCs for all familiar contexts have been constructed (either by programmers or by a program itself) can a general-purpose, knowledgeable question-answerer be built. Though it is difficult to estimate the percent of needed REPCs that have been constructed, it is probably well below 5%.

A REPC for a data object belongs to one of three levels: 1) isomorphism, 2) isolated features, and 3) relations among features. An isomorphic REPC involves a one-to-one relationship between the parts of the object and the parts of the REPC. Usually it also implies that the parts of the REPC interact in a manner analogous to the ways in which the corresponding parts of the object interact. For example, one can represent a "black and white" visual image in a computer by using a two-dimensional matrix in which each matrix element corresponds to one region (pixel) in the image field, and the value of each element is a measure of the grey level of the corresponding image region.

If features, such as sub-images of circles or squares, are identified within either the image field or its isomorphic REPC, the image can be represented at the feature level in terms of a list of the features (commonly also called attributes or properties) that it has. The feature list REPC (e.g., circle, ball) is usually less complete than the isomorphic REPC because some of the data structure may not be expressible in terms of defined features.

After the features have been identified, the data object can be represented in relational form (e.g., "the circle on the block"). English is a level-3 representation, and although one can build an expert system by coding rules that act on features expressed in English (e.g., "swing if the ball is over the plate"), unless one has a level-1 (isomorphic) representation to back it up, it is subject to error and incompleteness. For example, without a level-1 representation of visual images, how would a system conveniently process geometric relationships (GELERNTER)? HOFSTADTER discusses representational formats for geometric relationships in terms of several interesting examples, including the "Bongard" problems. In these problems, a series of pictures of objects that exemplify a common organizational principle are presented, and the problem is to identify the organizational principle and apply it to additional pictures.

Various computer formalisms are used for REPCs at the three levels. At the isomorphic level the REPC must have a degree of freedom that corresponds, one-to-one, with each degree of freedom to be represented in the data object. Hence, one can always think of an isomorphic REPC as a state vector with n positions (dimensions) that correspond to n degrees of freedom in the data object (e.g., an image with n image points corresponds to an n-dimensional vector), and matrix representation is the usual format.

At level 2, various formalisms are used, including mainly simple attribute-value structures, such as data tables, linked lists, and data-pointer structures. These are reviewed in standard texts, such as that by MARTIN.

Level-3 REPCs involve an even wider variety of formalisms, chief of which are: relational databases, semantic data nets, predicate calculus (and related formal languages), and NL. The definition and use of tabular relational databases are reviewed by CODD (1979). The definition, history, and use of semantic nets are reviewed by BRACHMAN, from the initial conception of Quillian to the recent development of structured inheritance networks and property lists as exemplified by FRL (Frame Representation Language) (ROBERTS & GOLDSTEIN), KRL (Knowledge Representation Language) (BOBROW & WINOGRAD), OWL (SZOLOVITS ET AL.), and KLONE (Knowledge Language One). The definition and use of predicate calculus in conjunction with production systems and semantic nets are reviewed by NILSSON. Simplified level-3 REPCs that ignore many details that would be required by computational-reasoning systems have been proposed for information retrieval (CIGANIK).

Implemented Representations (REPCs)

Explicit representations of state vectors are feasible when: 1) the situation is characterized by n classes of values (e.g., n horses running a race), 2) the computer can efficiently manage n data cells, and 3) the values of the n cells can be determined or estimated in acceptable time. A simple example of such a system is the game of tic-tac-toe. Any position in the game can be characterized in terms of a vector with nine positions (there is no higher level of detail or additional degrees of freedom that are inherent to a position in tic-tac-toe). Even complicated games can be represented in terms of state vectors—e.g., chess (WILKINS), which uses plans and features rather than exhaustive search of the game tree and statistical evaluation—but NL interfaces for these games have not yet been built. Still, in Wilkins' PARADISE program, the MACLISP code itself reads like English. The program has intermediate levels of problem representation lying between the state vector and the solution that constitute plans. These plans contain variables such as "attack kingside" and "safemove" that guide the selection of moves rather than specifying them, as in simpler problem domains, e.g., tic-tac-toe. The following code shows a plan that was constructed by PARADISE (Pattern Recognition Applied to Directing Search) in response to a particular game position.

```
(((WN N5) (((BN N4)   (SAFEMOVE WR Q7) (((BK NIL)
(SAFECAPTURE WR BR)) ((ANYBUT BK) (SAFECAPTURE
WR BK)))) ((BN N4) (CHECKMOVE WR Q7) (BK NIL)
(SAFECAPTURE WR BQ)))) ((THREAT (PLUS (EXCHVAL
WN N5) (FORK WR BK BR))) (LIKELY 0) ((THREAT (PLUS
(EXCHVAL WN N5)  (EXCH WR BQ))) (LIKELY 0)))
```

A rough translation of this code reads:

> Play N-N5. If Black captures the knight, attempt to safely move the rook on Q1 to Q7. Then, if black moves his king anywhere, try to safely capture the black rook on R7, and if black moves any piece other than his king, try to safely capture the king with the rook. As an alternative, after black captures the knight, attempt to safely move the rook on Q1 to Q7 with check. Then, if black moves his king anywhere, try to safely capture the black queen with the rook.

Even those who do not play chess will recognize a plausible train of thought here that corresponds to the familiar way in which language is used.

The best chess-playing program in the world today is probably Chess 4.6 (NEWBORN). The difference between the methods used by Chess 4.6 and

PARADISE seems to reflect a parallel competition in ALP. Chess 4.6 works by evaluating the consequences of all possible moves for a given number of turns by each player, which it does very efficiently. PARADISE analyzes only a few moves, but it does that analysis within a model of strategy. Similarly, in IR, today's commercial systems generate retrievals by cataloging the positions of all words in a database and by accessing them efficiently. Meanwhile, some research IR systems access only a limited number of words within a model of meaning (SCHANK & KOLODNER).

Because many such games are characterized by a few degrees of freedom, they are readily represented as state vectors. Adventure (DECUS) is a state-vector type of game, and it simulates NL dialog in a rudimentary way. Games with more degrees of freedom (e.g., football) are sometimes simulated by ignoring or grouping the degrees of freedom (detail). Similar reduced-detail representations have been successfully created and interfaced with NLP routines for complicated practical problems. Among these are the compilation of commodities data (STANSFIELD) and the recording of the medical features of a patient (ROBERTSON ET AL.; SAGER & HIRSCHMAN; SLAMECKA ET AL.), including electrolyte imbalance (PATIL).

The research area of electric circuit design/trouble shooting/education, reviewed by STEELS, has received considerable attention in the past four years, including at least 40 publications, some of which involve systems with NL interfaces. This area is well suited to a net representation since the underlying order of circuits is similar to a net, with circuit components (resistors, diodes, capacitors, transistors, etc.) as the nodes and with wires as the links.

One of the broadest applications areas is that of graphics and image processing. There is a system for understanding stories about images (painting) (CHARNIAK). There is a system for analyzing stick figures of humans, called SKELETON (HERMAN). There is a system for interpreting statements from drawn algebraic relationships (PURCELL) using OCR. WALTZ & BOGGESS argue that graphic representation is central to NL understanding, and there are several systems that construct graphic display while driven by NL commands. There are also a number of systems that represent geometric relationships among physical objects, either for general interest in the problem (LEHNERT & BURSTEIN) or as a part of a system to drive a robot or a manipulator (BINFORD ET AL.; MARR & NISHIHARA; WINOGRAD, 1972). These various applications may involve REPC levels 1, 2, or 3. Collectively, these areas are very active and are represented by more than 100 publications during the past four years.

Automatic programming is another domain in problem representation in which the computational structure that has been developed is strong enough so that it is worthwhile to construct an NL interface. MCCUNE reviews this area and some steps towards implementation. At least 15 other papers cover this area, including those by GREEN & BARSTOW and GINSPARG.

Military applications also rank high as computational models for which NL interfaces would be desirable. Among the tasks of the defense sector are monitoring a sensor network that contains numerical data as well as NL materials. The signals in this network are used to prompt appropriate defense activities. The high priority of this work has led to the development of several systems that have some NL capability (e.g., SILVA & MONTGOMERY). During the past three years, at least 15 unclassified publications have appeared in this area. Other areas that have been represented as computational models include: chemical computations (BUCHANAN & FEIGENBAUM); human attitudes (SCHANK, 1979b); social acts (SCHANK, 1979b); and mechanical devices [a forced-air furnace (RIEGER, 1977)].

Discourse Representation (REPNL)

A REPNL is the internal representation of an NL dialog. To check if a particular sentence "makes sense," one performs the operations indicated by the sentence, either on the object or on its REPC. Thus, for the sentence, "The circle is on the box," either I look at the circle and the box, or the system looks at its REPC of the circle and the box, and we try to verify the extent to which the assertion is true. The key property of the REPNL is to express the candidate sentence in terms of the functions that the system uses to manipulate its REPCs (THOMAS). If the system were to use English for REPNL, it would suffer some logical problems, chiefly those of ambiguity. For example, every time an ambiguous word or phrase (e.g., "plants and air pollution," meaning plants-vegetation or plants-industrial) appears in the NL stream, the REPNL notation should have a mechanism for distinguishing the different cases and for specifying the appropriate information to be instantiated. The resolution of apparent ambiguities can be logically complicated. If an entered sentence requires more than one subject expert module for its interpretation (e.g., the expert for chess and the expert for European history) and if those experts are to communicate directly, they need a medium for communication, and that medium must make explicit what each expert alone knows. That is, if the two experts are A and B, and their expertise is "a" and "b," then a message from A to B cannot contain any items that refer to "a" for interpretation—i.e., all "a" information must be explicit. One way this can be done is by explicitly disambiguating English by using tags (e.g., plants-vegetation) (WINOGRAD, 1972).

Adequacy Studies of REPNLs

A number of authors have reported on the apparent inadequacies of various REPNLs, usually under the following protocol. In step 1 a structure is proposed that accounts for a given number of features. In step 2 the structure is tested and is found to be adequate for one domain but to fail for others. In step 3 the failure modes are identified, and new features to be used in subsequent tests are proposed.

WOODS noted that the assertion of a link in a semantic net is ambiguous because it could be interpreted intensionally or extensionally. This is a special case of the general question of the representation of belief, which is reviewed by MCDERMOTT & DOYLE. ZADEH believes that truth should be represented as a continuous variable and interpreted via "fuzzy logic." DOYLE & LONDON looked at the consequences of having a database that contained statements of belief and of adding new assertions to such a system while trying to maintain logical consistency. When fuzzy truth values are used, the addition of a new assertion can lead to revised truth values for all the old assertions whose truth was known with less than certainty. For example, the discovery that the earth is not the center of the universe changed many people's beliefs in a wide variety of contexts. The literature of the past four years on computer representation and manipulation of data contains at least 40 publications on the formal structure of belief.

SCHANK (1979b) analyzed several abstract kinds of metaphorically expressed social and historical relationships present in the Gettysburg Address and developed a new notation to represent them—"triangle relations." Questions of anaphora were explored by WEBBER and about ten others. At least 25 other publications discussed aspects of representation purported to be inadequately represented by current formalisms. Additional shortcomings will continue to be identified for we are far from a complete theory of REPNL.

Several authors reported on mechanisms for structuring dialogs that are made up of several sentences (BROWN; MANN ET AL.; MOORE ET AL.). The problems include the identification and representation of general structures, such as theme, purpose, and speaker attitudes. SCHANK (1979b) reported on the representation of speaker attitudes derived from NL.

NL DATA ABSTRACTION

Parsing is the process of making the logical relationships among words in a text explicit. If this process is carried out by methods that do not involve reference to a REPC, the parse is syntactic; otherwise, it is semantic. MARCUS reported the development of a new syntactic parser, which is notable for its strong correspondence to traditional grammar structures and for its claim that it involves no backtracking because it never has to revise its strategy. Clearly this isn't the end of the story because many sentences are semantically ambiguous even though their syntax might be unambiguous. Other sentences are syntactically and semantically ambiguous. Sager has shown that an essentially syntactic parse can be successful at parsing NL into a table format for NL taken from a discipline (e.g., medical research) in which the grammatical structures that are used are highly standardized by informal conventions (GRISHMAN & HIRSCHMAN; SAGER & HIRSCHMAN). RIEGER (1976) reported work on a system in which each word is represented by an expert, and the parse is decided by a "dialog" among the experts, each of whom contributes some information based on the explicit context (i.e., the words) in which it finds itself. Several NL parsing systems have been developed, based on augmented transition networks (ATN) that are readily interfaced to specific applications [e.g., LIFER (HENDRIX)]. Two theses presented methods for the automatic parsing of NL newspaper stories (CULLINGFORD; DE JONG), with the intention of making the results available to a question-answering system. The question-answering works sometimes. By identifying the failure modes, the system can be modified to perform better. This scenario of improvement is likely to persist until better REPC formalisms are developed. I know of no practical production systems for day-to-day operations that use databases created by parsing NL sources, although the systems above approach this goal. However, many databases created by other means are accessed by NL methods (discussed below).

DATABASE RETRIEVAL

Any database can be coordinated for retrieval using keyword methods, whether the database elements are predicate calculus formulas, nodes joined by semantic net links, structured records coordinated through schemas, or sequential NL bibliographic records. Usually, preprocessing a database to produce index files (relating terms to the numbers of the records in which they occur) greatly improves real-time response. Such file inversion is the method of choice in commercial bibliographic systems, although alternatives based on tree structures (MARTIN), linked list formalisms (e.g., SCHANK & KOLODNER), and statistical ordering principles (SALTON, 1980a) are also used. For small files (thousands of records or less) the file organization is much less crucial than for large files, where hardware limitation on storage volume and processing time limit the feasible processing options. However, the costs associated with creating and storing index files or other derived structures (which may be much larger than the original data file itself) may be unwarranted for files that are processed only infrequently or for which user requests may be batched and direct processing is more efficient (SCHIPMA). For situations in which the retrieval task is to find a data element with a particular value in a database, systems exist that accept the request in NL.

A typical bibliographic record contains a title and an abstract field (among others) that are expressed in NL. In the past 15 years much of the work in bibliographic retrieval has concerned procedures that improve retrieval by the use of statistical estimates of meaning (e.g., clustering, as discussed below). NL techniques that are knowledge based have not made inroads into the commercial area, but the situation may change soon. The statistical techniques are little used commercially, although their contribution to retrieval efficiency is well documented in experimental systems.

One of the most well known and fertile statistical approaches to retrieval is clustered file organization (SALTON, 1980a). Records that share a higher proportion of words are also likely to share more concepts than records that don't. This principle is the NL estimation step. Accordingly, a database could be structured so that records with more terms in common are physically closer. A query then specifies a point in the space and results in the retrieval of records closest to the query point. User relevance judgments on those records can then be used to distort the record space and to identify new records with likely relevance. Because this procedure is based on the direct coordination of records, index files are not needed; thus, storage requirements are much less than those for inverted file organization. Another advantage is that because it is based on statistical associations, it is likely to capture jargon and technical language that a novice searcher might not think of or recognize. Unfortunately, it is expensive to establish the initial cluster file organization, and this method is a radical departure from the inverted file

126 DAVID BECKER

structure software that is commercially in place. SALTON (1979) has presented evidence for performance superiority for his methods and has proved mathematical theorems that predict the performance gains. Clustering research has been actively done by many groups during the past five years, resulting in at least 50 publications.

Recently, several research groups have explored the feasibility of using the clustering principle in conjunction with inverted file organization for bibliographic data. The idea is to give up the space gains associated with cluster file organization but to keep the recall and precision gains. This is done by using the clustering principle on selected inverted file data, thus avoiding the heavy processing costs associated with clustering the whole file. [Efficient clustering algorithms require time proportional to N (log N), where N is the number of records to be clustered.] A typical search, using these protocols, begins with a Boolean search expression, which results in an initial retrieved set (R1). Subsequent results are derived by statistical analysis of R1 and sometimes of other records that share terms with R1. One simple procedure is to break R1 into groups; then perhaps manual judgment of a few members of each group will be sufficient to decide whether or not the whole group is relevant (PREECE). Another idea is to compare the frequency of each term in R1 with its frequency in the whole database and then report the terms present at unusually high frequency (which characterize R1) so that the searcher can modify his strategy accordingly (DOSZKOCS). This algorithm (AID) has been implemented at the U.S. National Library of Medicine (NLM). Another idea is to label each term manually with the name of the discipline in which it is defined (e.g., magnetism is defined in physics) so that when either record clustering or AID-like term referral analysis is done, it can be restricted to terms that are relevant to specific disciplines (BECKER ET AL.). Another technique is to construct a thesaurus of terms, based on co-occurrence in a document collection, and then do retrieval experiments by representing each document in terms of the clusters. When these clusters are adjusted to increase their statistical independence, the retrieval performance is significantly improved (CRAWFORD). In related techniques, terms that are statistically identified from R1 are used to augment the inverted file search retrieval strategy (NOREAULT ET AL.). Similarly, BURKET ET AL. describe a full-text retrieval system that features vocabulary clustering options as part of its repertoire. In this case, one use of this option is to characterize the kind of document being examined by the distribution of the terms that it contains. All these methods lead to improved retrieval. The mathematical measures of retrieval performance and statistical association that are used for applications in this area are reviewed by MCGILL ET AL.

Another idea is to identify simple syntactic structures [e.g., citing statements (O'CONNOR, 1980a) and "answer passages" (O'CONNOR, 1980b)] that can enhance retrieval performance in keyword-based search. Significant indexing phrases have been identified by a system using several interdependent rules (MAEDA ET AL.) instead of the more usual identification based on phrase frequency or association frequency. SALTON (1979) has analyzed the frequencies of isolated terms in a document collection within the context of a model of their "discrimination efficiency" for retrieval. Another

approach is to weight the terms used in the retrieval according to their correlation with relevance as determined from previous searches. Various mathematical formulations of the problem are plausible, depending on one's
assumptions about term distribution characteristics in the text. SALTON
(1980a) and SPARCK-JONES report logical and empirical support for these
methods.

The future of statistical-keyword techniques (e.g., indexing, abstracting,
Boolean retrievals) for NL files is unclear. Thesauri and dictionaries that map
keywords into larger categories, such as clusters or disciplines, can make an
appreciable contribution to retrieval performance. If a time comes when NL
files are stored in an explicit, disambiguated, propositional form, then
statistical-keyword techniques are likely to be replaced by rule-based systems
that are based on exact match. However, it is also possible that files will continue to be stored in NL format and that the querying routines will contain
sophisticated logic that will use statistical methods and automate the thought
processes now used by online searchers. SMITH reviews the status of such
studies. In the short term, commercial and user-group software packages are
becoming available for keyword search of files on mini- and microcomputer
systems (*COMPUTER BUSINESS NEWS;* RUCKDESCHEL).

Several systems have been and are being developed to provide an NL interface to the user, even though NL analysis techniques are not applied to the
data elements themselves. The idea is to make the interface "user friendly"
and to lessen the amount of system-specific information that a user must
learn.

For example, CO-OP provides an NL interface to any database in CODASYL
(Conference on Data Systems Languages) standard format (KAPLAN). CO-
OP also has logic to avoid misleading answers for loaded questions, such as,
"How many of the students in Geometry 101 got an A," when there were no
students in that class. Another system of this type is ROBOT, which invokes
database functions in response to NL commands (HARRIS). Still another
system is the query structure that is planned for the Chemical Substances Information Network (CSIN) system of the Environmental Protection Agency
(EPA) and the federal User Prompted Graphic Data Evaluation (UPGRADE)
system (MILASK & FULLERTON). Several such NL front-end systems are
reviewed by GAINES.

PROMIS (Problem Oriented Medical Information System) is a functioning
integrated medical information system for patient care. It includes database
facilities for individual medical histories, tests, and physician reasoning that
underlies diagnosis. Users interact with the system through menu-select simulated NL screens that are currently generated by more than 30,000 data
frames that average 600 characters each (ROBERTSON ET AL.).

At a more ambitious level are those systems that play an active role in the
creation of the database and then provide retrieval services for it—e.g., LISP
(Linguistic String Project). Using stop/restriction lists and transformation
rules based on the theory of Harris, this system builds what is essentially a
relational database from NL input and then provides NL-prompted retrievals
on it (SAGER & HIRSCHMAN).

128   DAVID BECKER

INFERENCE

Suppose that a database contains representations for the assertions: A → B and B → C. If one searched this database for the assertion A → C, more than retrieval is called for because the desired item is not explicitly present in the database although the logically equivalent components are.

Approaches to resolve this problem depend on the nature of the database. The situation is relatively simple for databases of geometric theorems because the truth of any assertion can be tested by the system in several ways: sample figures (GELERNTER), proof procedures, and precedence. The situation for databases built on experimental observations is more complicated for several reasons: 1) all premises are not explicit; 2) all observations have a corresponding probability of error; and 3) not all observations are explicitly entered or considered. Hence, databases of experimental data are subject to belief revision (as discussed before) and incomplete cataloging of logical consequences.

A more usual case, however, is a request for data that may be obtained from the database by the application of general rules. For example, if the database contains the ages of a company's employees, a system could report their average age by using a rule to define average in terms of the REPC. Many database systems of this type have appeared in the past three to five years, and many of them have NL interfaces. Some are referred to as "toy systems" because, like that of WINOGRAD (1972), their activities are so limited that they are at best prototypes for systems that could perform useful operations. However, other systems can be used fully in day-to-day operations (FREIHERR; GAINES; HOOVER; YASAKI).

The CYRUS system (SCHANK & KOLODNER) has a database of facts on the life of Cyrus Vance. Conceptual dependency diagrams are used as the REPC format. In response to queries (e.g., Did Cyrus Vance talk to Mrs. Kosygin at the party on November 25, 1974), the system derives answers by using a hierarchy of 25 common-sense rules designed to mimic the way people use memory to answer questions when direct answers are not immediately available (either not stored in the database or not indexed in an obviously accessible manner).

The MYCIN system is notable for its significant success in arriving at medical diagnoses from symptoms reported to it and from available patient medical histories through a series of rules (adapted from the responses of doctors) and a sophisticated probability assessment module. This is not a toy system, and the systematics that were developed for deriving system rules from interaction with experts may well lead to the automation of rule generation in general. Although the interface is not truly NL (only a subset of English grammatical responses are allowed), it is interactive and has much of the feel of a true NL interface (SHORTLIFFE ET AL.).

SOPHIE is a CAI system for electronic circuit design and servicing (BROWN & BURTON). It accepts a wide variety of NL sentences from the user and responds by modifying the representation of the circuit under study or by giving requested parameter values or by asking questions.

GUS is a computerized travel consultant that communicates in NL with a traveler about flight schedules and related contingencies. It optimizes flight parameters by applying rules that are organized into "standard flight plan" frames to a database of flight information (BOBROW ET AL.).

BELIEVER is an NL analysis system that enters descriptions of simple events and refers to stored scripts to infer probable causes and the intentions of the actors (SRIDHARAN & SCHMIDT) (for the domain specified by the user of BELIEVER).

BLAH is an NL system that does tax computations (WEINER). It can explain the logic that it used to resolve the computational choices available, and its principal goal is to structure those explanations into a convenient and easily understood format.

DENDRAL is the world's best synthetic organic chemist in the sense that it can predict chemical reactions and coordinate them into synthetic pathways. It does not have an NL interface but is one of the first practical inferential systems (BUCHANAN & FEIGENBAUM).

Although it is difficult to make the concepts precise, the "number" of rules required to do the various kinds of processing described in this chapter varies over a wide range. Commercial bibliographic retrieval packages typically support about five functions (e.g., exact term match, term truncation, and three Boolean combinations). The number of rules required to simulate a searcher is not known. Tic-tac-toe requires about seven rules. The chess program by WILKINS has about 200. HEARSAY has about 500 to guide speech recognition. MYCIN (SHORTLIFFE ET AL.) has about 300 (ARDEN), and DENDRAL has thousands (BUCHANAN & FEIGENBAUM). One machine translator has about 100,000 rules (GARFIELD), and PROMIS has over 30,000 frames of 600 characters each.

In the years to come, it seems likely that many areas of knowledge will be represented in rule systems and that these systems will contain many rules. There will also be a great need for systems that automate rule generation, as has been done in TIERSA (DAVIS; DAVIS ET AL.).

SUMMARY

Fueled by rapidly decreasing hardware costs, the rapidly growing size of the participating research and development (R&D) community, economic incentive in the marketplace, and a growing repertoire of available algorithms, ALP applications are becoming more sophisticated and widespread. These applications include WP, database processing, publishing, and expert question-answering systems. Funding impetus is shifting from NSF, the Department of Defense, and the National Institutes of Health, to the private sector for some major activities. Although many questions on knowledge representation and manipulation must be resolved before many NLP tasks involving inference can be fully automated, promising research paths are being pursued. Currently, expert modules have been constructed for about a dozen contexts. When perhaps ten times that number have been constructed, the serious questions of communication between expert modules can be addressed at a practical level, and meaning level processing of general databases can be attempted. Upcoming developments include automatic detection of a wide class of English syntax errors, enhanced use of voice communication with the computer, a richer variety of English language subject experts, and statistics/dictionary-based aids to online bibliographic search.

BIBLIOGRAPHY

ADAMS, R. C.; CLEAVE, G. A. 1979. CICERO Typesetting Manual. Melbourne, Australia: Aeronautical Research Labs; 1979. 130p. (ARL/ STRUC NOTE-453). NTIS: AD-A074 399/7.

AI MAGAZINE. La Canada, CA: American Association for Artificial Intelligence. Available from: Bruce Buchanan, Stanford University Department of Computer Science, Palo Alto, CA 94305.

ALLEN, JOHN. 1979. An Overview of LISP. Byte. 1979; (8):10-16, 118-122. ISSN: 0360-5280.

ARDEN, BRUCE W. 1980. What Can Be Automated? The Computer Science and Engineering Research Study (COSERS). Cambridge, MA: MIT Press; 1980. 934p. ISBN: 0-262-01060-7.

BECKER, DAVID S.; HORWITZ, IRA M.; KIRK, SAM A. 1979. AI Methods for Large Bibliographic Files. Chicago, IL: IIT Research Institute; 1979 June. 51p. Available from: D. S. Becker, IIT Research Institute, 10 W. 35th Street, Chicago, IL 60616.

BECKER, DAVID S.; PYRCE, SHARON R. 1977. Enhancing the Retrieval Effectiveness of Large Information Systems. Chicago, IL: IIT Research Institute; 1977. 162p. NTIS: PB: 266-008.

BERNHARD, ROBERT. 1981. COMPUTERS II. Minis and Mainframes. IEEE Spectrum. 1981; 18(1):42-46. ISSN: 0018-9235.

BINFORD, T. O.; LIU, C. R.; GINI, G.; CINI, M.; ISHIDA, T. 1977. Exploratory Study of Computer Integrated Assembly Systems. Stanford, CA: Stanford University, 1977. 256p. NTIS: PB 289-295/1ST.;

BOBROW, D. G.; KAPLAN, R. M.; KAY, M.; NORMAN, D. A.; THOMPSON, H.; WINOGRAD, T. 1977. GUS: A Frame-Driven Dialog System. Artificial Intelligence. 1977; 8(2):155-173. ISSN: 0004-3702.

BOBROW, D. G.; WINOGRAD, T. 1977. An Overview of KRL, A Knowledge Representation Language. Cognitive Science. 1977; 1(1):3-46. ISSN: 0364-0213.

BRACHMAN, RONALD J. 1979. On the Epistemological Status of Semantic Networks. In: Findler, Nicholas V., ed. Associative Networks—Representation and Use of Knowledge by Computers. New York, NY: Academic Press; 1979. 3-46. ISBN: 0-12-256380-8.

BRODIE, MICHAEL L. 1980. Computer Science and Technology: Data Abstraction, Data Bases and Conceptual Modelling: An Annotated Bibliography. College Park, MD: Maryland University; 1980. 91p. NTIS: PB 80-183833.

BROWN, DAVID C.; KWASNY, STAN C. 1977. A Natural Language Graphics System. Columbus, OH: Ohio State University; 1977. 110p. (OSU-CISRC-TR-77-8). NTIS: AD A045 946/1ST.

BROWN, GRETCHEN P. 1977. A Framework for Processing Dialogue. Cambridge, MA: Massachusetts Institute of Technology; 1977. 76p. (Report no. MIT/LCS/TR-182). NTIS: AD-A042 370/7ST.

BROWN, J. S.; BURTON, R. 1975. Multiple Representations of Knowledge for Tutorial Reasoning. In: Bobrow, D. G.; Collins, A. M., ed.

Representation and Understanding. New York, NY: Academic Press; 1975. 311–349. ISBN: 0-12-108550.

BUCHANAN, B. G.; FEIGENBAUM, E. A. 1978. Dendral and Meta Dendral. Artificial Intelligence. 1978; 11(1):5–24. ISSN: 0004-3702.

BUCHANAN, B. G.; MITCHELL, T. 1978. Model-Directed Learning of Production Rules. In: Waterman, D. A.; Hayes-Roth, Frederick, eds. Pattern Directed Inference Systems. New York. NY: Academic Press; 1978. 297–312. ISBN: 0-12-737550-3.

BUNDERSON, C. VICTOR. 1978. Authoring Systems vs. Authoring Languages for Instructional Systems Development: Implications for the Department of Defense. Columbus, OH: Battelle Columbus Labs; 1978. 46p. NTIS: AD-A071 082/2ST.

BURKET, T. G.; EMRATH, P.; KUCK, D. J. 1979. The Use of Vocabulary Files for On-Line Information Retrieval. Information Processing & Management. 1979; 15(6):281–289. ISSN: 0306-4573.

BUSINESS WEEK. 1981. At Sears, "Thumbs Up" to the Video Catalog. Business Week. 1981 May; 33–34. ISSN: 0007-7135.

CHARNIAK, EUGENE. 1978. On the Use of Framed Knowledge in Language Comprehension. New Haven, CT: Yale University; 1978. 71p. (RR-137). NTIS: AD-A062-680/4ST.

CHARNIAK, EUGENE; RIESBECK, CHRISTOPHER K.; MCDERMOTT, DREW V. 1980. Artificial Intelligence Programming. Hillsdale, NJ: Lawrence Erlbaum Associates; 1980. 323p. ISBN: 0-89859-004-3; LC: 79-22120.

CIGANIK, M. 1979. Metainformational in Action in the Process of the Automatic Semantic Analysis. Information Processing & Management. 1979; 15(4):195–203. ISSN: 0306-4573.

CODD, E. 1979. Extending the Data Base Relational Model to Capture More Meaning. ACM Transactions on Database Systems. 1979; 4(4): 397–434. ISSN: 0362-5915.

COMPUTER BUSINESS NEWS. 1981. Information Retrieval Program Runs Under CP/M. Computer Business News. 1981: 4(2):22. ISSN: 0162-5853.

CRAWFORD, ROBERT G. 1979. Automatic Thesaurus Construction Based on Term Centroids. The Canadian Journal of Information Science. 1979; 4:124–136. ISSN: 0380-9218.

CULLINGFORD, RICHARD E. 1978. Script Application: Computer Understanding of Newspaper Stories. New Haven, CT: Yale University; 1978. 213p. (Doctoral thesis). NTIS: AD-A056 080/5ST.

DAMERAU, FRED J. 1976. Automated Language Processing. In: Williams, Martha E., ed. Annual Review of Information Science and Technology: Volume 11. Washington, DC: American Society for Information Science; 1976. 107–161. ISSN: 0066-4200; ISBN: 0-87715-212-8; LC: 66-25096.

DAVIS, R. 1978. Acquisition in Rule Based Systems—Knowledge about Representations as a Basis for System Construction and Maintenance. In: Waterman, D. A.; and Hayes-Roth, Frederick, eds. Pattern Directed Inference Systems. New York, NY: Academic Press; 1978. 99–134. ISBN: 0-12-737550-3.

DAVIS, R.; BUCHANAN, B.; SHORTLIFFE, E. 1977. Production Rules as a Representation for a Knowledge Based Consultation Program. Artificial Intelligence. 1977; 8:15–45. ISSN: 0004-3702.

DE JONG, GERALD F. 1979. Skimming Stories in Real Time: An Experiment in Integrated Understanding. (Doctoral thesis). New Haven, CT: Yale University; 1979. 238p. NTIS: AD-A071-432/9ST.

DECUS. 1980. International 1980/1981 DECUS Program Library. (PDP-11/VAX Software Catalog). Maynard, MA: Digital Equipment Corp.; 1980. 173p.

DOSZKOCS, TAMAS E. 1978. AID, An Associative Interactive Dictionary for Online Searching. Online Review. 1978; 2(2):163-173. ISSN: 0309-314X.

DOYLE, JON; LONDON, PHILIP. 1980. A Selected Descriptor Indexed Bibliography to the Literature on Belief Revision. Cambridge, MA: Massachusetts Institute of Technology; 1980. 45p. NTIS: AD-A084 821/8.

ELLIS, CLARENCE A.; NUTT, GARY J. 1980. Office Information Systems and Computer Science. Computing Surveys. 1980; 12(1): 27-60. ISSN: 0010-4892.

ELMORE, ROBERT W.; AGARWAL, KRISHNA K. 1980. An Information Retrieval System. BYTE. 1980; 5(10):114-150. ISSN: 0360-5280.

ERDMAN, LEE D.; HAYES-ROTH, FREDERICK; LESSER, VICTOR R.; REDDY, D. RAJ. 1980. The HEARSAY-II Speech-Understanding System: Integrating Knowledge to Resolve Uncertainty. Computing Surveys. 1980; 12(2):213-253. ISSN: 0010-4892.

FREIHERR, GREGORY. 1980. The Seeds of Artificial Intelligence. Rockville, MD: Research Resources Information Center; 1980. 74p. (NIH Publication no. 80-2071). Available from: Superintendent of Documents, U.S. Government Printing Office, Washington, DC 20440.

GAINES, B. R. 1979. Logical Foundations for Data Base Systems. International Journal of Man Machine Studies. 1979; 11(4):481-500. ISSN: 0020-7373.

GARFIELD, EUGENE. 1980. Can Machines be Scientific Translators? Current Contents. 1980; (33):5-9. ISSN: 0163-2574.

GELERNTER, H. 1963. Realization of a Geometry Theorem Proving Machine. In: Feigenbaum, Edward A.; Feldman, Julian, eds. Computers and Thought. New York, NY: McGraw Hill Book Company; 1963. 134-152. LC: 63-17596.

GINSPARG, JERROLD M. 1978. Natural Language Processing in an Automatic Programming Domain. Palo Alto, CA: Stanford University; 1978. 173p. (Doctoral thesis). (STAN-CS-78-671).

GOODSTEIN, DAVID. 1980. Output Alternatives. Datamation. 1980. 26(2):122-130. ISSN: 0011-6963.

GREEN, C.; BARSTOW, D. 1978. On Program Synthesis Knowledge. Artificial Intelligence. 1978; 10(3):241-279. ISSN: 0004-3702.

GRISHMAN, R.; HIRSCHMAN, L. 1978. Question Answering from Natural Language Medical Data Bases. Artificial Intelligence. 1978; 11(1): 25-43. ISSN: 0004-3702.

GROSZ, B. 1977. The Representation and Use of Focus in Dialogue Understanding. Menlo Park, CA: Stanford Research Institute; 1977. (Technical Note no. 151).

HALL, PATRICK A. V.; DOWLING, GEOFF R. 1980. Approximate String Matching. Computing Surveys. 1980; 12(4):381-402. ISSN: 0010-4892.

HARRIS, L. R. 1977. User Oriented Data Base Query with the Robot

Natural Language Query System. International Journal of Man-Machine Studies. 1977; 9(6):697-713. ISSN: 0020-7373.

HECKEL, PAUL. 1980. Designing Translator Software. Datamation. 1980; 26(2):134-138. ISSN: 0011-6963.

HENDRIX, GARY G. 1977. LIFER: A Natural Language Interface Facility. In: Proceedings of the 2nd Berkeley Workshop on Distributed Data Management and Computer Networks; 1977; Berkeley, CA. 196-201. (TID-4500-R65). Available from: University of California at Berkeley, Berkeley, CA 94704.

HERMAN, MARTIN. 1977. Understanding Stick Figures. College Park, MD: University of Maryland; 1977. 40p. (Report no TR-603). NTIS: AD-A047 817/2ST.

HOFSTADTER, DOUGLAS R. 1980. Godel, Escher, Bach = An Eternal Golden Braid. New York, NY: Vintage Books; 1980. 777p. ISBN: 0-394-74502-7.

HOOVER, THOMAS. 1980. Conversations with a Computer. Readers Digest. 1980; 117(699):13-21. ISSN: 0034-0375.

HUTCHINS, W. J. 1978. Machine Translation and Machine-Aided Translation. Journal of Documentation (U.K.). 1978; 34(2):119-159. ISSN: 0022-0418.

JONG, STEVEN. 1981. Word Processing Software Roundup. Personal Computing. 1981; 5(1):26-33. ISSN: 0192-5490.

KAPLAN, S. JERROLD. 1978. Indirect Responses to Loaded Questions. In: Waltz, David L., ed. TINLAP-2: Theoretical Issues in Natural Language Processing-2: Proceedings of the Association for Computational Linguistics and the Association for Computing Machinery (ACM) 2nd Joint Meeting; 1978 July 25-27; Urbana, IL. New York, NY: Association for Computing Machinery; 1978. 202-209. Available from: ACM, P.O. Box 12105, Church Street Station, New York, NY 10249.

KINNUCAN, PAUL. 1980. Word Processing Systems Sport Innovative Features. Mini-Micro Systems. 1980; 13(8):35-37. USPS: 0059-0470.

KNUTH, D. 1979. TEX and METAFONT: New Directions in Typesetting. Bedford, MA: Digital Press; 1979. 256p. ISBN: 0-932376-02-9.

LEHNERT, WENDY; BURSTEIN, MARK H. 1979. The Role of Object Primitives in Natural Language Processing. New Haven, CT: Yale University; 1979. 33p. (Report no. RR-162). NTIS: AD-A069 861/ST.

LOWERRE, B. T. 1976. The HARPY Speech Recognition System. Pittsburgh, PA: Carnegie Mellon University Department of Computer Science; 1976. 78p. (Technical report).

MAEDA, TAKASHI; MOMOUCHI, YOSHIO; SAWAMURA, HAJIME. 1980. An Automatic Method Extracting Significant Phrases in Scientific or Technical Documents. Information Processing & Management. 1980; 16(3):119-128. ISSN: 0306-4573.

MALLER, V. A. J. 1980. Retrieving Information. Datamation. 1980; 26(9):164-172. ISSN: 0011-6963.

MANAGEMENT INFORMATION SYSTEMS WEEK. 1981. Patent Database Adds Graphics to Text. Management Information Systems Week. 1981 April 5; 1: 12. ISSN: 0199-8838.

MANN, W. C.; SCRAGG, G.; ARCHIBOLD, A. A. 1977. Working Papers in Dialogue Modeling: Volume 2. Marina Del Rey, CA: University of

134   DAVID BECKER

Southern California; 1977. 105p. (Report no. ISI/RR-77-56). NTIS: AD-A037 107/0ST.

MARCUS, MITCHELL. 1979. An Overview of a Theory of Syntactic Recognition for Natural Language. Cambridge, MA: MIT Artificial Intelligence Lab; 1979. 256p. NTIS: AD-A078 066/8.

MARR, D.; NISHIHARA, H. K. 1976. Representation and Recognition of Three Dimensional Shapes. Cambridge, MA: MIT Artificial Intelligence Lab; 1976. (AIM-M-377). NTIS: AD-A031 882/4ST.

MARTIN, JAMES. 1975. Computer Data-Base Organization. Englewood Heights, NJ: Prentice Hall, Inc.; 1975. 558p. ISBN: 0-13-165506-X.

MCCUNE, BRIAN P. 1979. Building Program Models Incrementally from Informal Descriptions. Palo Alto, CA: Stanford University; 1979. (STAN-CS-79-772). 144p. NTIS: AD-A086-504/8.

MCDERMOTT, DREW; DOYLE, J. 1980. Non-Monotonic Logic I. Artificial Intelligence. 1980; 13(1,2):41-72. ISSN: 0004-3702.

MCGILL, MICHAEL; KOLL, MATTHEW; NOREAULT, TERRY. 1979. An Evaluation of Factors Affecting Document Ranking by Information Retrieval Systems. Syracuse, NY: Syracuse University; 1979. 119p. (NSF-IST-78-10454). NTIS: PB 80-119506.

MILASK, LAURANCE J.; FULLERTON, STEVEN. 1978. The UPGRADE System—User's Overview. Washington, DC: Council of Environmental Quality; 1978. 47p. NTIS: PB-296 719/8ST.

MOORE, JAMES A.; LEVIN, JAMES A.; MANN, WILLIAM C. 1977. A Goal Oriented Model of Natural Language Interaction. Marina Del Rey. CA: University of Southern California; 1977. 59p. (Report no. ISI/ RR-77-52). NTIS: AD-A037 111/2ST.

NEWBORN, MONROE M. 1979. Recent Progress in Computer Chess. Advances in Computers. 1979; 18:59-117. ISBN: 0-12-012118-2. LC: 59-15761.

NILSSON, NILS J. 1979. A Framework for Artificial Intelligence. Menlo Park, CA: Stanford Research Institute; 1979. 96p. NTIS: AD-A068 188/2ST.

NOREAULT, TERRY; KOLL, MATTHEW; MCGILL, MICHAEL. 1977. Automatic Ranked Output from Boolean Searches in SIRE. Journal of the American Society for Information Science. 1977; 28(6):333-339. ISSN: 0002-8231.

O'CONNOR, JOHN. 1980a. Answer Passage Retrieval by Text Searching. Journal of the American Society for Information Science. 1980; 31(4): 227-239. ISSN: 0002-8231.

O'CONNOR, JOHN. 1980b. Citing Statements: Recognition by Computer and Use to Improve Retrieval. In: Benenfeld, Alan R.; Kazlauskas, Edward J., eds. Communicating Information: Proceedings of the American Society for Information Science (ASIS) 43rd Annual Meeting: Volume 17: 1980 October 5-10; Anaheim, CA. White Plains, NY: Knowledge Industry Publications, Inc. for ASIS; 1980. 177-179. ISSN: 0044-7870; ISBN: 0-914236-3-3.

PATIL, RAMESH S. 1979. Design of a Program for Expert Diagnosis of Acid Base and Electrolyte Disturbances. Cambridge, MA: Massachusetts Institute of Technology; 1979. 42p. (Report no. MIT/LCS/TM-132). NTIS: AD-A078 413-2.

PETERSON, JAMES L. 1980. Computer Programs for Detecting and Correcting Spelling Errors. Communications of the ACM. 23(12):676-687. ISSN: 0588-8069.

POWELL, P. B.; THOMPSON, P. 1978. Natural Language and Voice Output for Relational Data Base Systems. In: Proceedings of the Association for Computing Machinery (ACM) Annual Conference; 1978 Dec. 4-6. 585-595. Available from: ACM, PO Box 12105, Church Street Station, New York, NY 10249.

PREECE, SCOTT E. 1973. Clustering as an Output Option. In: Waldron, Helen J.; Long, Raymond F., eds. Innovative Developments in Information Systems: Their Benefits and Costs; Proceedings of the American Society for Information Science (ASIS) 36th Annual Meeting: Volume 10; 1973 October 21-25; Los Angeles, CA. Washington, DC: ASIS; 1973. 189-190. ISSN: 0044-7870; ISBN: 0-87715-410-4; LC: 64-8303.

PURCELL, STEPHEN C. 1977. Understanding Hand Printed Algebra for Computer Tutoring. Cambridge, MA: Bolt Beranek and Newman; 1977. 71p. (BBN-3749). NTIS: AD-A053 805/8ST.

RABINER, L. R.; WILPON, J. G.; ROSENBERG, A. E. 1980. A Voice-Controlled, Repertory-Dialer System. The Bell System Technical Journal. 1980; 59(7):1153-1163. ISSN: 0005-8580.

RAUZINO, VINCENT C. 1981. The Looming Battle between Data Base Machines and Software Data Base Management Systems. Computerworld. 1981; 15(1):8,10-12. ISSN: 0127-0420.

RIEGER, CHARLES. 1976. Viewing Parsing as Word Sense Discrimination. In: Dingwall, W. O., ed. A Survey of Linguistic Science. New York, NY: Greylock Publishers; 1976. 356p. LC: 78-60709; ISBN: 0-89223-014-2.

RIEGER, CHARLES. 1977. Spontaneous Computation in Cognitive Models. Cognitive Science. 1977; 1(3):315-354. ISSN: 0364-0213.

RIEGER, CHARLES; GRINBERG, MILT. 1978. The Declarative Representation and Procedural Simulation of Causality in Physical Mechanisms. College Park, MD: University of Maryland: 1978. 31p. (TR-513). NTIS: AD-A037 953/7ST.

RIESBECK, CHRISTOPHER K. 1979. Representations to Aid Distributed Understanding in a Multi-Program System. In: Findler, N. V., ed. Associative Networks—Representation and Use of Knowledge by Computers. New York, NY: Academic Press; 1979. 409-424. ISBN: 0-12-256380-8.

RIESBECK, CHRISTOPHER K.; CHARNIAK, EUGENE. 1978. Micro-SAM and Micro-ELI Exercises in Popular Cognitive Mechanics. New Haven, CT: Yale University; 1978. 48p. (RR-139).

ROBERTS, MICHAEL. 1980. Multiprocessing: Networks vs. Mainframes. Mini-Micro Systems. 1980; 13(10):121-128. USPS: 0059-0470.

ROBERTS, R. B.; GOLDSTEIN, I. P. 1977. The FRL Primer. Cambridge, MA: MIT Artificial Intelligence Lab; 1977. 23p. NTIS: AD-A053 306/7ST.

ROBERTSON, G.; MCCRACKEN, D.; NEWELL, A. 1979. The ZOG Approach to Man-Machine Communication. Pittsburgh, PA: Carnegie Mellon University; 1979. 215p. (Report no. CMU-CS-79-148). NTIS: AD-A081 088/7.

ROBINSON, ARTHUR L. 1979. Communicating with Computers by Voice. Science. 1979; 203(4382):734-736. ISSN: 0036-8075.

ROSEN, CHARLES A.; HAAS, NORMAN. 1980. Microcomputer-Based

Natural Language Understanding. Mountain View, CA: Machine Intelligence Corp.; 1980. 48p. NTIS: PB-80-187370.

ROSENBERG, RONALD. 1978. Ray Kurzweil Strikes Out in a New Direction. Mini-Micro Systems. 1978: 11(10):16–18. USPS: 0059-0470.

RUCKDESCHEL, FRED R. 1979. Basic Text Editor. Byte. 1979; 4(6): 156–164. ISSN: 0360-5280.

SAGER, NAOMI; HIRSCHMAN, LYNETTE. 1978. Information Structures in the Language of Science: Theory and Implementation. New York, NY: New York University; 1978. 187p. NTIS: PB-289 949/0ST.

SALTON, GERARD. 1979. SMART. In: Belzer, Jack; Holzman, Albert G.; Kent, Allen, eds. Encyclopedia of Computer Science and Technology: Volume 13. New York, NY: Marcel Dekker, Inc.; 1979. 137–172.

SALTON, GERARD. 1980a. Automatic Information Retrieval. Computer. 1980; 13(9):41–56. ISSN: 0018-9162.

SALTON, GERARD. 1980b. Automatic Term Class Construction Using Relevance. A Summary of Work in Automatic Pseudo-Classification. Information Processing & Management. 1980; 16(1):1–15. ISSN: 0306-4573.

SALTON, GERARD; WALDSTEIN, R. K. 1978. Term Relevance Weights in On-Line Information Retrieval. Information Processing & Management. 1978; 14(1):29–35. ISSN: 0306-4573.

SCHANK, ROGER C. 1979a. Reminding and Memory Organization. New Haven, CT: Yale University; 1979. 102p. (RR-170). NTIS: AD-A080 200/9.

SCHANK, ROGER C. 1979b. RE: The Gettysburg Address Representing Social and Political Acts. In: Findler, Nicholas V., ed. Associative Networks—Representation and Use of Knowledge by Computers. New York, NY: Academic Press; 1979. 327–362. ISBN: 0-12-256380-8.

SCHANK, ROGER C.; ABELSON, R. P. 1977. Scripts, Plans, Goals and Understanding: An Inquiry into Human Knowledge Structures. Hillsdale, NJ: Lawrence Erlbaum Associates; 1977. 248p. ISBN: 0-470-99033-3; LC: 76-51963.

SCHANK, ROGER C.; KOLODNER, JANET. 1979. Retrieving Information from an Episodic Memory or Why Computers' Memories Should Be More Like People's. New Haven, CT: Yale University; 1979. 35p. NTIS: AD-A071 445/1ST.

SCHIPMA, PETER B. 1980. Final Report: International Cancer Research Data Bank. Chicago, IL: IIT Research Institute; 1980. 256p. (IITRI-C6350-60A; Contract Number N01-C0-55221). Available from: IIT Research Institute, 10 W. 35th Street, Chicago, IL 60616.

SCHIPMA, PETER B.; BECKER, DAVID S. 1980. Text Storage and Display via Videodisk. In: Benenfeld, Alan R.; Kazlauskas, Edward J., eds. Communicating Information: Proceedings of the American Society for Information Science (ASIS) 43rd Annual Meeting: Volume 17; 1980 October 5–10; Anaheim, CA. White Plains, NY: Knowledge Industry Publications, Inc.; 1980. 103–105. ISSN: 0044-7870; ISBN: 0-914236-73-3.

SCHOICHET, SANDOR R. 1978. The LISP Machine. Mini-Micro Systems. 1978; 11(5):68–74. USPS: 059-470.

SCHUEGRAF, ERNST J. 1980. Associative Processors: Have They Finally Arrived? In: Benenfeld, Alan R.; Kazlauskas, Edward J., eds. Commu-

nicating Information; Proceedings of the American Society for Information Science (ASIS) 43rd Annual Meeting: Volume 17; 1980 October 5-10; Anaheim, CA. White Plains, NY: Knowledge Industry Publications, Inc.; 1980. 329-331. ISSN: 0044-7870; ISBN: 0-914236-73-3.
SHAPIRO, NEIL. 1980. PM Designs Your Personal Word Processor. Popular Mechanics. 1980; 154(1): 78-79,120. ISSN: 0032-4558.
SHOOR, RITA. 1981. Relational Data Base Management Systems: Fact and Fiction. Computerworld. 1981; 15(1):13. ISSN: 0127-0420.
SHORTLIFFE, E. H.; DAVIS, R.; AXLINE, S. G.; BUCHANAN, B. G.; GREEN, C. C.; COHEN, S. N. 1975. Computer-Based Consultations in Clinical Therapeutics: Explanation and Rule-Acquisition Capabilities of the MYCIN System. Computers and Biomedical Research. 1975; 8:303-320. ISSN: 0010-4809.
SHUTT, JOHN. 1980. 'ETHERNET' Is 1 of 2 OKd by the IEEE. MIS Week. 1980; 1(31):1,6. ISSN: 0199-8838.
SILVA, G.; MONTGOMERY, C. A. 1979. Satellite and Missile Data Generation for AIS. Woodland Hills, CA: Operating Systems, Inc.; 1979. NTIS: AD-A084 326/8.
SLAMECKA, VLADIMIR; CAMP, HENRY N.; BADRE, ALBERT N.; HALL, W. DALLAS. 1977. MARIS: A Knowledge System for Internal Medicine. Information Processing & Management. 1977; 13(5): 273-276. ISSN: 0306-4573.
SMITH, LINDA C. 1980. Artificial Intelligence Applications in Information Systems. In: Williams, Martha E., ed. Annual Review of Information Science and Technology: Volume 15. Washington, DC: Knowledge Industry Publications for the American Society for Information Science; 1980. 67-105. ISSN: 0066-4200; ISBN: 0-914236-65-2; LC: 66-25096.
SPARCK-JONES, KAREN. 1979. Experiments in Relevance Weighting of Search Terms. Information Processing & Management. 1979; 15(3): 133-144. ISSN: 0306-4573.
SRIDHARAN, N. S.; SCHMIDT, C. F. 1978. Knowledge Directed Inference in BELIEVER. In: Waterman, D. A.; Hayes-Roth, F., ed. Pattern-Direct Inference Systems. New York, NY: Academic Press; 1978. 361-379. ISBN: 0-12-737550-3.
STANSFIELD, JAMES L. 1977. COMEX: A Support System for a Commodities Expert. Cambridge, MA: MIT Artificial Intelligence Lab; 1977. NTIS: AD-A052 442/1ST.
STEELE, GUY LEWIS; SUSSMAN, GERALD JAY. 1980. Design of a LISP Based Microprocessor. Communications of the ACM. 1980; 23(11):628-644. ISSN: 0588-8069.
STEELS, LUC. 1979. Procedural Attachment. Cambridge, MA: MIT Artificial Intelligence Lab; 1979. 57p. (AI-M-543). NTIS: AD-A084 637/8.
SZOLOVITS, P.; HAWKINSON, L. B.; MARTIN, W. A. 1977. An Overview of OWL, A Language for Knowledge Representation. Cambridge, MA: Massachusetts Institute of Technology; 1977. 140p. MIT LCS-TM-86.
SZOLOVITS, P.; PAUKER, S. G. 1978. Categorical and Probabilistic Reasoning in Medical Diagnosis. Artificial Intelligence. 1978; 11(1): 115-144. ISSN: 0004-3702.
THOMAS, JOHN C. 1977. A Design-Interpretation Analysis of Natural

English—With Applications to Man-Computer Interaction. White Plains, NY: IBM Thomas J. Watson Research Center; 1977. 38p. NTIS: AD A056 121/7ST.

THORNDYKE, P. W. 1977. Cognitive Structures in Comprehension and Memory of Narrative Discourse. Cognitive Psychology. 1977; 9(1): 77-110. ISSN: 0010-0285.

TOSHIBA AMERICA INCORPORATED. 1981. Toshiba Document Filing System—DF-2000. Northbrook, IL: Toshiba America Inc.; 1981 June. 12p. Available from: Noriki Matsuzaki, Toshiba America, Inc.; 2900 MacArthur Boulevard, Northbrook, IL 60062.

U. S. NATIONAL RESEARCH COUNCIL. AUTOMATIC LANGUAGE PROCESSING ADVISORY COMMITTEE. 1966. Language and Machines: Computers in Translations and Linguistics. Washington, DC: National Academy of Sciences; 1966. 124p.

WALTZ, DAVID L.; BOGGESS, LOIS. 1979. Visual Analog Representations for Natural Language Understanding. Urbana, IL: University of Illinois; 1979. 29p. NTIS: AD-A081 956/5.

WEBBER, BONNIE L. 1978. Description Formation and Discourse Model Synthesis. In: Waltz, David L., ed. TINLAP-2: Theoretical Issues in Natural Language Processing-2: Proceedings of the Association for Computational Linguistics and the Association for Computing Machinery (ACM) 2nd Joint Meeting; 1978 July 25-27; Urbana, IL. New York, NY: Association for Computing Machinery; 1978. 42-50. Available from: ACM, P.O. Box 12105, Church Street Station, New York, NY 10249.

WEINER, J. L. 1980. BLAH, A System Which Explains Its Reasoning. Artificial Intelligence. 1980; 15(1,2):19-48. ISSN: 0004-3702.

WILKINS, DAVID. 1980. Using Patterns and Plans in Chess. Artificial Intelligence. 1980; 14(2):165-203. ISSN: 0004-3702.

WINOGRAD, TERRY. 1972. Understanding Natural Language. New York, NY: Academic Press; 1972. 256p. ISBN: 0-12-759750-6.

WINOGRAD, TERRY. 1980. Extended Inference Modes in Reasoning by Computer Systems. Artificial Intelligence. 1980; 13(1,2):5-26. ISSN: 0004-3702.

WOODS, W. A. 1975. Whats in a Link: Foundations for Semantic Networks. In: Bobrow, D. G.; Collins, A., eds. Representation and Understanding. New York, NY: Academic Press; 1975. 35-82. ISBN: 0-12-108550-3.

YASAKI, EDWARD K. 1980. AI Comes of Age. Datamation. 1980; 26(10):48-54. ISSN: 0011-6963.

ZACHARY, W. W. 1979. A Survey of Approaches and Issues in Machine-Aided Translation Systems. Computers and the Humanities. 1979; 13(1):17-28. ISSN: 0010-4817; ISBN: 0-08-024677-X.

ZADEH, L. A. 1978. PRUF—A Meaning Representation Language for Natural Languages. International Journal of Man-Machine Studies. 1978; 10(4):395-460. ISSN: 0020-7373.

ZAMORA, ANTONIO. 1980. Automatic Detection and Correction of Spelling Errors in a Large Data Base. Journal of the American Society for Information Science. 1980; 31(1):51-57. ISSN: 0002-8231.

5   Search Techniques

MARCIA J. BATES[1]
University of Washington, Seattle

INTRODUCTION

Scope

Search techniques are methods, heuristics, tactics, strategies, or plans that can be used by people in searching in manual or automated information systems. This chapter examines search techniques from a psychological point of view. It is the subjective experience of the human being who is doing the searching that is of interest—how a person thinks about and carries out information searching.

Because this is the first *ARIST* chapter solely on this topic, coverage goes back indefinitely, with emphasis on the period 1976-1980. Coverage is international and includes non-English materials.

Ironically, this topic is difficult to research because "searching" often covers all aspects of bibliographic searching, not just techniques, and narrower terms such as "search techniques" or "search theory" are not well established and generally used. Further, large areas of information science research that are not directly concerned with searching may nonetheless have implications for search techniques. The design of an information retrieval system, for example, determines in many respects what searching methods are possible on that system. This author chose to cover items that: 1) were retrieved by the literature search on "searching," "search techniques," and related terms, 2) were comparatively less likely to be covered in other chapters of this volume, and 3) proved to be strongly concerned with search techniques per se.

This chapter does not cover the following topics because they would extend coverage too much or because this reviewer is not qualified to evaluate them or both:

[1] Present address: Graduate School of Library and Information Science, University of California, Los Angeles, CA 90024.

- Searching procedures in internal computer file organization. Search optimization by people at the online interface is considered at length but not the internal programming design necessary to produce the system with which the user interacts.
- Chemical searching. For a start in this area, see ANTONY, MAIZELL, and RUSH.
- Searching techniques for specific databases or specific online search systems. While often ephemeral, the information provided in articles on these topics is nonetheless of considerable practical use. It is excluded because "search techniques," as a research area of information science, should be generated from principles and research results of general applicability. The excellent bibliographies by HALL & DEWE and HAWKINS (1980) include many references to articles on databases and online search systems.
- The reference (or pre-search) interview. Two extensive annotated bibliographies appeared in 1979 on this topic (CROUCH; NORMAN).

Domain

This section is included to illustrate a technique in the presentation of reviews and bibliographies that may be of great value to the searcher who subsequently uses that review or bibliography. The "scope" of a review (previous section) is the conceptual territory covered, whereas the "domain" is the bibliographical territory—i.e., the bibliographic sources searched to identify materials to review. Traditionally, the scope is well defined, while the domain is not mentioned at all.

However, a person who is doing a thorough search on a topic generally uses several bibliographic sources. A reader of this review, for example, who is researching "search techniques," may plan to look up the topic in other sources as well, such as *Information Science Abstracts* and *Library Literature*. If that reader is informed, through a domain statement, of the sources searched by this reviewer, then he or she will not have to duplicate the searching already done for this chapter. The reader who sees below that the past four years of *Information Science Abstracts* have been searched under the heading "Searching, search strategy, retrieval" then knows that it would be a waste of time in most instances to search those volumes under that topic again. Only when the scope of the person's interest is significantly different from that defined above—e.g., internal computer searching rather than human searching—is it worthwhile to go to sources that have already been covered. Thus, the searcher who is given both the scope and domain of a review or bibliography can design an efficient search strategy. This approach is elaborated by BATES (1976).

Described below is the domain—i.e., the sources, terms, and dates of coverage of the search for this chapter:

- *Library Literature*, 1970-1980. Bibliography—Teaching; Computer-stored bibliographic data (1976-1980 only); Information storage and retrieval; Instruction in library use (1976-1980 only); Reference librarians; Reference services; Research and the library; Research techniques; Searching, Bibliographical; Searching, Computer; Use studies (1976-1980 only).
- *Information Science Abstracts*, 1976-1979. (1980 issues not published at time of search.) Sec. 1.1: Conferences, publications, bibliographies (1977-1979 only); Sec. 5.8: Searching, search strategy, retrieval.
- *Library and Information Science Abstracts*, 1975-1980. Reference work (1978-1980 only); Searching (1978-1980 only); Strategies.
- *Resources in Education*, 1976-Jan. 1981, and *Current Index to Journals in Education*, 1976-Feb. 1981. [Both sources are online in the ERIC (Educational Resources Information Center) database.] Information retrieval; Information seeking; Library reference services (through July 1980); Reference services (Aug. 1980+); Search strategies.
- *Government Reports Announcements & Index*, 1970-Nov. 21, 1980 (Issue 24 of 1980). [The online form of this resource is the NTIS (National Technical Information Service) database.] All terms beginning with "Search" or "Searching."
- *Dissertation Abstracts International*, 1861-Jan. 1981. Searched in subject indexes through 1978 under terms: Information (1973-1978 only); Reference; Retrieval (1973-1978 only); Search; Searching; Seeking; Strategy. For 1979-Jan. 1981 scanned all dissertations under "Information Science" and "Library Science."
- *Business Periodicals Index*, July 1969-July 1980. Search theory.
- *Books in Print 1979-1980*, and *Books in Print Supplement 1979-1980*. Information science; Information services; Information storage and retrieval systems; Library science; Library science—Data processing; Reference services (Libraries); Searching, Bibliographical.

In addition, the extensive bibliographies by HALL & DEWE, HAWKINS (1980), and MURFIN & WYNAR were also searched and found helpful. The University of Washington shelf list catalog was searched; the useful Library of Congress (LC) classification numbers for this topic are Z699, Z699.3, Z711, and Z711.2. *Engineering Index* (COMPENDEX online) and *Computer and Control Abstracts* (INSPEC online, i.e., Information Services in Physics, Electrotechnology, Computers and Control) covered some information science literature on this topic but did not add to what was picked up in other sources. *Psychological Abstracts, Communication Abstracts*, and

Ergonomics Abstracts, which might be expected to be helpful, were unproductive. Due to the time lag in the coverage of abstracting and indexing services, major information science journals that cover search techniques were scanned for relevant articles through 1980.

DEFINITIONS

Because of its rapid development, the area of search techniques is plagued by vague terminology. The term "search strategy," in particular, is used with several meanings. Some definitions are proposed below.

Search mechanics—the methods or operations by which a database or service is accessed and a search is performed—i.e., the "how-to." This term includes the means of logging on and off a database, explanation of commands, and the mechanics of Boolean logic. For example, an article that explains the meaning of *OR*, *AND*, and *NOT* in a search statement and shows how to use them in searching would call this material "search mechanics" not "search strategy."

Search formulation—a search statement or series of statements expressing the search topic of a request. Working out an effective series of search statements for a particular topic can be difficult, and some searchers have consequently published their "search strategy" for a particular topic. It is suggested here that the term "search formulation" be used instead and that the term "search strategy" be reserved for the meaning below.

Search strategy—an approach to or plan for a whole search. A search strategy is used to inform or to determine specific search formulation decisions; it operates at a level above term choice and command use. For example, the "building-block" approach of Charles Bourne (MARKEY & ATHERTON) is a strategy. First, one combines with a Boolean *OR* the variant terms for each conceptual element of the request and enters each "building block" as a separate search statement. Then one combines all the resulting sets, using the *AND* operator, into a single master search statement. This strategy contrasts with Bourne's "citation pearl-growing" strategy, in which one combines and searches on a few specific terms immediately to retrieve citations that are then examined for candidate search terms to be added to the subsequent search formulation. These strategies can be understood and used independently of particular search topics.

Search formulation and *search profile.* The general meaning of profile is an outline or a biographical sketch of a person. This usage has been adapted in selective dissemination of information (SDI) systems to refer to a set of terms (or search statements) that describe the subject interests of a person who subscribes to an SDI service. The profile is run against records of newly arrived documents, and citations that match the user's interests are sent to him or her.

"Search profile" is also sometimes used in the sense of "search formulation"—i.e., a search statement or series of statements expressing a search topic. It is suggested here that these two phrases retain their distinct meanings—i.e., use "search profile" only to describe a person's interests, and use "search formulation" to describe those statements that express a search topic. Not only does this distinction keep the meaning of profile closer to its original English use, it also makes it possible to discuss any differences in techniques involved in the development of search profiles (of people) as distinct from search formulations (for specific search queries).

PROLOGUE: IS THERE ANY NEED TO IMPROVE SEARCH TECHNIQUES?

In a study published by Thomas Childers in 1971 (CROWLEY & CHILDERS), 25 New Jersey public libraries were each asked 26 reference questions over a period of three months. The questions were posed unobtrusively by anonymous callers. The librarians' responses indicated that even when they thought that something was unusual, they did not suspect that a study was being conducted. The questions were not difficult—e.g., "What does the phrase 'gnomes of Zurich' refer to?"

Of all questions asked, just 55% were answered correctly. Excluding those times when a librarian did not attempt to answer a question, 64% of the responses were correct. In other words, more than one out of every three answers was wrong. Similarly poor results were obtained in a large study for the Chicago Public Library by MARTIN, and in a recent small study by HOUSE.

CHILDERS repeated this approach recently in an even larger study for the Long Island public libraries. When answers were provided, 84% (compared with 64% above) were correct. However, these librarians frequently either failed to find an answer or referred the patron to another library or agency. An actual answer to the question was provided only 56% of the time (p926). Since 84% of these were correct, the probability of the patron's receiving a direct (not referred) and correct answer to a question was just 47% (reviewer's computation).

The situation is similar with online searching. Since most online searching is done for bibliographic work, the objective is usually not a correct answer but an adequate set of citations. FENICHEL (1980c), in summarizing the results of several studies of online searching, concluded that: 1) there is considerable room for improvement in the searching of many experienced searchers; 2) for both experienced and inexperienced searchers the major problems were with search strategy, not search mechanics (in these conclusions Fenichel does not distinguish between search formulation and search strategy); and 3) a "substantial group" of experienced searchers performs simple searches and makes little use of the interactive capabilities of online systems (p123).

In addition, in her own study, FENICHEL (1980b) found that the experienced online searchers were generally quite satisfied with their performance despite the fact that their own average recall score was 51% (p60). There seems to be a strong need to improve training in search techniques for librarians and information specialists.

MACHINE ENHANCEMENT OF HUMAN SEARCHING

In 1974 JAHODA (1974) concluded that it would be very difficult, if not impossible, to automate the processes involved in question analysis and search strategy development by reference librarians. His conclusion still holds in that most of the work reported in this section does not try to replace the central cognitive processes involved in information searching—i.e., the analysis of the question, the design of overall strategy, and the choice of information source(s) and acceptable search term(s). Most of the systems described here aid or augment the searcher's effort or simplify the searcher's work by masking multisystem complexities with an apparently simple, single system. However, some of these systems are beginning to move in on those cognitive processes. Jahoda's prediction may yet be disproved, and sooner than might have been thought.

Every automated information retrieval system can be seen as a machine enhancement of human searching. The discussion here is limited to systems that emphasize the "front end," that is, those systems that put new capabilities or search aids into the hands of the searcher.

One type of automated aid helps the searcher select a database or a manual information source. In 1968 WEIL described an automated system that would suggest the titles of biographical reference books to those who were seeking biographical information. Shortly thereafter, MEREDITH described a system for the instruction of library school students called REFSEARCH. A student would enter a reference query, and the system would produce a list of sources that would be likely to contain the answer. Both systems worked by categorizing reference sources according to various aspects of their coverage and matching those aspects with corresponding elements in the query.

More recently, BIVINS & PALMER (1979; 1980) described a prototype system called REFLES (Reference Librarian Enhancement System), which stores two types of information: 1) ephemeral information that cannot be found in reference sources, and 2) information about new and/or particularly useful reference sources. Librarians provide the information for the files and then access it using index terms that they develop and alter themselves.

Automated systems to help searchers select databases have been developed by WILLIAMS & PREECE (1977) and by MARCUS. The system of Williams and Preece, called Data Base Selector (DBS), ranks databases by the number of postings they have to a requester's search terms, applies various weighting factors (time, breadth of indexing, relative frequency of terms etc.), and then produces a ranked list of the databases with values to distinguish distance between ranks. The system by Marcus, part of CONIT (Connector for Networked Information Transfer), takes the natural language phrasing of the requester and does a keyword/stem search on the phrase in a multidisciplinary database. Classification codes found in the retrieved documents are then matched with a classification of databases to produce a ranked list of relevant databases.

Several systems have been developed to ease vocabulary selection and use in searching. Robert Niehoff and his colleagues (NIEHOFF; NIEHOFF &

KWASNY; NIEHOFF ET AL.) have developed VSS (Vocabulary Switching System), in which the user enters a term and receives a list of corresponding and related terms in several databases. Several different types of switching can be used. Examples are exact matching and stem phrase switching (stem each word in the candidate term, then use the stemmed phrase to access the stem phrase file). VSS is fully operational but still experimental. Switching can be done among six vocabularies (NIEHOFF).

DOSZKOCS has developed a system that uses statistical association to identify and to display terms related to those in the searcher's query. The system, known as AID (Associative Interactive Dictionary), has been implemented in the TOXLINE database of NLM. It is fully operational and requires less computer processing space than earlier experimental systems using statistical association.

DRABEK ET AL. have developed and pilot tested an online interactive system, called Query Analysis System, to aid sociology students in identifying search terms and bibliographic resources for their research. The student enters a term and gets back lists of other terms that are hierarchically above or below the entered term, as well as a list of relevant bibliographic sources. Drabek et al. developed a hierarchical list of sociology terms to create the system.

These systems provide assistance in one or two aspects of the search process. The systems described next simplify the searcher's task in broader ways. The database selection capability of CONIT described above is just one part of this system. MARCUS & REINTJES and MARCUS describe CONIT and its recent additions, respectively. CONIT is a computer interface, a "virtual" system, designed so that the searcher uses a single, simple command language although he or she is actually searching on three heterogeneous vendor systems, ORBIT, DIALOG, and MEDLINE. It also has a keyword/stem searching capability so that the naive user can enter a natural language term and have the system do more sophisticated searching than the user realizes, even on a controlled vocabulary if the stem matches. Author searches can also be made in a common format, thus eliminating concern about different punctuation rules on different databases. End users without professional training have achieved acceptable—but not yet optimal—results on CONIT.

WILLIAMS & PREECE (1980; 1981) and PREECE & WILLIAMS describe their design for a Total Transparent Information Retrieval System (TTIRS). They designed a generalized model of what such a system should look like and then implemented a "minitransparent" system on a microcomputer. The full system would contain "transparency aids" of various sorts, including automatic selectors for databases, communications network, and vendor. The minitransparent system, known as The Searcher's Workbench (TSW), can access Williams's and Preece's own DBS as well as VSS. TSW also enables the searcher to search several systems without knowing the specifics of any one system. Most entry is accomplished by touching points on the display, so the user seldom has to look away from the screen.

The Individualized Instruction for Data Access (IIDA) system has been developed by Charles Meadow and his colleagues (DREXEL UNIVERSITY & FRANKLIN INSTITUTE; LANDSBERG ET AL.; MEADOW; MEADOW &

EPSTEIN; MEADOW ET AL., 1977; MEADOW ET AL., 1978) to perform two functions: 1) to train new searchers and 2) to aid trained searchers as they go along in a search. The second function, the assistance mode, is of greater interest here. The program monitors searcher behavior and sends error messages and advice as needed. For example, the searcher may get a message if commands are repeated too often or if "thrashing" is observed. Thrashing occurs when the user shifts search objectives so rapidly that a particular line of reasoning cannot be completed (MEADOW). The searcher can also call up a menu of "help" options, which provide various kinds of useful information. (See the chapter by Elaine Caruso in this volume for further discussion.)

Search aids similar to those described above are also being developed commercially. These systems are not described here, but organizations developing them are the Franklin Institute (Philadelphia, PA), Computer Corporation of America (Cambridge, MA), and Williams and Nevin, Ltd. (Manchester, England).

Finally, efforts are proceeding to develop information retrieval systems of such sophistication that the user can enter a query in natural language without concern for search term selection or Boolean combination. Examples of this effort are the CITE (Current Information Transfer in English) system by DOSZKOCS & RAPP, and the THOMAS program by ODDY (1977a; 1977b). In conventional online systems the searcher manipulates the search formulation through several iterations, but in these systems the user provides relevance feedback only, and the system manipulates the formulation, in effect, for the user. By various means the search is expanded automatically to synonymous or related terms—i.e., the searcher does not have to provide the related terms. A prototype of CITE has been implemented on NLM's MEDLINE database. The THOMAS program is still experimental.

Oddy and N. Belkin are planning to develop THOMAS further, drawing on Belkin's concept of an information need as an anomalous state of knowledge, or "ASK" (BELKIN & ODDY). They argue that, in general, the user is unable to specify precisely what is needed to resolve that anomalous state and, therefore, for information retrieval, the user should be asked to describe the ASK, rather than to specify the information need in a conventional query. (See also BELKIN and BELKIN ET AL.)

PHYSICAL SEARCH

However one may think of an information search strategically, it is also a physical act, particularly in manual systems. One moves along shelves, and through files; one searches for a single item among many, which are physically arranged according to some principle. How can this effort be minimized for the desired results?

Physical search has long been of interest to the armed forces, especially the Navy, because of the need to find downed flyers or enemy vessels. There is a long tradition of mathematical work on search and reconnaissance theory, both in the military and in operations research. Here, only introductory and bibliographic sources are discussed for the work outside of information science.

Early military and operations research materials on search and reconnaissance theory are covered in a 1966 bibliography with abstracts compiled by ENSLOW. The 239-page bibliography published in 1979 with abstracts by KENTON updates coverage on maritime and aviation search and rescue. An old (1970) but excellent survey of the literature on physical search is provided by MOORE. The review begins with a chart of the various searching categories. For example, in one-sided searches the "distribution of the target is known to the searcher" (p11), and the target can be stationary or moving. In two-sided searches there is a conscious evader. Presumably, one-sided stationary-target searches are of most interest to us. Moore reviews the literature category by category. MORSE (1974) provides a somewhat briefer but more recent and less mathematical review of the search literature for public safety experts. The review includes visual scanning of an area.

One would expect this literature to provide a rich resource for the development of physical search theory in information science. Unfortunately, except for the now-aging work by Morse and Leimkuhler (discussed below) and a couple of tangential articles by Donald Kraft, a student of Leimkuhler's, this leap does not seem to have been made. Since this reviewer's knowledge of mathematics is not sufficient to enable a critical evaluation of their work, material found is simply mentioned.

Both LEIMKUHLER and MORSE (1972) deal with the optimal ordering of items in a file to facilitate efficient search. Morse is also concerned with the application of search theory to the browsing of files (MORSE, 1970a; MORSE, 1970b; MORSE, 1973). Kraft continues an operations research approach to searching, but the interest is only marginally in physical search (DEUTSCH & KRAFT; KRAFT & LEE).

Aside from Morse's work, studies on browsing appear to be almost nonexistent. The intriguing proposal made by LICKLIDER in the 1965 INTREX (Information Transfer Experiments) conference to compare several "browseries" was never carried out as far as can be determined. Each browsery was to be organized along different lines, and the study was to determine which mode of organization led to greatest browsing satisfaction and the most serendipitous discoveries of useful information.

Browsing *capabilities* have been built into automated systems, but the problem of how to *optimize* productive browsing in automated and manual systems apparently remains untested. It might be argued that as manual systems are replaced by automated ones and the physical location of an item becomes less important, the study of browsing becomes unnecessary. Nevertheless, the human being who interacts with the system remains the same, whether the system is manual or automated. Many years ago MILLER noted that physical location is a very important mental organizing principle for human beings. He argued that information scientists should take advantage of this in designing information systems, especially computer systems where a sense of spatiality is easily lost. A recent effort to use this human characteristic is a "spatial data management system" described by BOLT. It creates a "virtual spatial world. . .over which the user helicopters via joystick control" (abstract). Since it is expensive to develop browsing capabilities in automated systems, it seems worthwhile to divert some of those expenditures to determining the browsing needs and preferences of the human beings who will use the systems.

In related work, GREENE found that fewer references located through browsing were as useful as those found in other ways. He concludes that browsing is not as valuable as usually claimed and suggests that the tradition of open-stack access in American libraries be reevaluated. However, browsing is usually a supplementary technique, not a primary one. The question is not whether it works as well as other techniques but whether it locates references that would not be retrieved in other ways. The issue of open and closed stacks has also been studied by GOLDHOR, HYMAN (1971; 1972), and SHILL.

A final topic in physical search is sign systems. A coherent system of signs in libraries is being recognized as an essential ingredient in facilitating end user searches. POLLET & HASKELL edited what may be the definitive work on library sign systems. Psychological and human factors research is presented, as well as extensive information on the planning and design of library sign systems (see also POLLET). An extensive review by SPENCER & REYNOLDS evaluates research, theory, and practice on every aspect of sign use in libraries and museums.

THE PSYCHOLOGY OF SEARCHING

Psychological aspects of searching deal with how people do think and should think in the process of searching. Drawing on *The Inner Game of Tennis* by GALLWEY, WAGERS deals with, as it were, the Zen of information work. He suggests ways in which reference librarians can establish a state of mind that will enable them to get past psychological blocks to creative problem solving and to perform better as searchers.

Similarly, BATES (1979a) deals with the searcher who is stumped and unsure of how to proceed. She suggests "idea tactics," that is, mental devices to generate new ideas or solutions to problems in searching. For example, the tactic BREACH is "To breach the boundaries of one's region of search, to revise one's concept of the limits of the intellectual or physical territory in which one searches to respond to a query" (p282). This tactic deals with the situation in which a person cannot think of any more sources to search because of assumptions about limits to the search domain. Confronted initially with thousands of possible resources, one usually narrows a search to certain types of sources or locations. If the sources in that domain have been exhausted and the answer still is not found, the searcher who uses BREACH will remind himself or herself that there may be productive resources outside the initially defined domain.

BLAIR sets forth an intriguing analysis of searcher biases in online searching. He defines a "futility point criterion" (FPC)—i.e., the maximum size of retrieved set that the searcher is willing to examine to find a desired item—and a "prediction criterion" (PC)—i.e., a criterion that the term(s) searched under actually index the document of interest. The search has to meet both criteria for the searcher to be satisfied. However, online search formulations frequently yield postings sets that exceed the FPC, so the searcher must often satisfy the FPC first before the retrieved set can be examined to determine if the PC is satisfied. Blair is interested in what the searcher does and should do to meet the FPC and to optimize the chances of then meeting the PC.

He draws on the research of two psychologists, A. Tversky and D. Kahneman, to suggest that searchers may show systematic biases in search modification. Specifically, they may "anchor" to initial search terms and to the initial ordering of terms in the search formulation; that is, they may be reluctant to drop initial terms or to try them in the various combinatorial subsets that are possible. For example, there are 15 combinations—not permutations—of one or more terms in a set of four terms. Thus, when they revise their searches to meet the FPC, they may drop or replace only the terms added last and may not exploit all the possible combinatorial subsets of the terms that they have entered. He suggests that these subsets, with associated postings, be generated automatically by the system to make it easier for the searcher to evaluate all the possible results in the search term set. Blair's paper is a valuable contribution to the study of psychological factors in online searching. The next step is empirical testing to determine whether people do behave in this way and whether the combinatorial approach is helpful.

Although old (1964), the study by CARLSON, which observed three librarians doing bibliographic searching, remains one of the most productive on the psychological factors involved in searching. He noticed, for example, that the librarians would say they would return and check out a discrepancy, but they never did unless they wrote it down (p30).

Thorough and intriguing observations of manual searching are being done in Denmark by several researchers. PEJTERSEN studied 134 user-librarian conversations to determine the strategies used to help patrons find fiction materials. She identified five characteristic patterns of search. The most intriguing is what she calls an "empirical search strategy." In this pattern the librarian mentally stereotypes users and suggests similar materials to everyone in a given category. For example, "middle-aged women are repeatedly offered the same set of authors" (p115). Contrast this approach to an "analytical search strategy," in which the librarian analyzes and tailors the assistance to the need stated by the user.

INGWERSEN & KAAE present the most sophisticated model this reviewer has seen of what they call "the public library communication system from a cognitive viewpoint" (p75). This model includes not only document generator, librarian, user, and document but also the document representation and the mental "images" or representations of the information and information need that the various players have in their minds. Ingwersen and Kaae then illustrate and discuss their detailed transcription and analysis of "thinking-aloud" protocols taken from 20 librarians and nonlibrarians. (In other words, the searchers said out loud what they were thinking while they were searching, and the researchers recorded and analyzed these data.) Independent searches by librarians and by users as well as user-librarian negotiation were studied. [See also INGWERSEN ET AL. (1977; 1980). The most recent data appear in INGWERSEN & KAAE.] Other studies of manual searching have been done by KEEN (1977) and by JOHNSON.

The psychology of online searching was investigated by STANDERA. After questioning experienced searchers, he identified 17 phases of the online search and the pressure points along it. The points of highest pressure, interestingly, were strategy design and modification. Other studies of online searcher thinking and behavior have been done by MALLEN and SMETANA.

RESEARCH WITH IMPLICATIONS FOR SEARCH TECHNIQUES

Searching in General

An outstanding review of "The Process of Searching Online Bibliographic Databases" was published by FENICHEL (1980c). She covers all types of research on online bibliographic searching: theory, case studies, experiments, and questionnaire and interview surveys. She discusses individual studies and summarizes major results across several studies. Some of these results are discussed above.

BUCKLAND suggests that the dominant patterns of search in academic, special, and public libraries can be characterized, respectively, as high document specificity, high information specificity, and low document and information specificity. According to Buckland, these different patterns suggest different emphases in each type of library in collection development and access devices such as catalogs.

Online Strategies

The heart of a chapter on search techniques should be the section that describes research done to compare different strategies for their cost and productivity under different circumstances. Not a single study doing just that was found. Those discussed here deal with aspects of online search techniques but not with strategy comparison.

In a study published in 1977 by OLDROYD & CITROEN, 20 searchers from eight European countries searched the same two queries on ESA (European Space Agency) RECON (similar to Lockheed's DIALOG—this system is now known as ESA-IRS). The authors then examined the records of the searches to identify search patterns. Two results are striking: 1) searchers used two strategies predominantly; these resemble Bourne's citation pearl-growing and building-block strategies (described in Definitions section of this chapter); 2) searchers showed various poor searching techniques, such as a "tendency to lose sight of the basic logic" (p308), and inadequate attention to vocabulary and other differences among databases.

FENICHEL (1980a; 1980b; 1981) looked at the relationship between experience and performance of online searchers. Novices did surprisingly well, but experienced searchers often searched very simply—in half of their searches they did not modify their initial strategy.

Controlled Vocabulary vs. Free Text

In online searching studies much attention has been given to when and whether to search on controlled vocabulary or free text. In free-text searching one searches on terms or phrases that appear in the text of the record, as in the title and the abstract. In controlled vocabulary searching, one searches on the descriptors and identifiers that are assigned to each record by the database compilers.

ATHERTON & MARKEY review several studies on this question (p62–71), and ROSSON & ATHERTON provide an annotated bibliography. In the review by Atherton and Markey, specific combinations of elements searched on (e.g., controlled vocabulary, titles, abstracts, etc.) vary from study to study, and so comparison is difficult. All in all, the results are so mixed that simple conclusions cannot be drawn. The reader is referred to the above review and bibliography for details of studies as well as to the subsequently published articles by MARKEY ET AL. and CALKINS.

Manual vs. Online Searching

Another choice in searching strategy is whether to search manually or online. The comparison is usually viewed in terms of cost-effectiveness—i.e., which technique is cheaper for which types of searches. However, for search strategy it is more important to determine which type of search yields optimal retrieval.

Two recent studies provide excellent discussions of this question. JOHNSTON and JOHNSTON & GRAY report one study in which 75 searches on agricultural topics were processed both manually and online on several databases (and their corresponding manual sources), including CAIN (Cataloging and Indexing system of the U.S. National Agricultural Library, now called AGRICOLA), BIOSIS Previews (BioSciences Information Service of Biological Abstracts), Chemical Abstracts Condensates, and MEDLINE. Johnston lists 12 questions one should ask in determining which way to search. Generally, the coordination capability of online searching is its strong point, while the strength of manual searching is the ability of the searcher to interpret the applicability of candidate references to the query, particularly in cases of ambiguous terminology. In a similar study of 40 parallel searches on seven databases and their manual equivalents, ELCHESEN concludes that manual searches are better for extremely broad or extremely specific topics. Finally, DOLAN (1979b), in a helpful-hints article, describes types of online searches to avoid.

Bibliographic and Citation Index Searching

Both AYRES ET AL. and TAGLIACOZZO ET AL. found that users who approach a catalog have fully correct title information more often than fully correct author information. In the former study the figure is 90% to 75%; in the latter, it is 70% to 42%. Further, ORTIZ & CONNOLE found that searching on the "main entry" (a cataloging term for principal, or master record, usually author) is about 90% slower than searching by title.

These studies strongly suggest that a basic technique of bibliographic (vs. subject) searching should be to search on title first, at least in manual catalogs. However, the cataloging rules in effect until 1967 called for title (added) entries only some of the time; it is only since 1967 that virtually all books are cataloged under both author and title (see also HINKLEY). But, the preferability of title searching on post-1967 books seems clearly indicated, against the conventional author bias.

Some of the above research was done in connection with efforts to speed up technical processes (i.e., acquisitions and cataloging) in libraries, including the search and verification process associated with book purchasing. In a related study, MCCORMICK ET AL. wanted to see if online databases could be used to verify the accuracy (for publication purposes) of the citations provided by authors of scientific manuscripts. After looking up a sample of citations from the published fisheries literature, they concluded that online databases could be used to supplement (but not supplant) manual sources and were accurate enough to be used for verification. However, the 67 differences found (some quite minor) between initial citation and database citation in 112 matches calls into question the appropriateness of online databases for at least some kinds of verification.

CUMMINGS & FOX compared two methods of citation searching in a mathematical analysis of a "pseudo-random case." The first strategy is to generate additional citations by searching a citation index to determine who cites the items in the starting document's bibliography. The second strategy is to generate references by looking in the bibliographies of documents that cite the starting document. For reasonably sized bibliographies (greater than seven items) the latter strategy generates more citations.

Reference Work

Gerald Jahoda has studied the reference/searching process extensively and has developed instructional packages on this topic for library and information science students. In JAHODA (1977) and JAHODA ET AL. he presents six modules for instruction that correspond to six major decision points in the process of answering reference questions. He identified and refined those stages by having 23 scientific and technical reference librarians check them out during 20 searches (JAHODA, 1977). The steps are: 1) message selection; 2) selection of types of answer-providing tools; 3) selection of specific answer-providing tools; 4) selection of access points in titles; 5) selection of answer; and 6) query negotiation/renegotiation.

DE FIGUEIREDO, a student of Jahoda, developed a typology of errors that can be made at each of Jahoda's stages in the search process. She suggests actions to prevent these errors by individual librarians, library administrators, and library schools.

POWELL found a direct correlation between the percent of correct answers given to test questions by each of a group of 51 librarians and the size of their public library reference collections. Other analyses of his data showed other variables that are strongly related to reference performance— viz., number of reference questions received by each librarian in an average week and number of reference and bibliography courses completed by each. Thus, it appears that available resources, experience, and training all contribute to successful performance by searchers.

SEARCH HEURISTICS

This section focuses on the literature that gives aids or "tips" to help the information specialist, i.e., intermediary, search more effectively or efficiently. All textbook materials are discussed in the next section, and instructional or heuristic articles are covered here.

Several articles recommend a series of steps in conducting a search. The oldest item mentioned in this chapter is "Technique of Library Searching," published in 1936 by ALEXANDER. It is surprisingly, one might even say dismayingly, similar to a number of articles on the search process published in the ensuing 45 years. Although newer models vary in details, one would be hard put to say that Alexander's model is inferior or less developed than those published since his. His six steps (which include substeps by type of question) are: 1) identify the question precisely; 2) decide what type of material is most likely to have the answer; 3) array sources within that type in the order of likelihood of containing the answer; 4) locate the chosen items; 5) search the items in their order of likelihood; 6) if the answer is not found, retrace the previous steps.

The most notable innovation in modeling the search process since Alexander seems to be flowcharting, which received a burst of interest in the late 1960s and early 1970s. Eight flowchart models are reproduced by KATZ (1974, Vol. II). He collected several models from the literature and reproduced other models that were gathered by JAHODA & OLSON. Some are eight- or ten-step models of the whole reference process (including, for example, the reference interview); others, such as those of BUNGE and STYCH (1966), go into more detail on the search itself. Bunge's three-page flowchart contains more than 50 decision boxes and operation boxes. The decision boxes include such questions as "Should I consult catalog?" and "Is answer likely to be in magazines?" Stych's model is similarly detailed and sometimes mentions specific titles for the searcher to consider. In addition, a descriptive flowchart model appears in CARLSON, and prescriptive models appear in BURKHARDT and MARTINSON (1970; 1972).

More recently, flowchart models have appeared for online searching. DOLAN (1979a) flowcharts the formulation of the search before going online; MORROW models the online phase of the search. Morrow's model is intended for searching on ORBIT but is also useful as a prototype for bibliographic searching on other systems. The suggested sequences for narrowing and broadening searches are particularly useful.

154 MARCIA J. BATES

To say that the most notable innovation in 45 years of modeling the search process is flowcharting is to say little. On the whole, these models are disappointing. Modeling certainly seems to be a logical and necessary first step in understanding the search process, but now that this has been done, what has been gained? Do we really understand how top-flight searchers get their results, how best to teach fledgling information specialists, or how to design a machine to search for us? Cumulatively, the work so far constitutes a bare beginning.

The nature and usefulness of these models may be analyzed more easily by considering the four types of searching models categorized by BATES (1979b): 1) models for idealizing searching (ideal search patterns based on mathematical, system analytic, or other formal criteria of optimality); 2) models for representing searching (descriptions of actual human search behavior); 3) models for teaching searching; and 4) models for facilitating searching (helping the searcher during the process).

BENSON & MALONEY provide a model in which the principle of matching between the query and the system is paramount. One analyzes the query and then builds a "bibliographic bridge" to the information system by identifying the sources to be searched and translating the query into the language of the system.

BATES (1979b) takes a different tack in "Information Search Tactics." Instead of prescribing a sequence of actions, she proposes 29 different "tactics." A tactic is a move made to further a search. It can be used at any point in a manual or online search that seems appropriate. Each tactic has a mnemonically brief and striking name. The tactics are intended primarily to be facilitative and secondarily for teaching. For example, the tactic TRACE means to use information already found to derive additional search terms. One might use TRACE by looking for terms in the tracings on a catalog card or in the descriptor lists appended to citations printed out in an online search.

KENNINGTON deals with the need for government and industry librarians to scan their environments for the information that they will need to support the decision-making of their organizations. He suggests four "modes of scanning": 1) undirected viewing, 2) conditioned viewing, 3) informal search, and 4) formal search (p266-267). ROBBIN addresses the situation in which a client of a special library wishes to locate data for research purposes. Assuming that the library does not own the data, she describes, in a six-page list of steps, the "pre-acquisition process" to use in locating the data. Other articles that give advice or hints for searching in general or manually are those by BELTRAN, JOSEL, MACHURINA, STYCH (1967; 1972), and VORESS.

Turning now to articles that deal solely with online searching, advice appears regularly in four journal columns: 1) "Offlines" by Donna DOLAN in *Database*; 2) "Computer Ease" by Mary Ellen PADIN in *Online*; 3) "I Learned about Searching from That...," also in *ONLINE*; and 4) "Search Corner" in *ONLINE REVIEW*.

Along with the explosive growth in the use of online systems, there has been a burst of articles providing heuristics for online searching. ADAMS, DONATI, KNOX & HLAVA, and MARSHALL give advice (with some overlap in content) for optimizing online searching. Their advice is essential to effective use of current systems; in any but the simplest cases, a searcher who does not know these techniques will do a poor job. As in-depth online training becomes more standardized and universal, such articles will increasingly be supplanted by textbooks and courses in online searching (see next section).

Although many articles present sample searches, the examples of Adams illustrate the preparation and revision of search formulations particularly well. His discussion of techniques for broadening and narrowing searches points to an area that needs research. For example, if a search statement returns too many postings, what is the best way to narrow the search with minimal loss of relevant citations? The techniques that Adams mentions need to be tested and compared in a controlled study.

SMITH suggests Venn diagramming (that is, the use of intersecting circles or rectangles to provide a physical representation of Boolean combinations) to help both searcher and patron understand and formulate the search. MARTINEZ & ZAREMBER propose the use of the ordinarily disregarded Boolean operator *OR NOT* in certain specified cases. This counterintuitive proposal does seem to be appropriate and useful in certain narrowly defined situations, but it is not for the neophyte searcher.

Considerable interest has been shown in the searching of multiple databases. WANGER (1977) discusses how to select databases for searching, CONGER notes some of the differences among nine vendor systems, and HAWKINS (1978) gives an introduction to techniques of multiple database searching, with emphasis on the natural sciences. EPSTEIN & ANGIER and ANGIER & EPSTEIN concentrate on the behavioral sciences in two of the most thorough articles encountered on online searching. They go into great detail on the character of various behavioral science databases and provide examples of multiple database searches.

In contrast to this enthusiasm for multiple database searches, J. E. EVANS argues that in most cases only one database is needed. Searchers in his academic library switched from doing only 10% of their searches in a single database to 94%. User satisfaction, based on a "crude sampling," remained high. HAWKINS (1978), on the other hand, reports high use of and high user satisfaction with multiple database searches in special libraries. Different payment procedures and library type may be responsible for these different views.

Finally, STIBIC discusses the practical consequences for search strategy of another searching capability that may be widespread before too long: unlimited ranking (i.e., the output of document citations in ranked order of relevance to the patron's query). Once the citations that are most likely to be relevant appear at the beginning of a large postings set, the searcher can simply have printed out the first N citations, confident that subsequent citations will be less relevant. In such a case, it will not be so essential to try to reduce the number of postings returned on one's search formulation.

TEXTS AND SEARCH QUESTIONS

Online searching as a textbook topic is coming of age. Two recent texts supersede earlier ones not only in currency but also with regard to search strategy instruction. HENRY ET AL. have extracted the common searching features available on various online systems (truncation, saving searches, etc.) and discuss them in a general way, so that the student has a sense of the variety of searching tools that are available. A five-page appendix provides "A Checklist for Search Preparation and Search Strategy." LANCASTER deals with information retrieval systems (IRSs) in general and with online search systems as a subset of IRSs. His chapter "Selecting a Data Base and Searching It," is outstanding for its detailed consideration of hierarchical level, specificity, and exhaustivity in formulating a search. These elements can have considerable impact on the effectiveness of retrieval and are often neglected or misunderstood.

This chapter has excluded materials on individual databases, but an exception is made here to discuss *ONTAP*, the Online Training and Practice manual for searching the ERIC database. Charles Bourne originally developed this material, but it remained unpublished until MARKEY & ATHERTON made it available in 1978, with full credit to Bourne. It is an excellent manual and is valuable for searchers on essentially any database. It contains full descriptions of Bourne's five searching strategies: 1) building-block, 2) citation pearl-growing, 3) successive fractions, 4) most specific facet first, and 5) lowest postings facet first. (The first two strategies are defined in the Definitions section of this chapter.)

Texts on reference work generally emphasize manual searching, concentrating on reference sources and/or policies of a reference service, and give short shrift to search techniques. However, three recent texts do an excellent job of providing instruction on the search process itself (GROGAN, 1979; JAHODA & BRAUNAGEL; KATZ, 1978). Katz's book, now in its third edition, is a two-volume basic reference text covering both reference sources and services, including searching. Grogan's text is rich with examples and practical advice while retaining the broad picture. Jahoda and Braunagel concentrate on query negotiation and searching and provide exercises for every major step of these processes. For example, the student reader practices identifying appropriate subject terms for searching a query. Finally, GARFIELD explains how to do various types of searches in one kind of resource: citation indexes.

In research on and training for searching it is sometimes useful to have access to real questions. A collection of several thousand real queries and on-line searches has been developed for research purposes by Alina Vickery and her colleagues at the University of London (Central Information Service, Senate House, Malet Street, London, WC1E 7HU). They are hoping to put this collection into machine-readable form so that it will be more readily usable. Two books by GROGAN (1967; 1972) describe case studies in reference—i.e., real reference questions and how they were solved by a librarian.

Finally, SLAVENS reports a series of real reference interviews and lists several hundred practice questions, some real and some invented.

CONCLUSIONS

This chapter is the first in *ARIST* that is devoted wholly to search techniques. It is not entirely surprising, therefore, to find that this topic is at a relatively primitive stage of development. Sophisticated automated information retrieval systems are being developed that will give the searcher powerful capabilities, but we have only an elementary understanding of how the human searcher who will operate such systems does and should search.

Research is needed to compare and to test search strategies in both the manual and online environments. In online searching, testing is needed on techniques for narrowing and broadening searches and on the strategies of Bourne and others. There is apparently nothing comparable to Bourne's strategies for manual searching, and even his are for searching on a database that one has already selected. How should one select a database or manual source from among the many possible sources in the first place? Research is also needed on browsing and on the psychological processes involved in searching. Finally, and above all, we need to develop theory on the nature of the search process.

BIBLIOGRAPHY

ADAMS, ARTHUR L. 1979. Planning Search Strategies for Maximum Retrieval from Bibliographic Databases. Online Review. 1979 December; 3(4): 373–379. ISSN: 0309-314X.

ALEXANDER, CARTER. 1936. Technique of Library Searching. Special Libraries. 1936 September; 27(7): 230–238. ISSN: 0038-6723.

ANGIER, JENNIFER J.; EPSTEIN, BARBARA A. 1980. Multi-Database Searching in the Behavioral Sciences. Part 2: Special Applications. Database. 1980 December; 3(4): 34–40. ISSN: 0162-4105.

ANTONY, ARTHUR. 1979. Guide to Basic Information Sources in Chemistry. New York, NY: Wiley; 1979. 219p. (Information Resources Series). ISBN: 0-470-26587-6.

ATHERTON, PAULINE; MARKEY, KAREN. 1979. Part IV: The Redesign of the ERIC Data Base for Online Searching. In: Atherton, Pauline. Online Searching of ERIC: Impact of Free Text or Controlled Vocabulary Searching on the Design of the ERIC Data Base. Syracuse: NY: ERIC Clearinghouse on Information Resources; 1979. 1–71. (Chapter in a technical report). ERIC: ED 180431.

AUBRY, JOHN W. 1972. A Timing Study of the Manual Searching of Catalogs. Library Quarterly. 1972 October; 42(4): 399–415. ISSN: 0024-2519.

AYRES, F. H.; GERMAN, JANICE; LOUKES, N.; SEARLE, R. H. 1968. Author versus Title: A Comparative Survey of the Accuracy of the Information Which the User Brings to the Library Catalogue. Journal of Documentation (U.K.). 1968 December; 24(4): 266–272. ISSN: 0022-0418.

BATES, MARCIA J. 1976. Rigorous Systematic Bibliography. RQ. 1976 Fall; 16(1): 7-26. ISSN: 0033-7072.

BATES, MARCIA J. 1979a. Idea Tactics. Journal of the American Society for Information Science. 1979 September; 30(5): 280-289. ISSN: 0002-8231.

BATES, MARCIA J. 1979b. Information Search Tactics. Journal of the American Society for Information Science. 1979 July; 30(4): 205-214. ISSN: 0002-8231.

BELKIN, NICHOLAS J. 1980. The Problem of "Matching" in Information Retrieval. In: Harbo, Ole; Kajberg, Leif, eds. Theory and Application of Information Research: Proceedings of the 2nd International Research Forum on Information Science; 1977 August 3-6; Copenhagen, Denmark. London, England: Mansell Publishing; 1980. 187-197. ISBN: 0-7201-1513-2.

BELKIN, NICHOLAS J.; BROOKS, H. M.; ODDY, R. N. 1979. Representation and Classification of Anomalous States of Knowledge and Information for Use in Interactive Information Retrieval. In: Henriksen, Tor, ed. IRFIS 3: Proceedings of the 3rd International Research Forum in Information Science: Volume 2; 1979 August 1-3; Oslo, Norway. Oslo, Norway: Statens Bibliotekskole; 1979. 146-183. (Statens Bibliotekskole Publikasjoner 5). ISSN: 0332-5091.

BELKIN, N. J.; ODDY, R. N. 1979. Design Study for an Anomalous State of Knowledge Based Information Retrieval System. Birmingham, England: University of Aston, Computer Centre; 1979 September. 226p. (British Library Research and Development Report no. 5547).

BELTRAN, ALFRED A. 1971. The Craft of Literature Searching. Sci-Tech News. 1971 Winter; 25(4): 113-116. ISSN: 0036-8059.

BENSON, JAMES; MALONEY, RUTH KAY. 1975. Principles of Searching. RQ. 1975 Summer; 14(4): 316-320. (Also in Katz, Bill; Tarr, Andrea, eds. Reference and Information Services: A Reader. Metuchen, NJ: Scarecrow; 1978. 131-139. ISBN: 0-3108-1091-3). ISSN: 0033-7072.

BIVINS, KATHLEEN T.; PALMER, ROGER C. 1979. REFLES (Reference Librarian Enhancement System). In: Tally, Roy D.; Dueltgen, Ronald R., eds. Information Choices and Policies: Proceedings of the American Society for Information Science 42nd Annual Meeting: Volume 16; 1979 October 14-18; Minneapolis, MN. White Plains, NY: Knowledge Industry Publications, Inc.; 1979. 58-65. ISSN: 0044-7870; ISBN: 0-914236-47-4; LC: 64-8303; CODEN: PAISDQ.

BIVINS, KATHLEEN; PALMER, ROGER C. 1980. REFLES: An Individual Micro-Computer System for Fact Retrieval. Online Review. 1980; 4(4): 357-365. ISSN: 0309-314X.

BLAIR, DAVID C. 1980. Searching Biases in Large Interactive Document Retrieval Systems. Journal of the American Society for Information Science. 1980 July; 31(4): 271-277. ISSN: 0002-8231.

BOLT, RICHARD A. 1978. Spatial Data Management System. Cambridge, MA: Massachusetts Institute of Technology Machine Architecture Group; 1978 December 31. 61p. NTIS: AD A070 243/1GA.

BRAGA, MARIO JORGE FERREIRA. 1974. An Introduction to Search Theory. Monterey, CA: Naval Postgraduate School; 1974 March. 117p. (Master's thesis). NTIS: AD-777 878/0GA.

BUCKLAND, MICHAEL K. 1979. On Types of Search and the Allocation of Library Resources. Journal of the American Society for Information Science. 1979 May; 30(3): 143-147. ISSN: 0002-8231.

BUNGE, CHARLES A. 1967. Professional Education and Reference Efficiency. Springfield, IL: Illinois State Library; 1967. 101p. (Research Series no. 11).

BURKHARDT, MARGIT. 1971. Anwendung der Systematischen Heuristik bei Recherchen [Application of Systematic Searching Techniques]. Bibliothekar (Germany). 1971 September; 25: 628-632. (In German). ISSN: 0006-1964.

CALKINS, MARY L. 1980. Free Text or Controlled Vocabulary? A Case History Step-by-Step Analysis. . .Plus Other Aspects of Search Strategy. Database. 1980 June; 3(2): 53-67. ISSN: 0162-4105.

CARLSON, G. 1964. Search Strategy by Reference Librarians: Part 3 of the Final Report on the Organization of Large Files. Sherman Oaks, CA: Hughes Dynamics, Inc., Advanced Information Systems Division; 1964 March. 46p. NTIS: PB 166 192.

CHILDERS, THOMAS. 1980. The Test of Reference. Library Journal. 1980 April 15; 105(8): 924-928. ISSN: 0363-0277.

CONGER, LUCINDA D. 1980. Multiple System Searching: A Searcher's Guide to Making Use of the Real Differences between Systems. Online. 1980 April; 4(2): 10-21. ISSN: 0146-5422.

CROUCH, WAYNE W. 1979. The Information Interview: A Comprehensive Bibliography and an Analysis of the Literature. Syracuse, NY: ERIC Clearinghouse on Information Resources; 1979. 49p. ERIC: ED 180501.

CROWLEY, TERENCE; CHILDERS, THOMAS. 1971. Information Service in Public Libraries: Two Studies. Metuchen, NJ: Scarecrow Press; 1971. 210p. ISBN: 0-8108-0406-9; LC: 77-154298.

CUMMINGS, L. J.; FOX, D. A. 1973. Some Mathematical Properties of Cycling Strategies Using Citation Indexes. Information Storage and Retrieval. 1973 December; 9(12): 713-719. ISSN: 0020-0271.

DE FIGUEIREDO, NICE M. 1975. A Conceptual Methodology for Error Prevention in Reference Work. Tallahassee, FL: Florida State University; 1975 December. 313p. (Ph.D. dissertation). UMI: 76-13, 807.

DEUTSCH, DONALD R.; KRAFT, DONALD H. 1974. A Study of an Information Retrieval Performance Measure: Expected Search Length as a Function of File Size and Organization. Paper presented at the Annual Meeting of the Operations Society of America; 1974; Boston, MA. 27p. ERIC: ED 143373.

DOLAN, DONNA R., ed. Offlines. Database. (Regular column). ISSN: 0095-0033.

DOLAN, DONNA R. 1979a. Before You Touch the Terminal: Flowchart of the Search Formulation Process. Database. 1979 December; 2(4): 86-88. ISSN: 0162-4105.

DOLAN, DONNA R. 1979b. What Databases Cannot Do. Database. 1979 September; 2(3): 85-87. ISSN: 0162-4105.

DONATI, ROBERT. 1978. Spanning the Social Sciences: Searching Techniques When Online. Online. 1978 January; 2(1): 41-52. ISSN: 0146-5422; ERIC: EJ 179525.

DOSZKOCS, TAMAS E. 1978. AID, An Associative Interactive Dictionary for Online Searching. Online Review. 1978 June; 2(2): 163-173. ISSN: 0309-314X; ERIC: EJ 190832; UMI: 79-25741.

DOSZKOCS, TAMAS E.; RAPP, BARBARA A. 1979. Searching MEDLINE in English: A Prototype User Interface with Natural Language Query, Ranked Output and Relevance Feedback. In: Tally, Roy D.; Dueltgen,

Ronald R., eds. Information Choices and Policies: Proceedings of the American Society for Information Science 42nd Annual Meeting: Volume 16; 1979 October 14–18; Minneapolis, MN. White Plains, NY: Knowledge Industry Publications, Inc.; 1979. 131–139. ISSN: 0044-7870; ISBN: 0-914236-47-4; LC: 64-8303; CODEN: PAISDQ.

DOYLE, JAMES M.; GRIMES, GEORGE H. 1976. Reference Resources: A Systematic Approach. Metuchen, NJ: Scarecrow Press; 1976. 293p. ISBN: 0-8108-0928-1; LC: 76-7080.

DRABEK, THOMAS E.; SHAW, WARD; CULKIN, PATRICIA B. 1978. The Query Analysis System: A New Tool for Increasing the Effectiveness of Library Utilization by Sociology Students. Teaching Sociology. 1978 October; 6(1): 47–68. ISSN: 0092-055X; ERIC: EJ 189447.

DREXEL UNIVERSITY SCHOOL OF LIBRARY AND INFORMATION SCIENCE; FRANKLIN INSTITUTE RESEARCH LABORATORIES. 1980. Individualized Instruction for Data Access (IIDA). Philadelphia, PA: Drexel University School of Library and Information Science; Franklin Institute Research Laboratories; 1980 June. 68p. (Final report, NSF Grant no. DSI 77-26524; see also ERIC: ED 168462, ED 179195, ED 190080, ED 190081).

ELCHESEN, DENNIS R. 1978. Cost-Effectiveness Comparison of Manual and On-Line Retrospective Bibliographic Searching. Journal of the American Society for Information Science. 1978 March; 29(2): 56–66. ISSN: 0002-8231.

EMERSON, SUSAN VINCE. 1975. Problem-Oriented Literature Searching. Cleveland, OH: Case Western Reserve University; 1975. 185p. (Ph.D. dissertation). UMI: 75-19201.

ENSLOW, PHILIP H., JR. 1966. A Bibliography of Search Theory and Reconnaissance Theory Literature. Naval Research Logistics Quarterly. 1966 June; 13(2): 177–202. ISSN: 0028-1441.

EPSTEIN, BARBARA A.; ANGIER, JENNIFER J. 1980. Multi-Database Searching in the Behavioral Sciences. Part 1: Basic Techniques and Core Databases. Database. 1980 September; 3(3): 9–15. ISSN: 0162-4105.

EVANS, JOHN EDWARD. 1980. Database Selection in an Academic Library: Are Those Big Multi-File Searches Really Necessary? Online. 1980 April; 4(2): 35–43. ISSN: 0146-5422.

EVANS, LYNN. 1975. Search Strategy Variations in SDI Profiles. London, England: Institution of Electrical Engineers; 1975. 129p. (OSTI Report 5229; Institution of Electrical Engineers publication no. R75/21). ISBN: 0-85296-427-7.

FENICHEL, CAROL HANSEN. 1980a. An Examination of the Relationship between Searching Behavior and Searcher Background. Online Review. 1980 December; 4(4): 341–347. ISSN: 0309-314X; UMI: 79-26997.

FENICHEL, CAROL HANSEN. 1980b. Intermediary Searchers' Satisfaction with the Results of Their Searches. In: Benenfeld, Alan R.; Kazlauskas, Edward John, eds. Communicating Information: Proceedings of the American Society for Information Science 43rd Annual Meeting: Volume 17; 1980 October 5–10; Anaheim, CA. White Plains, NY: Knowledge Industry Publications, Inc.; 1980. 58–60. ISSN: 0044-7870; ISBN: 0-914236-73-3; LC: 64-8303; CODEN: PAISDQ; UMI: 79-26997.

FENICHEL, CAROL HANSEN. 1980c. The Process of Searching Online

Bibliographic Databases: A Review of Research. Library Research. 1980 Summer; 2(2): 107-127. ISSN: 0164-0763.

FENICHEL, CAROL HANSEN. 1981. Online Searching: Measures That Discriminate among Users with Different Types of Experiences. Journal of the American Society for Information Science. 1981 January; 32(1): 23-32. ISSN: 0002-8231; UMI: 79-26997.

GALLWEY, W. TIMOTHY. 1974. The Inner Game of Tennis. New York, NY: Random House; 1974. 141p. ISBN: 0-394-49154-8.

GARFIELD, EUGENE. 1979. Citation Indexing: Its Theory and Application in Science, Technology, and Humanities. New York, NY: Wiley; 1979. 274p. (Information Sciences Series). ISBN: 0-471-02559-3; LC: 78-9713.

GIERING, RICHARD H. 1975. Search Strategies and User Interface. Journal of Chemical Information and Computer Sciences. 1975 February; 15(1): 6-11. ISSN: 0095-2338.

GOLDHOR, HERBERT. 1972. The Effect of Prime Display Location on Public Library Circulation of Selected Adult Titles. Library Quarterly. 1972 October; 42(4): 371-389. ISSN: 0024-2519.

GREENE, ROBERT J. 1977. The Effectiveness of Browsing. College & Research Libraries. 1977 July; 38(4): 313-316. ISSN: 0010-0870.

GROGAN, DENIS JOSEPH. 1967. Case Studies in Reference Work. Hamden, CT: Archon Books; 1967. 166p. ISBN: 85157-004-6.

GROGAN, DENIS JOSEPH. 1972. More Case Studies in Reference Work. Hamden, CT: Linnet Books; 1972. 293p. ISBN: 0-208-01070-X; LC: 72-185911.

GROGAN, DENIS JOSEPH. 1979. Practical Reference Work. London, England: Clive Bingley; 1979. 144p. ISBN: 0-85157-275-8; LC: 79-41109.

HALL, JAMES LOGAN; DEWE, AINSLIE. 1980. Online Information Retrieval, 1976-1979: An International Bibliography. London, England: Aslib; 1980. 230p. ISBN: 0-85142-127-X.

HAWKINS, DONALD T. 1978. Multiple Database Searching: Techniques and Pitfalls. Online. 1978 April; 2(2): 9-15. ISSN: 0146-5422; ERIC: EJ 189033.

HAWKINS, DONALD T. 1980. Online Information Retrieval Bibliography, 1964-1979. Marlton, NJ: Learned Information, Inc.; 1980. 174p. ISBN: 0-938734-00-8.

HENRY, W. M.; LEIGH, J. A.; TEDD, L. A.; WILLIAMS, P. W. 1980. Online Searching: An Introduction. London, England: Butterworth; 1980. 209p. ISBN: 0-408-10696-4.

HINKLEY, WILLIAM. 1968. On Searching Catalogs and Indexes with Inexact Title Information. Chicago, IL: University of Chicago Graduate Library School; 1968 December. 51p. (Master's thesis). Available from: University of Chicago Library, Photoduplication Dept., 1100 E. 57th St., Chicago, IL 60637.

HOUSE, DAVID E. 1974. Reference Efficiency or Reference Deficiency. Library Association Record (U.K.). 1974 November; 76(11): 222-223. (Also in: Katz, Bill; Tarr, Andrea. Reference and Information Services: A Reader. Metuchen, NJ: Scarecrow Press; 1978. 140-144. ISBN: 0-3108-1091-3). ISSN: 0024-2195.

HYMAN, RICHARD JOSEPH. 1971. Access to Library Collections: Summary of a Documentary and Opinion Survey on the Direct Shelf

Approach and Browsing. Library Resources & Technical Services. 1971 Fall; 15(4): 479-491. ISSN: 0024-2527.

HYMAN, RICHARD JOSEPH. 1972. Access to Library Collections: An Inquiry into the Validity of the Direct Shelf Approach, with Special Reference to Browsing. Metuchen, NJ: Scarecrow Press; 1972. 452p. ISBN: 0-8108-0434-4.

INGWERSEN, PETER; JOHANSEN, THOMAS; TIMMERMAN, POVL. 1977. A Study of the User-Librarian Negotiation Process. In: Batten, W. E., ed. EURIM II: A European Conference on the Application of Research in Information Services and Libraries; 1976 March 23-25; Amsterdam, The Netherlands. London, England: Aslib; 1977. 203-207. ISBN: 85142-091-5.

INGWERSEN, PETER; JOHANSEN, THOMAS; TIMMERMAN, POVL. 1980. User-Librarian Negotiations and Search Procedures: A Progress Report. In: Harbo, Ole; Kajberg, Leif, eds. Theory and Application of Information Research: Proceedings of the 2nd International Research Forum on Information Science; 1977 August 3-6; Copenhagen, Denmark. London, England: Mansell Publishing; 1980. 160-171. ISBN: 0-7201-1513-2.

INGWERSEN, PETER; KAAE, SOREN. 1979. User-Librarian Negotiations and Information Search Procedures in Public Libraries: Analysis of Verbal Protocols. In: Henriksen, Tor, ed. IRFIS 3: Proceedings of the 3rd International Research Forum in Information Science: Volume 1; 1979 August 1-3; Oslo, Norway. Oslo, Norway: Statens Bibliotekskole; 1979. 71-106. (Statens Bibliotekskole Publikasjoner 5). ISSN: 0332-5091.

JAHODA, GERALD. 1974. Reference Question Analysis and Search Strategy Development by Man and Machine. Journal of the American Society for Information Science. 1974 May-June; 25(3): 139-144. ISSN: 0002-8231.

JAHODA, GERALD. 1977. The Process of Answering Reference Questions. A Test of a Descriptive Model. Tallahassee, FL: Florida State University, School of Library Science; 1977 January. 219p. (For related document see ED 111421). ERIC: ED 136769.

JAHODA, GERALD; BRAUNAGEL, JUDITH SCHIEK. 1980. The Librarian and Reference Queries: A Systematic Approach. New York, NY: Academic Press; 1980. 175p. ISBN: 0-12-379760-8; LC: 79-6939.

JAHODA, GERALD; BRAUNAGEL, JUDITH; NATH, HERBERT. 1977. The Reference Process: Modules for Instruction. RQ. 1977 Fall; 17(1): 7-12. ISSN: 0033-7072.

JAHODA, GERALD; OLSON, PAUL E. 1972. Models of Reference: Analyzing the Reference Process. RQ. 1972 Winter; 12(2): 148-156. ISSN: 0033-7072.

JOHNSON, ALLAN R. 1978. Problem Solving and the Reference Search. Chicago, IL: University of Chicago, Graduate Library School; 1978. 72p. (Master's thesis). Available from: University of Chicago Library, Photoduplication Dept., 1100 E. 57th St., Chicago, IL 60637.

JOHNSTON, SUSAN M. 1978. Choosing between Manual and On-Line Searching—Practical Experience in the Ministry of Agriculture, Fisheries and Food. Aslib Proceedings (U.K.). 1978 October/November; 30 (10-11): 383-393. ISSN: 0001-253X.

JOHNSTON, SUSAN M.; GRAY, D. E. 1977. Comparison of Manual and

SEARCH TECHNIQUES

Online Retrospective Searching for Agricultural Subjects. Aslib Proceedings (U.K.). 1977 July; 29(7): 253-258. ISSN: 0001-253X.

JOSEL, NATHAN A., JR. 1971. Ten Reference Commandments. RQ. 1971 Winter; 11(2): 146-147. ISSN: 0033-7072.

KATZ, WILLIAM A. 1974. Introduction to Reference Work. 2nd edition. New York, NY: McGraw-Hill; 1974. 2 volumes. ISBN: 0-07-033353-X, 0-07-033354-8; LC: 73-8658.

KATZ, WILLIAM A. 1978. Introduction to Reference Work. 3rd edition. New York, NY: McGraw-Hill; 1978. 2 volumes. ISBN: 0-07-033331-9, 0-07-033332-7; LC: 77-12539.

KEEN, E. MICHAEL. 1968. Search Strategy Evaluation in Manual and Automated Systems. Aslib Proceedings (U.K.). 1968 January; 20(1): 65-81. ISSN: 0001-253X.

KEEN, E. MICHAEL. 1977. On the Processing of Printed Subject Index Entries During Searching. Journal of Documentation (U.K.). 1977 December; 33(4): 266-276. ISSN: 0022-0418.

KENNINGTON, DON. 1977. Scanning the Operational Environment: The Librarian's Role. Journal of Librarianship (U.K.). 1977 October; 9(4): 261-269. ISSN: 0022-2232.

KENTON, EDITH. 1979. Search and Rescue Methods and Equipment (A Bibliography with Abstracts). Springfield, VA: National Technical Information Service; 1979 July. 239p. NTIS: PS-79/0649/8GA.

KNOX, DOUGLAS R.; HLAVA, MARJORIE M. K. 1979. Effective Search Strategies. Online Review. 1979 June; 3(2): 148-152. ISSN: 0309-314X.

KRAFT, DONALD H.; LEE, T. 1979. Stopping Rules and Their Effect on Expected Search Length. Information Processing & Management. 1979; 15(1): 47-58. ISSN: 0306-4573.

LANCASTER, F. WILFRID. 1979. Information Retrieval Systems: Characteristics, Testing and Evaluation. 2nd edition. New York, NY: Wiley; 1979. 381p. (Information Sciences Series). ISBN: 0-471-04673-6; LC: 78-11078.

LANDSBERG, M. KAREN; LAWRENCE, BARBARA; LORENZ, PATRICIA A.; MEADOW, CHARLES T.; HEWETT, THOMAS T. 1980. A Joint Industrial-Academic Experiment: An Evaluation of the IIDA System. In: Benenfeld, Alan R.; Kazlauskas, Edward John, eds. Communicating Information: Proceedings of the American Society for Information Science 43rd Annual Meeting: Volume 17; 1980 October 5-10; Anaheim, CA. White Plains, NY: Knowledge Industry Publications, Inc.; 1980. 406-408. ISSN: 0044-7870; ISBN: 0-914236-73-3; LC: 64-8303; CODEN: PAISDQ.

LEIMKUHLER, FERDINAND F. 1968. A Literature Search and File Organization Model. American Documentation. 1968 April; 19(2): 131-136.

LICKLIDER, J. C. R. 1965. Appendix I: Proposed Experiments in Browsing. In: Overhage, Carl F. J.; Harmon, R. Joyce. INTREX: Report of a Planning Conference on Information Transfer Experiments; 1965 September 3. Cambridge, MA: Massachusetts Institute of Technology Press; 1965. 187-197. LC: 65-28409.

MACHURINA, A. T. 1970. Ob intuitsii bibliografa i logike bibliograficheskogo razyskaniia: Iz opyta raboty s chitatel'skimi trebovaniiami [Bib-

liographer's Intuition and the Logic of Bibliographic Searching: Experience Based on Readers' Requests]. Sovetskaia Bibliografiia (U.S.S.R.). 1970;(2): 16-24. (In Russian). ISSN: 0038-5042.
MAIZELL, ROBERT E. 1979. How to Find Chemical Information. New York, NY: Wiley; 1979. 261p. ISBN: 0-471-56531-8.
MALLEN, MARIE-CHRISTINE. 1977. On-Line Information Retrieval: Operators' Behaviour and Opinions. On-Line Information: [Proceedings of the] 1st International On-Line Information Meeting; 1977 December 13-15; London, England. Oxford, England: Learned Information (Europe), Ltd.; 1977. 95-102. ISBN: 0-904933-10-5.
MARCUS, RICHARD S. 1980. Search Aids in a Retrieval Network. In: Benenfeld, Alan R.; Kazlauskas, Edward John, eds. Communicating Information: Proceedings of the American Society for Information Science 43rd Annual Meeting: Volume 17; 1980 October 5-10; Anaheim, CA. White Plains, NY: Knowledge Industry Publications, Inc.; 1980. 394-396. ISSN: 0044-7870; ISBN: 0-914236-73-3; LC: 64-8303; CODEN: PAISDQ.
MARCUS, RICHARD S.; REINTJES, J. FRANCIS. 1979. Experiments and Analysis on a Computer Interface to an Information-Retrieval Network. Cambridge, MA: Massachusetts Institute of Technology. Laboratory for Information and Decision Systems; 1979 April. 133p. (Report no. LIDS-R-900). ERIC: ED 190104.
MARKEY, KAREN; ATHERTON, PAULINE. 1978. ONTAP: Online Training and Practice Manual for ERIC Data Base Searchers. Syracuse, NY: ERIC Clearinghouse on Information Resources; 1978 June. 182p. ERIC: ED 160109.
MARKEY, KAREN; ATHERTON, PAULINE; NEWTON, CLAUDIA. 1980. An Analysis of Controlled Vocabulary and Free Text Search Statements in Online Searches. Online Review. 1980 September; 4(3): 225-236. ISSN: 0309-314X.
MARSHALL, DORIS B. 1980. To Improve Searching, Check Search Results. Online. 1980 July; 4(3): 32-47. ISSN: 0146-5422.
MARTIN, LOWELL A. 1969. Library Response to Urban Change: A Study of the Chicago Public Library. Chicago, IL: American Library Association; 1969. 313p. ISBN: 8389-0077-1; LC: 76-104040.
MARTINEZ, CLARA; ZAREMBER, IRVING. 1978. OR NOT: The Unused Operator. Journal of the American Society for Information Science. 1978 July; 29(4): 207-208. ISSN: 0002-8231.
MARTINSON, TOM L. 1970. A Simple Stratified Flow Chart for Compiling Subject Bibliographies in Geography. Special Libraries Association Geography and Map Division Bulletin. 1970 December; (82): 32-41. ISSN: 0036-1607.
MARTINSON, TOM L. 1972. Library of Congress Author Catalogs: A "Micro-Series" in the Stratified Flow Chart. Special Libraries Association Geography and Map Division Bulletin. 1972 March; (87): 12-16, 50. ISSN: 0036-1607.
MCCORMICK, JACK M.; TERRY, RITA B.; KOLLGAARD, JEFFERY R. 1979. Verification of Citations by Searching Computer Data Bases. In: Tally, Roy D.; Dueltgen, Ronald R., eds. Information Choices and Policies: Proceedings of the American Society for Information Science 42nd Annual Meeting: Volume 16; 1979 October 14-18; Minneapolis, MN. White Plains, NY: Knowledge Industry Publications, Inc.; 1979.

219-228. ISSN: 0044-7870; ISBN: 0-914236-47-4; LC: 64-8303; CODEN: PAISDQ.

MEADOW, CHARLES T. 1979. The Computer as a Search Intermediary. Online. 1979 July; 3(3): 54-59. ISSN: 0146-5422; ERIC: EJ 208344.

MEADOW, CHARLES T.; EPSTEIN, B. E. 1977. Individualized Instruction for Data Access. On-Line Information: [Proceedings of the] 1st International On-Line Information Meeting; 1977 December 13-15; London, England. Oxford, England: Learned Information (Europe), Ltd.; 1977. 179-194. ISBN: 0-904933-10-5.

MEADOW, CHARLES T.; HEWETT, THOMAS T.; RAFSNIDER, D. JEAN; TOLIVER, DAVID E.; EPSTEIN, BERNARD; EDELMANN, JANET V.; MAHER, ANN. 1977. Individualized Instruction for Data Access (IIDA) Final Design Report. Philadelphia, PA: Drexel University Graduate School of Library Science; 1977 July. 171p. ERIC: ED 145826.

MEADOW, CHARLES T.; TOLIVER, DAVID E.; EDELMANN, JANET V. 1978. A Technique for Machine Assistance to Online Searchers. In: Brenner, Everett H., comp. The Information Age in Perspective: Proceedings of the American Society for Information Science 41st Annual Meeting: Volume 15; 1978 November 13-17; New York, NY. White Plains, NY: Knowledge Industry Publications, Inc.; 1978. 222-225. ISSN: 0044-7870;ISBN: 0-914236-22-9; LC: 64-8303; CODEN: PAISDQ.

MEREDITH, JOSEPH C. 1971. Machine-Assisted Approach to General Reference Materials. Journal of the American Society for Information Science. 1971 May-June; 22(3): 176-186. ISSN: 0002-8231; ERIC: ED 060918.

MILLER, GEORGE A. 1968. Psychology and Information. American Documentation. 1968 July; 19(3): 286-289.

MOORE, MICHAEL L. 1970. A Review of Search and Reconnaissance Theory Literature. Ann Arbor, MI: University of Michigan Systems Research Lab.; 1970 January. 104p. NTIS: AD 700 333.

MORRIS, JACQUELYN M.; ELKINS, ELIZABETH A. 1978. Library Searching: Resources and Strategies. New York, NY: Jeffrey Norton; 1978. 129p. ISBN: 0-88432-004-9; LC: 77-9214.

MORROW, DEANNA I. 1976. A Generalized Flowchart for the Use of ORBIT and Other On-Line Interactive Bibliographic Search Systems. Journal of the American Society for Information Science. 1976 January-February; 27(1): 57-62. ISSN: 0002-8231.

MORSE, PHILIP M. 1970a. On Browsing: The Use of Search Theory in the Search for Information. Cambridge, MA: Massachusetts Institute of Technology Operations Research Center; 1970 February. 42p. NTIS: AD 702 920.

MORSE, PHILIP M. 1970b. Search Theory and Browsing. Library Quarterly. 1970 October; 40(4): 391-408. ISSN: 0024-2519.

MORSE, PHILIP M. 1972. Optimal Linear Ordering of Information Items. Operations Research. 1972 July/August; 20(4): 741-751. ISSN: 0030-364X; NTIS: AD A035 133/8GA.

MORSE, PHILIP M. 1970b. Search Theory and Browsing. Library Quarterly. 1970 October; 40(4): 391-408. ISSN: 0024-2519. Scarecrow Press; 1973. 246-261. (Chapter in a book). ISBN: 0-8108-0535-9.

MORSE, PHILIP M. 1974. Search Theory. Cambridge, MA: Massachusetts Institute of Technology Operations Research Center; 1974 January.

166   MARCIA J. BATES

100p. (Part of Study: Innovative Resource Planning in Urban Public Safety Systems). NTIS: PB 284 254/0GA.

MURFIN, MARJORIE E.; WYNAR, LUBOMYR R. 1977. Reference Service: An Annotated Bibliographic Guide. Littleton, CO: Libraries Unlimited; 1977. 294p. ISBN: 0-87287-132-0.

NEILL, S. D. 1975. Problem Solving and the Reference Process. RQ. 1975 Summer; 14(4): 310-315. ISSN: 0033-7072.

NIEHOFF, ROBERT T. 1980. The Optimization and Use of Automated Subject Switching for Better Retrieval. In: Benenfeld, Alan R.; Kazlauskas, Edward John, eds. Communicating Information: Proceedings of the American Society for Information Science 43rd Annual Meeting: Volume 17; 1980 October 5-10; Anaheim, CA. White Plains, NY: Knowledge Industry Publications, Inc.; 1980. 397-400. ISSN: 0044-7870; ISBN: 0-914236-73-3; LC: 64-8303; CODEN: PAISDQ.

NIEHOFF, ROBERT T.; KWASNY, STAN. 1979. The Role of Automated Subject Switching in a Distributed Information Network. Online Review. 1979 June; 3(2): 181-194. ISSN: 0309-314X.

NIEHOFF, ROBERT T.; KWASNY, STAN; WESSELLS, MICHAEL. 1979. Overcoming the Database Vocabulary Barrier—A Solution. Online. 1979 October; 3(4): 43-54. ISSN: 0146-5422.

NORMAN, O. GENE. 1979. The Reference Interview: An Annotated Bibliography. RSR: Reference Services Review. 1979 January/March 7(1): 71-77. ISSN: 0090-7324.

ODDY, ROBERT N. 1977a. Information Retrieval through Man-Machine Dialogue. Journal of Documentation (U.K.). 1977 March; 33(1): 1-14. ISSN: 0022-0418.

ODDY, ROBERT N. 1977b. Retrieving References by Dialogue Rather Than by Query Formulation. Journal of Informatics. 1977 April; 1(1): 37-53.

OLDROYD, BETTY K.; CITROEN, CHARLES L. 1977. Study of Strategies Used in Online Searching. Online Review. 1977 December; 1(4): 295-310. ISSN: 0309-314X.

ONLINE. I Learned About Searching From That... Online. (Regular column). ISSN: 0146-5422.

ONLINE REVIEW. Search Corner. Online Review. (Regular column). ISSN: 0309-314X.

ORTIZ, RICHARD J.; CONNOLE, THOMAS P. 1973. Bibliographic Searching: Main Entry vs. Title Access, A Comparative Time Study. 1973 August. 136p. (A research paper presented to the faculty of the University of Denver Graduate School of Librarianship). ERIC: ED 112950.

PADIN, MARY ELLEN, ed. Computer Ease. Online. (Regular column). ISSN: 0146-5422.

PEJTERSEN, ANNELISE MARK. 1979. Investigation of Search Strategies in Fiction Based on an Analysis of 134 User-Librarian Conversations. In: Henriksen, Tor, ed. IRFIS 3: Proceedings of the 3rd International Research Forum in Information Science: Volume 1; 1979 August 1-3; Oslo, Norway. Oslo, Norway: Statens Bibliotekskole; 1979. 107-131. (Statens Bibliotekskole Publikasjoner 5). ISSN: 0332-5091.

POLLET, DOROTHY. 1976. New Directions in Library Signage: You Can Get There from Here. Wilson Library Bulletin. 1976 February; 50(6): 456-462. ISSN: 0043-5651.

POLLET, DOROTHY; HASKELL, PETER C., comps., eds. 1979. Sign Systems for Libraries: Solving the Wayfinding Problem. New York, NY: R. R. Bowker; 1979. 269p. ISBN: 0-8352-1149-5; LC: 79-11138.

POLLOCK, JOSEPH J. 1977. Search Properties of Printed and Machine-Readable Files. In: Fry, Bernard M.; Shepherd, Clayton A., comps. Information Management in the 1980s: Proceedings of the American Society for Information Science 40th Annual Meeting: Volume 14; 1977 September 26–October 1; Chicago, IL. White Plains, NY: Knowledge Industry Publications, Inc.; 1977. Microfiche, fiche 6, frame F14, 24x reduction. (Abstract appears in hard copy on page 23). ISSN: 0044-7870; ISBN: 0-914236-12-1; LC: 64-8303.

POWELL, RONALD R. 1978. An Investigation of the Relationships between Quantifiable Reference Service Variables and Reference Performance in Public Libraries. Library Quarterly. 1978 January; 48(1): 1-19. ISSN: 0024-2519; UMI: 77-9147.

PREECE, SCOTT E.; WILLIAMS, MARTHA E. 1980. Software for the Searcher's Workbench. In: Benenfeld, Alan; Kazlauskas, Edward John, eds. Communicating Information: Proceedings of the American Society for Information Science 43rd Annual Meeting: Volume 17; 1980 October 5–10; Anaheim, CA. White Plains, NY: Knowledge Industry Publications, Inc.; 1980. 403-405. ISSN: 0044-7870; ISBN: 0-914236-73-3; LC: 64-8303; CODEN: PAISDQ.

ROBBIN, ALICE. 1977. The Pre-Acquisition Process: A Strategy for Locating and Acquiring Machine-Readable Data. Drexel Library Quarterly. 1977 January; 13(1): 21-42. ISSN: 0012-6160.

ROSSON, MICHAEL L.; ATHERTON, PAULINE. 1979. Part V: Online Searching Using Free Text or Controlled Vocabulary; 1970-1978: An Analyzed and Annotated Bibliography. In: Atherton, Pauline. Online Searching of ERIC: Impact of Free Text or Controlled Vocabulary Searching on the Design of the ERIC Data Base. Syracuse, NY: ERIC Clearinghouse on Information Resources; 1979. 1-39. (Chapter in a technical report). ERIC: ED 180431.

RUSH, JAMES E. 1978. Handling Chemical Structure Information. In: Williams, Martha E., ed. Annual Review of Information Science and Technology: Volume 13. White Plains, NY: Knowledge Industry Publications, Inc.; 1978. 209-262. ISSN: 0066-4200; ISBN: 0-914236-21-0; LC: 66-25096; CODEN: ARISBc.

SHILL, HAROLD B. 1980. Open Stacks and Library Performance. College & Research Libraries. 1980 May; 41(3): 220-226. ISSN: 0010-0870.

SLAVENS, THOMAS P., ed. 1978. Informational Interviews and Questions. Metuchen, NJ: Scarecrow Press; 1978. 154p. ISBN: 0-8108-1102-2; LC: 77-18502.

SMETANA, F. O. 1974. Mapping Individual Logical Processes in Information Searching. Research Triangle Park, NC: North Carolina Science and Technology Research Center; 1974 November. 24p. (NASA Report no. N75-19074). NTIS: N75-19074/4GA.

SMITH, SALLYE WRYE. 1976. Venn Diagramming for On-Line Searching. Special Libraries. 1976 November; 67(11): 510-517. ISSN: 0038-6723; ERIC: EJ 148437.

SPENCER, HERBERT; REYNOLDS, LINDA. 1977. Directional Signing and Labelling in Libraries and Museums: A Review of Current Theory and Practice. London, England: Royal College of Art Readability of

Print Research Unit; 1977. 117p. (TRC Report no. T78-6187; BLRD Report no. 5415).

STANDERA, O. R. 1978. Some Thoughts on Online Systems: The Searcher's Part and Plight. In: Brenner, Everett H., comp. The Information Age in Perspective: Proceedings of the American Society for Information Science 41st Annual Meeting: Volume 15; 1978 November 13-17; New York, NY: White Plains, NY: Knowledge Industry Publications, Inc.; 1978. 322-325. ISSN: 0044-7870; ISBN: 0-914236-22-9; LC: 64-8303; CODEN: PAISDQ.

STEVENS, MARY ELIZABETH. 1974. Strategies for Organizing and Searching. In: Fenichel, Carol, ed. Changing Patterns in Information Retrieval. Washington, DC: American Society for Information Science; 1974. 47-79. ISBN: 0-87715-106-7; LC: 66-29616.

STIBIC, VLADO. 1980. Influence of Unlimited Ranking on Practical Online Search Strategy. Online Review. 1980 September; 4(3): 273-279. ISSN: 0309-314X.

STYCH, F. S. 1966. The Flow Chart Method. RQ. 1966 Summer; 5(4): 14-17. ISSN: 0033-7072.

STYCH, F. S. 1967. The Flow Chart Method and Heraldic Enquiries. RQ. 1967 Summer; 6(4): 169-174. ISSN: 0033-7072.

STYCH, F. S. 1972. Decision Factors in Search Strategy. RQ. 1972 Winter; 12(2): 143-147. ISSN: 0033-7072.

SWENSON, SALLY. 1965. Flow Chart on Library Searching Techniques. Special Libraries. 1965 April; 56(4): 239-242. ISSN: 0038-6723.

TAGLIACOZZO, RENATA; ROSENBERG, LAWRENCE; KOCHEN, MANFRED. 1970. Access and Recognition: From Users' Data to Catalogue Entries. Journal of Documentation (U.K.) 1970 September; 26(3): 230-249. ISSN: 0022-0418.

VAN CAMP, ANN. 1979. Effective Search Analysts. Online. 1979 April; 3(2): 18-20. ISSN: 0146-5422.

VORESS, HUGH E. 1963. Searching Techniques in the Literature of the Sciences. College & Research Libraries. 1963 May; 24(3): 2u9-212. ISSN: 0010-0870.

WAGERS, ROBERT. 1980. Reference and Information Service: The Inner Game. Wilson Library Bulletin. 1980 May; 54(9): 561-567. ISSN: 0043-5651.

WANGER, JUDITH. 1977. Multiple Database Use: The Challenge of the Database Selection Process. Online. 1977 October; 1(4): 35-41. ISSN: 0146-5422.

WANGER, JUDITH. 1979. Evaluation of the Online Search Process: A Preliminary Report: [Proceedings of the] 3rd International Online Information Meeting; 1979 December 4-6; London, England. Oxford, England: Learned Information (Europe), Ltd.; 1979. 1-11. ISBN: 0-904933-21-0.

WANGER, JUDITH. 1980. Evaluation of the Online Search Process: Paper presented at the National Online Information Meeting; 1980 March 25-27; New York, NY. 10p. ERIC: ED 190143.

WEIL, CHERIE B. 1968. Automatic Retrieval of Biographical Reference Books. Journal of Library Automation. 1968 December; 1(4): 239-249. ISSN: 0022-2240.

WILLIAMS, MARTHA E.; PREECE, SCOTT E. 1977. Data Base Selector for Network Use: A Feasibility Study. In: Fry, Bernard M.; Shepherd,

Clayton A., comps. Information Management in the 1980s: Proceedings of the American Society for Information Science 40th Annual Meeting: Volume 14; 1977 September 26–October 1; Chicago, IL. White Plains, NY: Knowledge Industry Publications, Inc.; 1977. Microfiche, fiche 10, frame C13, 24x reduction. (Abstract appears in hard copy on page 34). ISSN: 0044-7870; ISBN: 0-914236-12-1; LC: 64-8303.

WILLIAMS, MARTHA E.; PREECE, SCOTT E. 1980. Elements of a Distributed Transparent Information Retrieval System. In: Benenfeld, Alan R.; Kazlauskas, Edward John, eds. Communicating Information: Proceedings of the American Society for Information Science 43rd Annual Meeting: Volume 17; 1980 October 5–10; Anaheim, CA. White Plains, NY: Knowledge Industry Publications, Inc.; 1980. 401–402. ISSN: 0044-7870; ISBN: 0-914236-73-3; LC: 64-8303; CODEN: PAISDQ.

WILLIAMS, MARTHA E.; PREECE, SCOTT E. 1981. A Mini-Transparent System Using an Alpha Microprocessor. In: Williams, Martha E.; Hogan, Thomas H., comps. Proceedings of the National Online Meeting; 1981 March 24–26; New York, NY. Medford, NJ: Learned Information, Inc.; 1981. 499–502. ISBN: 0-938734-02-4.

6 Online Information Retrieval Systems

DONALD T. HAWKINS
Bell Laboratories

INTRODUCTION

More than ten years of dialup online information retrieval service have passed. In the online retrieval area, much developmental activity occurred during 1967-1972 (BOURNE, 1980; SUMMIT, 1980a). In 1967, Lockheed Missiles and Space Co. (now also known as Lockheed Information Systems) inaugurated remote terminals for online retrieval at the Ames Research Center of the National Aeronautics and Space Administration (NASA) and at NASA's headquarters in Washington, DC. During the next few years similar activities took place concurrently at the National Library of Medicine (NLM) and at System Development Corp. (SDC). Apparently the first dialup service was NLM's MEDLINE (Medical Literature Analysis and Retrieval System Online), inaugurated on October 29, 1971 (MCCARN & LEITER). Lockheed and SDC let commercial contracts for online retrieval service in 1972, and Mead Data Central, Inc., offered access in the early 1970s to the *Psychological Abstracts* database with its PADAT (*Psychological Abstracts* Direct Access Terminal) system. Online retrieval has been in the forefront of the unprecedented activity and technological advance in the library and information science world. PEMBERTON arbitrarily chose the date of the Online-'80 conference—November 1980—as the tenth anniversary of online retrieval. (The true date is impossible to determine because of the many concurrent events occurring as online retrieval developed.)

Many software features of the early systems still exist virtually unchanged, but today's powerful enhancements, such as online document ordering, truncation in free-text searching, and 1200-baud searching via the public networks, were then far in the future. The databases available then comprised one or two dozen instead of today's hundreds. Although online retrieval was seen as a useful technique for some libraries, it was often regarded as merely a supplement to standard manual information retrieval techniques. Others, however, saw its potential:

> ...the movement toward rapid interactive access to major public and commercial databases is now very strong, and it will probably not be many years before satisfying experience with this mode of information access will help it become not merely an experimental innovation but the standard means of using centrally (or regionally) held data.

> Preface, *ARIST* (1972)

From its small beginnings, online searching has become an indispensable tool; it is now solidly established in academic, industrial, government, and (recently) public libraries. Its growth in the past ten years has been phenomenal, and its success is illustrated by the publication of an article about it in the prestigious business periodical, *Fortune* (KIECHEL). M. E. WILLIAMS (1978) briefly reviewed the state of the art as of late 1977 and identified several trends for the future. Among these were a more transparent user interface and the disappearance of software differences among systems (see the section on The User Interface).

The first mention of today's well-known online retrieval systems in *ARIST* was by BERUL in Volume 4; he gave a brief description of DIALOG and ORBIT (Online Retrieval of Bibliographic Information Time-Shared). Online systems have been the subject of several chapters in succeeding *ARIST* volumes. Most recently, MCCARN (1978) reviewed the literature up to about 1977 in Volume 13. WANGER (1979a) reviewed education and training for online systems in Volume 14. This chapter focuses on the major developments since McCarn's review.

The rapid spread of online retrieval systems has been paralleled by a concurrent growth in the literature. HAWKINS (1980d) publishes an annual bibliography on the subject in *Online Review;* through 1979, the entries totaled more than 1,700. A concatenated bibliography, containing the material in the original bibliography and the first three annual updates, was recently published by Learned Information, Inc. (HAWKINS, 1980c). The bibliometric characteristics of the literature of online retrieval were studied by HAWKINS (1978a). He also identified the major journals and authors in the field. At the time of his study, articles on online retrieval were dispersed among many library and information science journals; today they are concentrated in the three journals dedicated to this field: *Online, Database*, and *Online Review*.

The continuing popularity of online retrieval in the literature is shown by the number of recent major works on the topic. A recent monograph edited by HOOVER (1980a) contains a wealth of useful information, primarily for library managers who may be unfamiliar with the topic. HALL (1977) wrote a sourcebook on online searching that is a detailed treatment of the subject and an excellent reference work. It includes descriptions of the major online systems and a listing of available databases. A recent textbook on online searching by HENRY ET AL. is a thorough treatment at the tutorial level. A brief history is included, as well as a chapter on the management of search services. The book is enhanced by numerous examples and seven appendices that give examples of searches on major systems. Many of the examples are taken from European search systems. A new journal, *SCIENCE & TECHNOLOGY LIBRARIES*, began publication in 1980, and its first issue was devoted to planning for online search services in libraries. The *Journal of the American Society for Information Science* (*JASIS*) recently inaugurated a "Perspectives" section that contains tutorial articles on subjects of current interest in information science. The first section had five articles on online searching (CRAWFORD & REES). Finally, in a monograph based on a series of interviews with online searchers, ATHERTON & CHRISTIAN relate many of the searchers' experiences. Although this work is somewhat dated, it is still useful for those who are contemplating the introduction of online services because of its case-history approach.

Conferences are a recent addition to the online information retrieval scene. Probably the first conference devoted solely to online retrieval was held in Pittsburgh in 1977 (KENT & GALVIN). More recently, commercial organizations have entered the conference area (BRENNER, 1980). The International Online Meeting in London (annually since 1977) and the National Online Meeting in New York (1980) were both sponsored by Learned Information. Online, Inc. sponsored Online-'79 and Online-'80. All these conferences drew large numbers of attendees.

In 1977 the major vendors of bibliographic online retrieval services already mentioned were joined by Bibliographic Retrieval Services, Inc. (BRS). The Canadian Online Enquiry (CAN/OLE) service is used primarily in Canada and is operated by the Canadian Institute for Scientific and Technical Information (CISTI). QL Systems (R. CRAWFORD), of Kingston, Ontario, offers access to about 35 databases, some of which are bibliographic. ALLEY ET AL. review the history and development of online services in Canada. (For a discussion of other online retrieval vendors, see the section on The European Scene.) BAHR (1980a) reviews the three major nongovernment U.S. online service vendors: Lockheed Information Systems, SDC, and BRS.

For the most part, bibliographic online information retrieval vendors have spent the past decade in developing software and in acquiring databases. Recently some of these vendors have been acquired by other organizations. SDC was acquired by Burroughs, Inc., and BRS was bought by Information Handling Services, itself a subsidiary of Indian Head, Inc. It is too early to tell what effect these changes will have on the future of the online retrieval business, but they do show that it has caught the eye of some large concerns that seem to see a significant potential for long-range financial growth. M. E. WILLIAMS (1981b) summarizes the mergers and acquisitions that have occurred recently as well as the databases brought online during 1980.

The rest of this chapter discusses developments in bibliographic and non-bibliographic databases and systems, the user interface, search service management, training and education of searchers, the European scene, and other issues. The emphasis is on bibliographic retrieval systems. Generally, coverage is limited to the period since the reviews by McCarn and Wanger. Bibliographic utilities and cataloging systems (such as OCLC, Inc.) are not covered.

BIBLIOGRAPHIC DATABASES

A wealth of bibliographic information is available online, and more becomes available each month (CHRISTIAN; SHENTON). The number of databases available through Lockheed, SDC, BRS, and NLM now totals well over 200; Lockheed alone has over 100 databases online. M. E. WILLIAMS (1980; 1981b) reports a dramatic increase in the number of databases available online in both 1979 and 1980. With so much information, the searcher sometimes has difficulty deciding which vendor to use and which database to access first. Further, many searches are interdisciplinary, often requiring several databases and possibly more than one vendor. An online database of databases, or subject index, can therefore be very useful. Online indexes have been developed by Lockheed (DIALINDEX), SDC [Database Index (DBI)], and BRS (CROSS). To use these systems, the searcher typically enters a Boolean expression that is evaluated against the inverted files of databases chosen by the searcher. (Lockheed, BRS, and SDC allow a group of files to be selected by subject if the searcher wishes.) The advantage of online indexes is that a search can be performed on the latest version of the inverted files of several databases quickly and conveniently. ANTONY describes DBI in some detail; DOLAN (1980) does the same for CROSS and compares it with DBI. DIALINDEX, being newer, does not seem to have been described in the literature yet.

Printed database directories and indexes are available. The most comprehensive and detailed is the one compiled by WILLIAMS ET AL. and published by ASIS. Now in its second edition, this directory lists 528 online and publicly available databases. Information about each is presented in eight categories, such as availability, charges, subject matter, and user aids. Indexes by name, subject, and producer complete the directory. A directory of 116 online bibliographic databases with an appendix of 40 additional databases was published by HALL (1979). Each database is classified as discipline oriented or problem oriented. Subject indexes to the databases are provided by the vendors; one was also published by TEITELBAUM & HAWKINS. WILLIAMS & BRANDHORST (1977; 1978; 1979) have published lists of databases available online, and SILCOFF has done the same for searchers in Canada. Similar lists also appear periodically in *Online Review*.

In addition to search aids issued by the online service vendors and database producers, detailed database descriptions appear regularly in *Database* and *Online*. Because there are so many, not all are mentioned here. Instead, the focus is on some of the general types of bibliographic databases that have recently become prominent. (SHENTON discusses many of the available databases, categorized by broad subject area.)

Newspaper Databases

Competition among newspaper databases has intensified. The established leader has been the New York Times Information Bank. It is excellent for searching for specific names of companies, people, or places, but its software has limitations, particularly with a 300-baud terminal (AVENY). One must also use the Information Bank's thesaurus. Plans have been announced to replace the present software with a new version that will overcome many of the shortcomings. At least four new databases now compete with the Information Bank. Since they are mounted on established systems, searchers will not need to learn additional software commands if they are unfamiliar with the Information Bank. National Newspaper Index (NNI) on DIALOG contains information from not only the *New York Times,* but also the *Wall Street Journal* and the *Christian Science Monitor.* Its companion file, NEWSEARCH, is a first because it is updated daily. (Aveny's paper compares the Information Bank with NNI.) SDC's Newspaper Index (NDEX) has information from seven major U.S. regional newspapers (other than those in NNI). Full-text newspaper databases are beginning to appear, such as that containing the full text of the Toronto *Globe and Mail* (NASH; RHYDEN) and NEXIS, produced by Mead Data Central, Inc., the producers of the full-text legal database LEXIS. HOGAN reviews the three available newspaper databases and the plans for NEXIS.

Legal and Patent Databases

LARSON & WILLIAMS review legal databases in *ARIST,* Volume 15. They give a detailed description of the major online full-text systems [such as LEXIS, JURIS (Justice Retrieval and Inquiry Systems), and WESTLAW] and conclude that the number of legal searching systems and databases will grow. Since their review was written, Lockheed has introduced the Legal Resource Index (LRI). It is the only *bibliographic* database devoted exclusively to the legal field. It contains information from more than 600 law journals and several law newspapers. Because it is accessed through DIALOG, its users need not obtain a special dedicated terminal or learn a new system, as they must with LEXIS and similar systems.

Patent databases are closely allied to legal databases. The major databases containing such information are Derwent's World Patents Index (WPI), available through SDC, and IFI's CLAIMS databases, available through Lockheed. *Chemical Abstracts (CA)* is an important source of chemical patent information, and petroleum patents are in the APIPAT database of the American Petroleum Institute (API). The review of online patent information by KABACK is excellent and thorough. KABACK ET AL. present an in-depth review of APIPAT.

Chemical Databases

Developments in chemical databases continue steadily. Many of these are discussed by BUNTROCK (1979a) in a series of columns in *Database.* A re-

176 DONALD T. HAWKINS

cent advance is the expansion of the chemical dictionary files to include all the substances entered into the *Chemical Abstracts* (*CA*) Registry System since 1972—an important and useful tool for chemical searchers. Lockheed and SDC have extended their online coverage of chemistry back to 1967. Tutorial papers by HULEATT (1979b) and OPPENHEIM on searching the *CA* database are useful for searchers who do not have a chemistry background. Oppenheim's paper contains a helpful and clear explanation of elementary chemical nomenclature and structure diagrams.

Chemical Abstracts Service (CAS) has recently entered the online retrieval arena as a service vendor, having long enjoyed a favorable reputation as a database producer. Its CAS ONLINE service (FARMER & O'HARA) is a substructure searching system; the user enters "screens" of data, and the system responds with the substances that meet the desired criteria. If the user has a graphics terminal, diagrams of the chemical structures can be displayed on the screen. The entire CAS Registry file of over five million compounds will soon be searchable. CAS ONLINE will be useful to organizations that manufacture and use many chemicals; however, the bibliographic files will still have to be used because CAS ONLINE retrieves only abstract numbers and structures.

Medical and Toxicological Databases

NLM's MEDLINE was one of the first online searching systems to become widely available. Many of its initial features are virtually unchanged today, but the system has by no means been stagnant (MCCARN, 1979a; 1979b). Text word searching has been added, a welcome development for those who use MEDLINE infrequently and may have difficulties with strict dependence on the controlled Medical Subject Headings (MeSH) vocabulary. Several databases have been added to the system, including Audiovisuals Online (AVLINE), the Registry of Toxic Effects of Chemical Substances (RTECS), and Toxicology Data Bank (TDB). TDB is an interesting and useful database of both numeric and textual toxicological information (BAWDEN; BAWDEN & JACKSON). BRIDGES reviews the databases that contain medical and toxicological information.

Except for a brief period on SDC, MEDLINE was long available only through NLM. However, BRS included it among the databases on its system, and Lockheed expects to offer it shortly. Searchers are thus entirely freed from the MeSH vocabulary because BRS and Lockheed are free-text indexed systems. BURROWS & KYLE compare MEDLINE searching on NLM and BRS.

Excerpta Medica complements MEDLINE in many cases and overlaps it in others (BLAIR, 1980b; POWELL). It was once available online through Informatics, Inc., and, after a hiatus, it is now accessed through DIALOG.

Other Bibliographic Databases

Online databases have historically concentrated on technical subjects, probably because database producers in those areas pioneered computer-aided publication methods and therefore already possessed a machine-readable product. Early online databases were a byproduct of the publication process. Today online retrieval is an industry in its own right. The available databases are no longer confined to technical areas but have moved into the social sciences and the humanities (the "soft" sciences) (HOCK) and even the popular literature. Magazine Index is one of the first online databases to contain material of interest to the public (SLADE & KELLY). Other online databases in the soft sciences include Art Bibliographies Modern (SHENG), MLA (Modern Language Association) Bibliography (MACKESY), United States Political Science Documents (USPSD) (PILACHOWSKI), and Philosopher's Index. A database of biographical information, the first of its kind, will soon be available on DIALOG.

The energy files on the DOE/RECON (Department of Energy/Remote Console) system may soon be publicly available (WALKER & LUEDKE). At present, there are 23 databases in the system, most of them government sponsored and relating to energy or nuclear technology. The system is maintained at Oak Ridge National Laboratory and is available to DOE, its contractors, and a few other libraries and information centers. Its public availability will be an important addition to the repertoire of databases available.

The intense and ongoing activity in the online bibliographic database area shows no sign of abating. New databases are being offered by the service vendors every month, and existing databases are being changed (WILLIAMS & BRANDHORST, 1979). Further information can be found in recent issues of *Online* and *Database*.

NONBIBLIOGRAPHIC DATABASES

This section presents nonbibliographic databases (such as those containing numeric information) from the viewpoint of the library or information center. Such systems have existed for a long time, particularly in the financial and economic areas, but they have begun to spread into the library world only recently. Interest in them by information professionals is growing rapidly, and even though the systems originally were designed for end users, nonbibliographic online services are beginning to appear in corporate libraries and information centers. Because nonbibliographic services were designed for specific markets, there are some important differences between them and bibliographic ones (WANGER & LANDAU). For example, no single vendor offers access to many nonbibliographic databases; users must deal with a variety of systems, vendors, commands, and contract requirements. There is no "supermarket" system, such as DIALOG, which offers access to several databases in a wide variety of subjects. Since many nonbibliographic systems are highly specialized, their market is small and their minimum charges are high. The searcher usually needs a thorough knowledge of the subject to use a nonbibliographic system intelligently; therefore, the end user performs much of the searching on nonbibliographic databases.

Information on nonbibliographic systems appears in various sources, many of which are newsletters or specialized reports. Relatively few papers on them appear in professional journals. Well-attended sessions on nonbibliographic online systems were held at the 1979 ASIS National Meeting and at Online-'79. Presentations by CONGER and by ROBBIN at the ASIS meeting contain noteworthy discussions of users' needs. A symposium on problems in the retrieval of numeric data was held at the fall 1979 meeting of the American Chemical Society; papers by CARTER and HAWKINS (1980e) describe some problems associated with numeric data retrieval and some possible solutions. An "online handbook" (PESTEL & RUBIN) would satisfy many of today's numeric data needs, particularly in the physical sciences. It would not only allow rapid lookup of numeric data, but it would also allow one to locate a substance according to desired properties.

LUEDKE ET AL. reviewed nonbibliographic databases in *ARIST*, Volume 12. Since then, Cuadra Associates, Inc., an independent consulting firm, has conducted a series of seminars on them and has done much to promote awareness of these systems in the library and information science community (*INFORMATION MANAGER*). Cuadra's *Directory of Online Databases*, edited by LANDAU ET AL., lists approximately 600 databases from more than 90 online vendors and contains information on both bibliographic and nonbibliographic databases. They are characterized as either "reference" (bibliographic or referral) or "source" (numeric, textual-numeric, properties, or full-text) databases. Data on producer, online service vendor, and content are provided, and so are several useful indexes. The directory is updated quarterly. A list of nonbibliographic databases online also appears periodically in *Online Review*.

The NIH-EPA (National Institutes of Health–Environmental Protection Agency) Chemical Information System (CIS) has grown from one or two databases of spectroscopic information to a full-fledged textual and numeric information system of great interest to chemists. At the heart of CIS is the Structure and Nomenclature Search System (SANSS). With it, a user can identify a substance from its name, structure, formula, or *CA* Registry Number. SANSS can also report where in the CIS files information on the substance can be found. Alternatively, the user can enter a numeric data file (mass spectroscopy, for example), identify a substance, and then use SANSS to obtain further data. Spectroscopic, toxicological, and crystallographic information are available on CIS. A recent and useful addition to CIS is a database containing items on chemicals from the *Federal Register*. The inclusion of *CA* Registry Numbers considerably enhances the utility of this database. BERNSTEIN & ANDREWS, HELLER & MILNE (1979; 1980), HELLER ET AL., and MILNE & HELLER describe CIS and its databases. We have not yet seen papers describing users' experiences with CIS; these would be useful and informative.

Some other useful online nonbibliographic systems include the ManLabs-NPL (National Physical Laboratory) Materials Databank (produced by Man-Labs, Inc., Cambridge, MA) (HAWKINS, 1979; KAUFMAN & NESOR), containing thermochemical and phase diagram information on a wide variety of inorganic chemicals, and LABSTAT, produced by the Bureau of Labor Statistics (MENDELSSOHN; TRIMBLE). LABSTAT contains data on price indexes and unemployment statistics, for example, in the form of time series; the system is expected to be publicly available through NTIS (National Technical Information Service) in the near future.

The Dow-Jones News Retrieval (DJNR) service combines numeric and textual information on stock prices with news from the Dow-Jones news wire (BEMENT; MOULTON). DJNR combines continuous updating (material is entered within 90 seconds of its appearance on the news wire) with retrospective retrieval. Unfortunately, Boolean capabilities and many of the powerful features of other systems are not yet available on DJNR.

One interesting type of online nonbibliographic database is the technology information exchange, such as Control Data's TECHNOTEC (JONES) and Dr. Dvorkovitz Associates' Licensable Technology. These contain descriptions of technology available for license.

THE USER INTERFACE

Much research has been done on the interface between the user and the bibliographic online search system. Under this broad heading fall not only such important issues as the need for an intermediary but also the practical methods of developing a successful search strategy, the conduct of the search (HOOVER, 1980b), the quality of the database, and the conduct of the reference interview between the searcher and the user. The user interface is crucial to the success of the search, whether the "user" is the searcher who acts as the intermediary or is the one who needs the information. SALTON reviews online retrieval systems from a theoretical point of view and describes some of the improvements to the user interface that are discussed below. BOYLE & MILLER compare some of the software features of an in-house system developed at Marathon Oil Co. with SDC's ORBIT. They conclude that many of the features of the commercial system, although useful, may not be needed in an in-house system that will be used by only a few searchers. For example, set history display would require an impractical amount of development effort to implement. Although their in-house searching system was not as versatile as ORBIT, its performance was acceptable.

End-User Searching

Most bibliographic online searches today are done by an intermediary rather than by the end user for good reasons. The substantial procedural differences among systems and the structural differences among databases seem to require the skills of a person who can devote much time to mastering the techniques of online searching. Financial considerations often dictate the use of an intermediary who, presumably, can search more efficiently as learning occurs. P. W. WILLIAMS (1977) summarizes the arguments for and against the use of an intermediary and shows that there can be a severe cost penalty when an intermediary is not used. In common with many other searchers, he concludes that the best mode of operation is to have the intermediary and the end user work together on the search. KRENTZ discusses some pitfalls for the end user and arrives at the same conclusion.

MEADOW (1979a) compares online searching with computer programming and finds many behavioral similarities. In its early days, programming was done only by those who were closely involved with the hardware, using low-level or assembly languages. The subsequent development of high-level languages, such as COBOL and FORTRAN, has opened up program writing to end users, leaving the more difficult tasks to the system programmers and specialized personnel. Meadow forecasts a similar scenario for online searching; the CONIT (Connector for Networked Information Transfer) and IIDA (Individual Instruction for Data Access) systems (MARCUS & REINTJES; MEADOW, 1979b) are steps toward searching by the end user.

CONIT and IIDA function as intermediaries between the searcher and the system, interpreting error messages, performing the logon procedures, changing files and systems, and diagnosing inefficient searching. Although they are still under development and are somewhat elementary, they represent an important advance in the user–system interface and show promise.

Subject switching (NIEHOFF & KWASNY; NIEHOFF ET AL.), another aid to the user, is an attempt to merge the thesauri, or vocabularies, from several databases and to provide synonym controls. The user enters the desired term, and the system responds with a list of synonymous terms and an indication of the source vocabularies. The vocabulary subject switching system (VSS) at Battelle can also generate statistics on its performance and can handle stems and variant spellings.

A third approach toward removing the barriers for the end user has been taken by DOSZKOCS (1978a; 1978b) and DOSZKOCS & RAPP, who have developed an interface to MEDLINE that eliminates the command structure of the software. The system, called Current Information Transfer in English (CITE), processes the search request, identifies the terms, performs a weighted logic search, and presents the ranked output to the user. The searcher can provide dynamic relevance feedback to the system for automatic search modification. Systems such as CITE will have a major effect on online retrieval as they become fully developed.

Minicomputers and microcomputers have had a profound and far-reaching impact on our lives, extending even into the home, and they are affecting online retrieval as well (BLAIR, 1980a; BUTLER). Systems based on these computers are being developed by information brokers and other organizations to do such things as unify the software of different retrieval systems (e.g., translate DIALOG commands into ORBIT format) and standardize logon procedures (P. W. WILLIAMS, 1979; 1980). These chip-based systems will eventually free today's searchers from the burden of learning several sets of software commands to access all the databases they need.

Database Quality

Today's many bibliographic online databases vary widely in quality. Some have a well-controlled vocabulary; others are completely free text. Spelling errors, especially in free-text databases, can cause important references to be missed because the online searching software uses a character string-matching algorithm. BOURNE (1977) studied 11 databases and found that the frequency of spelling errors ranged from 23% for ABI/INFORM to 0.5% for BIOSIS (BioSciences Information Service). (Since Bourne's work, ABI/INFORM has regenerated the database with a controlled vocabulary and has presumably eliminated many of the errors.) According to Bourne, many searchers place the blame for spelling errors on the search vendor instead of on the database producer, where it belongs. The vendor is precluded from making changes to the databases because of copyright regulations, and the database producers are not motivated to correct errors because of the labor and expense involved. Therefore, the problem is not likely to disappear soon. Some database producers have developed error-checking and validation systems; ZAMORA describes the one in use at CAS. Such systems cannot rectify past errors, but they will help to ensure that future entries will be reliable. NORTON cites some errors in databases and calls for a consumer movement among online searchers to express dissatisfaction to the producers.

Evaluation of Searches and Searchers

As far as the end user is concerned, evaluation of any search, manual or online, seems simple: was the desired information retrieved or not? However, other factors are involved—e.g., the cost of the search, the speed of the response, and the form in which the results were presented. A typical evaluative study usually involves a questionnaire and tabulation of the results. (FOSDICK and JAHODA ET AL. have published examples.) BLAIR (1980a) discusses some methods for evaluating online searches and gives sample questionnaires. Most published surveys give similar results: the respondents are pleased with online retrieval, especially the speed with which the information is obtained, the low cost, and the power and flexibility of the systems.

Evaluation of searchers is more difficult and more subjective than evaluation of searches because a person's performance is measured. Certification of searchers has been the subject of some debate, but most searcher evaluation is probably done by conventional methods of performance appraisal. The State University of New York (SUNY) has developed a screening test and training program for searchers (DOLAN & KREMIN). VAN CAMP lists ten desirable traits for a good online searcher. In an attempt to quantify the learning experience of online searchers, FENICHEL (1978; 1980; 1981) made a detailed analysis of searches done by persons with different levels of experience. Her study considered general familiarity with online searching and familiarity with the database. Novice searchers did surprisingly well, and searchers who had the most searching experience and the most database experience achieved the highest recall. Fenichel also found an enormous variation in searching behavior, which made it difficult to interpret some of her results.

The Reference Interview

For the end user a search usually begins with an interview with the search intermediary. Although there is a sizeable body of literature on the reference interview, interviewing techniques have come under renewed scrutiny. MCCARN (1978) devoted a section of his review to the role of the intermediary and discussed the part played by the reference interview. He noted that the intermediary has been thrust into prominence in the library world largely as a result of the emergence of online retrieval. AUSTER & LAWTON, in a particularly interesting study, analyzed the negotiation process for online searches by recording 44 pre-search interviews. They then studied the transcripts, identified verbal and nonverbal behavior, and arrived at a preliminary model of the process. Although their work was hampered by the lack of videotapes of the interviews (which would have added the messages of body language to the study), it is a valuable study of the reference interviewing process. CORSON also recorded searching sessions and derived a general model of a search. She concludes that the mood or tone of the conversation plays a major part in a successful search interview. An informal approach helps to build trust and confidence between the searcher and the user. KNAPP has studied the reference interview from a more practical view, citing many examples of typical interviewing strategies and techniques. Among these are the use of open-ended questions, Venn diagramming, conceptualization, and analysis. She rightly concludes that the reference interview in the computer-based setting is not radically different from many of the standard techniques that have been used in libraries for years.

Use of Online Systems in Reference Work

Online services are moving out of the specialized information retrieval units of many libraries and are appearing in the general reference service. In this setting, they are used for answering short queries, verifying references for interlibrary loans (ILL), checking authors' names, and a host of similar tasks. SWEETLAND describes these uses in a small special library that provides a high level of service to its users. KUSACK examines the pros and cons of integrating online searching with traditional reference service vs. keeping it a visible, separate activity. He advocates a large measure of integration and makes several recommendations for the establishment of the service. KLUGMAN describes the issues in the use of online retrieval at the General Library of the University of California at Berkeley (UCB). She discusses the interview, marketing of the service, and the integration of online systems with traditional reference services. Some of the problems that must be faced in a large library such as that of UCB are human ones, in which some reference librarians may feel uneasy with computers and terminals. There are also economic issues, such as charging for searches and paying for training, as well as interaction with the users and document delivery. Klugman is optimistic about the future of online retrieval systems and the role of the intermediary in the academic library.

Search Strategy

Search strategy continues to be popular in the online literature. It is the means by which the searcher communicates with the system and is often the key to a successful search. Columns by BUNTROCK (1979a), DOLAN (1979), HAWKINS & MENDENHALL, and PADIN in *Online* and *Database* are useful for searchers who are seeking hints, tips, or shortcuts. Padin's column, "Computer Ease," usually explains how the computer treats certain types of search statements and new software features. The column by Hawkins and Mendenhall, "I Learned About Searching From That...," offers shortcuts, pitfalls, and unusual strategies; Buntrock's "Chemcorner" deals with online chemical searching, and Dolan's "Offlines" treats miscellaneous topics. Contributions to these columns are welcome and actively solicited. Other helpful and practical search strategy techniques are described by ADAMS. MARSHALL stresses the need for searchers to review the output of a search and lists 31 pitfalls.

In formulating search strategy, one is often faced with the choice between free-text terms and a controlled vocabulary. Happily, the searcher usually has a choice. Some databases (MEDLINE is a prime example) that formerly allowed only controlled vocabulary searching now allow free text as well. Case studies of free-text vs. controlled vocabulary searching have been made by ANTONY ET AL., CALKINS, and MARKEY ET AL. Markey et al. found that free-text searches on ERIC had higher recall, and controlled vocabulary searches had higher precision; a combination of both is the preferred approach. Based on these results, Markey et al. suggest some new searching aids for ERIC, such as an online rotated descriptor or identifier display and some linkage between controlled and uncontrolled vocabulary terms.

There are three basic approaches to search strategy: 1) "building block," 2) "successive fractions," and 3) "citation pearl growing" (BUNTROCK, 1979b; MARKEY & ATHERTON). In the building-block approach, concepts are developed separately, then combined with Boolean logic to produce the result. The successive-fraction search starts with a large set on what may be a somewhat vague subject and successively intersects additional concepts to narrow the search to the desired size and specificity. Finally, the citation pearl-growing method begins with one citation that is either known or has been found in the database. Its indexing terms are examined and "recycled" into the search to retrieve additional citations. This process can be repeated as often as desired until the strategy is formulated. Most searches probably use a combination of these techniques.

Another approach to search strategy was taken by BATES (1979a; 1979b). In an excellent pair of papers, she defined 29 search tactics and 17 idea tactics. A search tactic is a move made to further a search. Bates classified them into four broad categories: 1) monitoring tactics, 2) file structure tactics, 3) search formulation tactics, and 4) term tactics. Idea tactics help to generate new ideas or to solve problems that are encountered during the search. They were grouped into "idea-generating" or "pattern-breaking" tactics. These two articles represent an unusually detailed and thorough analysis of the search process and the interaction between the user and the online system.

Information needs today are becoming increasingly interdisciplinary. The searcher must therefore be prepared to search several databases and to be comfortable with switching frequently from one to the other. Multi-database searching calls for special techniques and can present several problems for searchers (HAWKINS, 1978b).

SEARCH SERVICE MANAGEMENT

Organizing and managing an online searching service continues to be a popular topic in the literature. HAWKINS (1980b) reviewed this area in detail in a chapter of Hoover's guide to online services, and SEBA edits a regular column in *Online* entitled "Management Outpost." HOOVER (1979) published a useful article giving practical advice and experiences on organizing and managing an online searching service in an academic library.

In many environments, the decision to institute online services is made only after a formal proposal is prepared by those desiring the service. MARTIN outlines the structure, content, and presentation of a typical proposal. In an excellent paper, PENSYL & WOODFORD relate the history of the online searching service at the Massachusetts Institute of Technology (MIT) libraries. Service was first offered locally at the branch libraries, and then it was centralized. Now, some consideration is again being given to a partial decentralization. The paper by Pensyl and Woodford is a detailed and thorough description of the management and practices of the MIT search service and provides a good model for anyone who is considering the introduction of online retrieval in a large library system. For those in federal libraries, BERGER & CERUTTI describe the special policies that must be followed.

Online information retrieval systems first appeared in special, technical, and academic libraries. More recently, they have begun to be used in public libraries. Their acceptance there is growing as more databases of interest to the general public, such as Magazine Index and National Newspaper Index, become available. The issue of costs is usually more important in public libraries than in other types because of the limited public library budgets. Several programs using grants and similar types of funding have helped to introduce online services into public libraries. JOHNSON describes the online retrieval program at the San Jose, CA, public library, which was one of the original libraries in the well-known DIALIB project. WATERS & MANN discuss the online services at the Dallas, TX, public library. They offer access to DIALOG and ORBIT as well as to a nonbibliographic database on bills before the Texas state legislature. Although they charge users of the service, they hope that they can soon offer it at a reduced cost or at no cost.

Impact of Online Systems on Libraries

Rarely does a technique enter a field and completely revolutionize it in as short a period as online retrieval has done. Papers that describe its impact in the library continue to appear. HAWKINS (1980f) describes the first six years of online searching in the Bell Laboratories Library Network. Online systems were directly responsible for several major operational changes there.

WERNER surveyed more than 700 health science libraries in the United States and Canada that were using MEDLINE. She also found that online systems had a major impact and that many libraries had instituted fees for the service (see the section on Costs and Statistics below). PIERMATTI & BOLLES describe the planning of the online service at a state university and the fee structure. Online retrieval at Rutgers University is offered to all New Jersey citizens as well as to the faculty and students at the university. The effects of online retrieval systems on Congress (GREGORY), the Executive Office of the President (KADEC & MANCHER), and a public library in England (CONVEY) have also been described. M. E. WILLIAMS (1977) reviews the National Program for Library and Information Services [proposed by the National Commission on Libraries and Information Science (NCLIS)] as it relates to online services and their impact on libraries. With online systems making their mark on information retrieval, libraries must become fully familiar with them and their vendors. BLUE and PLOSKER & SUMMIT, in helpful papers, list some questions to be asked in the selection of a vendor.

Online retrieval is also affecting libraries in terms of marketing their services (BAHR, 1980b; SHAPIRO) by thrusting marketing techniques into prominence. For many if not most library users, computer retrieval of information is new, and they must be made aware of its potential. A carefully orchestrated marketing program can benefit an online retrieval service, but it takes time, and its cost may be significant. Word-of-mouth advertising by satisfied customers is very effective, and online demonstrations play a major role.

Equipment

Historically, 300-baud terminals have been widely used for online searching. Since they are usually acoustically coupled and hence do not require an external modem, they offer portability and ease of use. Only a telephone line is needed to establish a connection. However, 300-baud terminals are not as efficient or as cost-effective for browsing online thesauri or for obtaining preliminary search results. With the development of modems that can operate at 1200 baud and the establishment of 1200-baud nodes in many major cities on both the Tymnet and Telenet networks, searching at the higher communication speed has spread and is becoming more popular. In a well-known paper, STEWART compared 300-baud and 1200-baud searching. He found that average connect time per search increased, but the number of offline prints decreased when searches were done at 1200 baud. He also observed that searchers will queue up for the 1200-baud terminal even when a 300-baud one is available. Similar experiences are described by BLAIR (1980c).

WITIAK ET AL. developed an interesting application of telephone conferencing for online searching. Using two terminals and four telephones, they worked out a method of doing an online search when the requester and searcher are at different locations. One pair of telephones is used for voice communication. The other pair connects the searcher's terminal to the online searching system. Then, with an internal conferencing connection, the requester's terminal is "slaved" to the searcher's. The requester's terminal responds simultaneously with the searcher's, and the effect is the same as if the searcher and requester were conducting the search at the same place. SHENTON & LANDSBERG discovered that conference searching at 1200 baud presents problems that do not exist at 300 baud, because of the addition of modems. (Witiak et al. used acoustically coupled terminals.) The addition of an "interface unit" to the configuration allows 1200-baud conference searching. GRAHAM uses the term "simultaneous remote search" in describing conference searching.

Online Ordering and Document Delivery

The wide use of online systems and services has meant that end users have easy access to much more information than before. Most information centers have observed a corresponding increase in their ILL volume and have had to turn to new fulfillment sources to meet the increasing requests (MCKEE & WILLIAMS). The column by COLBERT in *Online* notes sources for obtaining various types of documents.

One of the early online ordering facilities is on the CAN/OLE system (LEBLANC). This service is linked to a central in-house collection of documents. The user isolates a single citation and then can order the corresponding document. The system prepares a request form that is similar to the standard ILL form and sends it to the document-fulfillment organization. One of the files contains the locations of serials in over 250 Canadian libraries. This file is searchable by the user, so that the location of the document (especially if it is in the in-house collection) can be ascertained before the order is placed. LeBlanc reports that 90% of the requests were filled from the in-house collection over an eight-month period.

Online ordering of documents has been available for some time through SDC's Electronic Maildrop service and recently through Lockheed's DIAL-ORDER system (GIBBS & LASZLO). With either system, the user enters an order for documents and directs it by a code to the desired supplier. The order is stored by the search service and retrieved later by the document-fulfillment supplier; all further interaction is then between the requester and the supplier. Both systems differ from CAN/OLE in that the user not only has a wide choice of vendors for fulfillment but also can direct the order to the desired vendor. The CAN/OLE system is linked only to CISTI. These systems are an interesting application of electronic mail (JOSEPHINE).

Costs and Statistics

Many papers on the economics and statistics of online retrieval continue to appear and are welcomed by managers of information retrieval activities. DRINAN reviews the financial management of an online search service and gives a sample budget. With such an emphasis on economics, there is an urgent need for a standard method of collecting and reporting searching data. HAWKINS & BROWN have proposed a standard in which a search is defined in terms of the classical "reference transaction" as the answer to a request, regardless of the number of databases accessed. Although their proposed standard poses a few difficulties, particularly for searches that use offline back files, it is a notable start in the attempt to bring about standardization in the wealth of statistical data that can be generated by an online search service.

Analyzing the cost factors in online searching is not necessarily straightforward, and many elements are easy to overlook. ALMOND & NELSON have proposed a detailed cost model, involving the number of keystrokes in the search statement, the terminal speed, and other factors. Their model is probably too complex for the average searcher to use for a practical estimation of search costs. ELCHESEN published a particularly useful and detailed analysis of costs and reviewed previous studies. The monograph by SAFFADY on the economics of searching covers terminal selection, search aids, and other nonrecurring expenses on a fairly simplistic and tutorial level. HOOVER (1979) compared costs of searches run on three major systems—Lockheed's DIALOG, SDC's ORBIT, and BRS's. SDC's charges were slightly higher than Lockheed's, and BRS's were slightly lower. On the other hand, Lockheed has more databases online, while BRS maintains only a portion of many of its databases online.

Online searching is generally thought to be more cost-effective than manual searching, and several recent studies confirm this (FLYNN ET AL.; KIDD; MAGSON). EAST reviewed the literature in this area. In most studies of online vs. manual searching, online costs are usually measured using data averaged over many searches, and manual costs are estimated. Because the latter are difficult to measure, their estimates vary widely. According to Flynn et al., manual searching can cost up to five or six times as much as online searching. However, their study is somewhat controversial, judging from the comments it generated. FARRADANE questioned their estimates of manual search times, and both he and BLICK suggest that a combination of online and manual searches is necessary for completeness. Blick makes the important point that some of the time saved by online searching must be spent in such tasks as training and reading manuals. The letter by CLEVER-DON presents some data showing that manual searching can be more cost-effective in some circumstances. Clearly, more study is needed.

In contrast to many other services, the cost of online searching has remained remarkably stable. Recently, however, it has been rising as database producers increase their royalty charges. According to BARWISE, royalty charges now account for 20-40% of the direct searching costs, and they may double by 1985. Computing and communications costs may decrease somewhat in the immediate future, but net searching costs will surely increase (see the section on Migration, below). SUMMIT (1980b) presents the issue of costs from the viewpoint of the online service vendor.

EDUCATION AND TRAINING

The education and training of online searchers has assumed an important place in the literature, as shown in a recent *ARIST* chapter (WANGER, 1979a) and a chapter in Hoover's monograph (KUROKI). BELLARDO ET AL. compiled a bibliography on the training of searchers. More recently, the three arenas of training—search service suppliers, database producers, and library schools—were reviewed by BOURNE & ROBINSON, and ROBINSON described the training at the Computerized Information Service of the University of California. The relationship between training and searcher proficiency is being studied for NLM by Cuadra Associates (WANGER, 1979b). HARDY discussed education and training from a database supplier's point of view. She stressed that a knowledge of the loading of the same databases by different search vendors, although of major importance, is a neglected area of training. She believes that basic training in online retrieval should be the province of library schools, that strategy and advanced techniques should be taught by search service vendors, and that database characteristics, including file loading, should be taught by the database producer. Such a training program would be thorough, but it probably would involve more time than a searcher (or organization) would wish to commit. LOWRY describes the content of a course in online retrieval given in an academic institution; HEYER discusses in-house training in a special library.

The training program at the University of Pittsburgh (DUNCAN ET AL.) is well known. Monthly classes attract a spectrum of attendees, from novices to expert searchers who are seeking a refresher course. A locally developed emulator, called TRAINER, simulates DIALOG, ORBIT, and BRS. This keeps online costs reasonable, and each trainee is allowed extensive practice at a terminal. TRAINER has now been installed at Carnegie-Mellon University, where it was received very favorably (CARUSO).

Training by conventional means is possible when the trainees can be assembled in a classroom; when this is not possible, special techniques must be used. Demonstrations and terminal experience are crucial for success. Normal audio communications must be supplemented by video links so that students can see the action at the terminal. In British Columbia, where much of the population is dispersed over a wide area, satellite communication has been used successfully to train searchers in remote areas (SIMMONS). Although this technique has problems, it shows great promise.

THE EUROPEAN SCENE

Online retrieval systems penetrated Europe somewhat later than the United States, and although their growth rate was initially a little slower, it has been rapid in recent years. The conferences sponsored by Learned Information, Ltd., each December in London have done much to increase the awareness of online systems in Great Britain as well as in Europe. A recent addition to the European online scene has been a German conference on online information retrieval, held in Cologne in May 1979 and 1980.

Systems and Databases

At the beginning of European online activity, the major American vendors marketed their services in a more-or-less traditional manner, establishing representatives or field offices in several major European cities. Such activity, of course, continues today. However, in the past two or three years, some European services have been marketed in the United States. BLAISE (British Library Automated Information Service) was exhibited at Online-'79, and one or two French systems were displayed at the 1980 National Online Meeting in New York. Although the amount of searching now being done from America on European systems is probably small, it will increase.

BLAISE (COLLINGE; HOLMES) is interesting because it is not only a retrieval system but also an online cataloging system that uses its own text editor and a document request system for catalog production. Although it is used mainly to produce the British National Bibliography, it is also an important online system for British users who wish to search MEDLINE or MARC (Machine-Readable Cataloging). The Swedish system 3RIP, currently under development (EDSTRÖM & WALLIN; LÖFSTRÖM), shows promise as an online search service. Apparently, it is not yet generally available; published papers do not mention what databases (if any) are loaded on it.

The European Space Agency (ESA) in Frascati, Italy, operates the Information Retrieval Service (IRS), which contains a growing number of databases, including many that are mounted by American vendors. It uses the Quest retrieval software, which was developed from RECON.

European databases are becoming increasingly widespread. Almost half of the databases available on DIALOG in late 1979 were of European origin (TOMBERG, 1979). Tomberg reports that more bibliographic databases are produced in Europe than in the United States, while the reverse is true for nonbibliographic databases. (However, the U.S. databases contain more citations than the European ones.) He attributes the geographic shift in bibliographic databases from the United States to Europe to four factors: 1) the linguistic advantage of Great Britain, 2) the linguistic disadvantage of the other countries, 3) the many international organizations headquartered in Europe, and 4) the inadequate coverage of non-U.S. material by some U.S. databases. Tomberg thinks that more European nonbibliographic databases should be made available online.

Communications

The major barrier to the spread of online retrieval abroad is the high cost of overseas telecommunications. Since European telephone systems are controlled and operated by the governments, costs tend to be higher and protocols more complex. The development of networks for data transmission has improved the situation greatly and has contributed to the spreading and increased use of online retrieval systems (TOMBERG, 1978). The EURONET-DIANE (Direct Information Access Network for Europe) network went into operation in 1980 and is already proving useful (MAHON, 1978a; MAHON, 1978b; RIGG). A similar network, SCANNET, operates in Scandinavia (ABRAHAMSSON). EURONET-DIANE links nine countries, including Great Britain and the European continent, and provides ready access to ESA's IRS system, BLAISE, and other hosts. As of October 1980, there were 23 hosts accessible through EURONET, and several more were imminent. There is much activity in Europe as the European countries are striving to enhance their positions in the online retrieval and communications area. International Packet Switched Service (IPSS), operated by British Telecom (formerly the telecommunication section of the British Post Office), allows communication across the Atlantic in both directions at $20–$30 per hour between nodes. IPSS connects to Tymnet and Telenet, and the connection is not seen by the user. The arrival of Tymnet and Telenet in the United States provided a substantial impetus to online searching in its early days, and IPSS will probably have a similar effect in Great Britain and the spread of European systems into the United States. Some initial experiences in accessing European online retrieval systems from North America have been reported (CLINTON & GRENVILLE).

The growth of EURONET and the imposition of service charges by the European postal, telephone, and telegraph (PTT) organizations on international data transmission are causing concern among the U.S. online retrieval service vendors. In two similar papers, CUADRA and BRENNER (1979) discuss the effect of these charges on online retrieval services. Summit also raised the issue at the 1979 conference of the Institute of Information Scientists (*ONLINE REVIEW*). Because of the higher charges imposed on Europeans who use Tymnet or Telenet, EURONET, which offers access to ESA (a European service), has a competitive advantage. According to Brenner, Cuadra, and Summit, revenues to U.S. service vendors could therefore be reduced, leading to a compensating increase in prices to U.S. customers. They ask, "Since many of the U.S. databases are produced with public funds, should access to them be hindered or limited because of actions taken by foreign governments?" Cuadra suggests several possible strategies, including restricting access to U.S. databases, higher royalties for overseas users, and the formation of a cartel among database producers. At present, the dire predictions of Cuadra and Brenner do not seem to have occurred: the U.S. online service industry is healthy and growing, and although some database royalties have increased, the price of connect time for searching has not increased.

OTHER TOPICS

Economic and Policy Issues

Migration. Online information retrieval originated as a byproduct of the publication process. As abstracts and indexes began to be produced by computer photocomposition and typesetting, the machine-readable version became available for other purposes, including online retrieval. In the early days of machine-readable databases, the printed and online versions coexisted happily. However, as the use of online databases increased, users began to cancel their subscriptions to the printed versions. This phenomenon is termed "migration." It has far-reaching economic implications for database users and online searchers because until now the cost of online databases has been heavily subsidized by their printed counterparts. As migration becomes more severe, pricing will undergo extensive changes so that database producers can remain economically viable. M. E. WILLIAMS (1981a) believes that migration is immaterial to the database industry and that competition between printed and online products is not unusual. She presents a detailed analysis of 13 years of revenue and expense data from one (anonymous) database producer. Between 1968 and 1972, the producer operated at a deficit, reaching the breakeven point in 1972. From 1972 to 1975, profits grew. They then turned down until the breakeven point was reached again in 1979. During the same period, prices for both the printed and online versions of the database were raised, with the online price showing a sharp upturn in 1979. This database has experienced migration, but Williams attributes the decline in profits to a combination of factors. She examines several possible courses of action for the database producer and concludes that the only effective way to reverse the slide in profits is to raise prices. Her paper is an impressive analysis of the economic issues affecting the online database business today and is one of the few based on actual data.

TRUBKIN (1980) analyzes the economics of database publishing and describes some efforts at Data Courier, Inc. (of which she is president) to determine the magnitude of migration for their databases. She illustrates how a 10% inflation rate can cut a healthy profit in half in just three years if revenues remain constant. Migration of only a few subscribers, at today's online rates, has a severe impact on profit. Data Courier's evidence, although fragmentary, shows that migration is not a serious problem yet, but it is beginning to be. A concrete example of migration is the study made at Texas Christian University (TCU) by PFAFFENBERGER & ECHT, in which the printed version of *Science Citation Index* (*SCI*) was cancelled in favor of online access only. Even though the cost of searching *SCI* online is four times higher for nonsubscribers as for subscribers to the printed version, the small use of the printed *SCI* at TCU did not warrant a continued hardcopy publication. Users of the database seemed satisfied with the decision to drop the printed version. If this study signals a major trend, online users can expect to see sharply increased database royalty charges soon.

Database restrictions. BRENNER (1979) and CUADRA have suggested possible methods of restricting access to databases. MOLSTER examines political and other reasons for limiting access and asks if they are necessary. In the final analysis, the overriding concern is economic. Access rights may be restricted to limit competition, to guarantee income to a certain service vendor or producer, or to prevent loss of revenue. Several methods, including access fees, the requirement to purchase the printed version (an answer to the migration problem), and geographical concerns, are used. Molster attributes a myriad of contractual arrangements today to the fast growth of the online industry and speculates that in time only a few types of contracts will be needed. Although he does not provide a definite answer to his question (probably because there is none), he feels that information should be made as widely available as possible.

Copyright. TRUBKIN (1979) notes that online databases, which are copyrighted, may contain information (such as abstracts) that is taken from the copyrighted material of others. She calls this a "copyright quandary" for database publishers and gives a good nonlegal review of the situation.

Fees for service. The issue of fees for online service has been hotly debated during the past few years, but the debate seems to be subsiding. Many libraries have been forced to institute charging schemes because of budgetary limitations; charging algorithms vary widely. COOPER considered both economic and policy issues in fee charging through an examination of online searching as a case study. On the one hand, it can be argued that because most public libraries are supported by tax dollars, information should be available without charge to all who need it. Online retrieval is therefore regarded as simply another tool to be used in fulfilling requests. CRAWFORD & THOMPSON take this approach in a college library. On the other hand, online searching is an expensive service, and each search is tailored to one user and probably does not benefit others. As Cooper points out, the introduction of charges for library services is a radical departure from the past. TEITELBAUM-KRONISH describes the charging scheme at New York University and reports virtually no objections to the fees. The effect of charging on demand was closely studied in the DIALIB project (COOPER & DEWATH) that was conducted in several public libraries in California. Not surprisingly, when fees were introduced, demand fell sharply. HUTSON found the same result with medical users. She also cites similar experiences at several other libraries and information centers. Fees for online searching limit access to information for those who cannot pay. Fees also have a great influence on those who could pay but are unwilling to. Clearly, user education is needed if demand for online retrieval in a fee-for-service environment is to be maintained.

Special Applications of Online Systems

Private files. Private files, mounted by an online service and available for searching only to their owner, are a burgeoning area of online activity. All three major online vendors offer this service, although they differ in the amount of assistance they provide to the user (SWANSON). At present, the file must be submitted to the vendor in properly formatted and machine-readable form. However, BRS and Lockheed offer an online data entry service. SDC will design and create the file for the customer. All of the vendors can transform an existing machine-readable file to their internal format and will do so for a fee. Typically, charges for private file service include a loading fee, a storage fee, a fee for updates, and the usual searching, communications, and offline printing fees. Privacy is ensured by additional password systems and the guarantee of nondisclosure of the client's identity.

Machine-readable output (MRO). Output from online searches can be obtained in machine-readable form, either as magnetic tape analogous to offline prints (HAWKINS, 1980a) or directly from the terminal, using a tape cassette or similar device (HULEATT, 1979a). MRO is useful in the compilation of large bibliographies and avoids the costly, time-consuming, and error-prone data-entry process. Special editing techniques may need to be developed because of the large volume of information involved. Hawkins describes the use of MRO at Bell Laboratories. Duplicate items present in several databases are detected by using the CODEN of the publication along with date and pagination information. Huleatt's method of MRO involves capturing the information as it is transmitted to the terminal using a cassette recorder, and then editing and reformatting it. Unfortunately, this method is too costly for large volumes of information. MRO is a useful and logical extension of online searching capabilities; its main drawback lies in the negotiations required among the user, database producer, and online vendor.

Professional Aspects of Online Searching

Online searching is generally thought to increase the professional status of the searcher, particularly in the bibliographic world of information. It has created new positions in many organizations (STUKENBROKER), and it has enhanced the perception of the searcher in the eyes of the user. For the non-bibliographic database user, it has provided significant new tools, including report generators and data analyzers. The involvement with the computer and its advanced technology, increased productivity, and the power of online systems have all contributed to the increase in job satisfaction and prestige of the searcher. However, in a thought-provoking paper (which won the Best Paper Award at the 1979 National Online Meeting), NIELSEN examines both sides of the professionalism question and applies some sociological models to online searching. He notes that searchers are enthusiastic, not only about the technology but about their role in using it. In the long run, there may be a deprofessionalizing aspect because advancing technology will make access to online systems easier for the end user. The role of the intermediary will probably change from that of practitioner to that of specialist and consultant.

Information brokers. Online retrieval has spawned a host of information brokerage organizations that provide searches to the public for a fee. Most of these organizations consist of one or two individuals but a few are large, well-established firms that have simply integrated online retrieval into their other services. BELLOMY (1977; 1979) describes his experiences, traces the history of information brokers, and speculates that they will spread and that technology will have a major impact on their activities.

User groups. Online user groups have sprung up in many areas of the world (BERGER & QUINT; MOORE). They have been useful in bringing pressure on vendors and database producers as needed and in providing a forum for searchers to share experiences (HUNTER). MOORE describes the formation and activities of the Nova Scotia Online Consortium, which represents 16 libraries using five online searching systems. The activities of this consortium are typical of many user groups. The National Online Circuit (GONZALEZ; HLAVA) is a loose federation of groups. It meets at national meetings, notably the National Online Meeting's Forum for Online User Groups, ASIS and other organizations. It provides an exchange of newsletters, and issues a directory of user groups. Online user groups run the gamut from formal and structured organizations to loose and informal ones that meet irregularly.

CONCLUSION

The first decade of online retrieval systems and services has seen them grow from experimental curiosities into large and expanding commercial enterprises. They have made a major impact on virtually every phase of the reference process and have revolutionized the techniques of information retrieval. Nonbibliographic databases, after penetrating the business and financial area, are also beginning to make themselves felt as they grow and expand into the library world. In the most recent *ARIST* chapter on online services, written in 1978, McCarn stated that although online systems were not a passing fad, they were in their infancy. He observed that the computer, while breeding the new role of the information professional, had led to rigidity and less freedom. Now software is being made more flexible, and the user interface has been improved. It is even acceptable to charge for online services. Online retrieval systems have emerged from their infancy and are maturing. Their second decade promises to be one of excitement and further growth.

BIBLIOGRAPHY

ABRAHAMSSON, SIXTEN. 1977. SCANNET—det nordiska datanaetet foer I D-tjaenster [SCANNET—the Nordic Data Network for ID Services]. Nordisk Tidsskrift. 1977; 64(4): 97-101. (In Swedish).

ADAMS, ARTHUR L. 1979. Planning Search Strategies for Maximum Retrieval from Bibliographic Databases. Online Review. 1979 December; 3(4): 373-379. ISSN: 0309-314X.

ALLEY, DOREEN; LAWFORD, HUGH; WOLTERS, PETER. 1978. Canadian Online Use: Trends, Implications, Policies. In: Proceedings of the 6th Canadian Conference on Information Science; 1978 May 10-13; Montreal, Canada. Ottawa, Canada: Canadian Association for Information Science; 1978. 61-94. ISSN: 0703-3247; ISBN: 0-920420-01-X.

ALMOND, J. ROBERT; NELSON, CHARLES H. 1978. Improvements in Cost Effectiveness in Online Searching. I. Journal of Chemical Information and Computer Sciences. 1978 February; 18(1): 13-15. ISSN: 0095-2338.

ANTONY, ARTHUR L. 1979. The Database Index. Database. 1979 December; 2(4): 28-33. ISSN: 0162-4205.

ANTONY, ARTHUR L.; WEIMER, SALLY; EDEN, VERONICA. 1979. An Examination of Search Strategy and an Online Bibliographic System Pertaining to Library and Information Science. Special Libraries. 1979 March; 70(3): 127-134. ISSN: 0038-6723.

ATHERTON, PAULINE; CHRISTIAN, ROGER L. 1977. Librarians and Online Services. White Plains, NY: Knowledge Industry Publications, Inc.; 1977. 124p. ISBN: 0-914236-13-X.

AUSTER, ETHEL; LAWTON, STEPHEN B. 1979. The Negotiation Process in On-Line Bibliographic Retrieval. Canadian Journal of Information Science. 1980 May; 4(5): 86-98.

AVENY, B. 1979. Competition in News Databases. Online. 1979 April; 3(2): 36-38. ISSN: 0146-5422.

BAHR, ALICE H. 1980a. Producers and Vendors of Bibliographic Online Services. 65-96. See reference: HOOVER, RYAN E., ed. 1980a.
BAHR, ALICE H. 1980b. Promotion of Online Services. 161-179. See reference: HOOVER, RYAN E., ed. 1980a.
BARWISE, T. P. 1979. The Cost of Literature Search in 1985. Journal of Information Science Principles and Practice (England). 1979 October; 1(4): 195-201. ISSN: 0165-5515.
BATES, MARCIA J. 1979a. Idea Tactics. Journal of the American Society for Information Science. 1979 September; 30(5): 281-289. ISSN: 0002-8231.
BATES, MARCIA J. 1979b. Information Search Tactics. Journal of the American Society for Information Science. 1979 July; 30(4): 205-214. ISSN: 0002-8231.
BAWDEN, DAVID. 1979. Chemical Toxicology Searching. Database. 1979 June; 2(2): 11-18. ISSN: 0162-4105.
BAWDEN, DAVID; JACKSON, F. T. 1978. Online Searching for the Toxicology of Chemical Substances. In: Proceedings of the 2nd International Online Information Meeting; 1978 December 4-6; London, England. Oxford, England: Learned Information, Ltd.; 1978. 195-204. ISSN: 0-904933-15-6.
BELLARDO, TRUDI; JACKSON, M. VIRGINIA; PIKOFF, HOWARD. 1979. Education and Training for Online Searching: A Bibliography. RQ. 1979 Winter; 19(2): 137-142. ISSN: 0033-7072.
BELLOMY, FRED O. 1977. The Information Brokerage Scene in America. In: Proceedings of the 1st International On-Line Information Meeting: 1977 December 13-15; London, England. Oxford, England: Learned Information, Ltd.; 1977. 215-223. ISBN: 0-904933-10-5.
BELLOMY, FRED O. 1979. Die privatwirtschaftliche Informationsversorgungsszene (Information Brokerage) in den USA [The Information Brokerage Scene in the USA]. Nachrichten für Dokumentation (Germany). 1979 January; 30(1): 17-20. ISSN: 0027-7436.
BEMENT, JAMES H. 1978. DJNR: What Is It? How to Use It. Online. 1978 July; 2(3): 39-40. ISSN: 0146-5422.
BERGER, MARY C.; QUINT, BARBARA. 1980. Online User Groups. 233-249. See reference: HOOVER, RYAN E., ed. 1980a.
BERGER, PATRICIA W.; CERUTTI, ELSIE. 1980. The Management of Online Reference Search Services in Federal Libraries. Science & Technology Libraries. 1980 Fall; 1(1): 81-107. ISSN: 0194-262X.
BERNSTEIN, HERBERT J.; ANDREWS, LAWRENCE C. 1979. NIH-EPA Chemical Information System. Database. 1979 March; 2(1): 35-49. ISSN: 0162-4105.
BERUL, LAWRENCE H. 1969. Document Retrieval. In: Cuadra, Carlos A.; Luke, Ann W., eds. Annual Review of Information Science and Technology: Volume 4. Chicago, IL: Encyclopedia Britannica, Inc.; 1969. 203-227. ISBN: 0-85229-147-7; LC: 66-25096.
BLAIR, JOHN C., JR. 1980a. Measurement and Evaluation of Online Services. 127-159. See reference: HOOVER, RYAN E., ed. 1980a.
BLAIR, JOHN C., JR. 1980b. Online Drug Literature Searching: Excerpta Medica. Online. 1980 October; 4(4): 13-23. ISSN: 0146-5422.
BLAIR, JOHN C., JR. 1980c. Utilization of 1200 Baud for On-Line Retrieval in a Health Science Library. Bulletin of the Medical Library Association. 1980 July; 68(3): 294-297. ISSN: 0025-7338.

BLICK, A. R.   1980.   On-Line vs. Manual—The Cost-Effectiveness Debate.
Journal of Information Science Principles and Practice (England).   1979
October; 1(4): 236–237.   (Letter to the Editor).   ISSN: 0165-5515.
BLUE, RICHARD I.   1979.   Questions for Selection of Information Re-
trieval Systems.   Online Review.   1979 March; 3(1): 77–83.   ISSN:
0309-314X.
BOURNE, CHARLES P.   1977.   Frequency and Impact of Spelling Errors
in Bibliographic Databases.   Information Processing & Management.
1977; 13(1): 1–12.   ISSN: 0306-4573.
BOURNE, CHARLES P.   1980.   On-Line Systems: History, Technology,
Economics.   Journal of the American Society for Information Science.
1980 May; 31(3): 155–160.   ISSN: 0002-8231.
BOURNE CHARLES P.; ROBINSON, JO.   1980.   Education and Training
for Computer-Based Reference Services: Review of Training Efforts to
Date.   Journal of the American Society for Information Science.   1980
January; 31(1): 25–35.   ISSN: 0002-8231.
BOYLE, STEPHEN O.; MILLER, A. PATRICIA.   1980.   Feature Compari-
son of an In-House Information Retrieval System with a Commercial
Search Service.   Journal of the American Society for Information
Science.   1980 September; 31(5): 309–317.   ISSN: 0002-8231.
BRENNER, EVERETT H.   1979.   Euronet and its Effects on the U.S. In-
formation Market.   Journal of the American Society for Information
Science.   1979 January; 30(1): 5–8.   ISSN: 0002-8231.
BRENNER, EVERETT H.   1980.   On-Line Relegates ASIS to the Miasma.
Bulletin of the American Society for Information Science.   1980 April;
6(4): 2.   (Letter to the Editor).   ISSN: 0095-4403.
BRIDGES, KITTY.   1981.   Environmental Health and Toxicology: An In-
troduction for the Online Searcher.   Online.   1981 January; 5(1): 27–
34.   ISSN: 0146-5422.
BUNTROCK, ROBERT E.   1979a.   Chemcorner.   Database.   1979 March;
2(1): 33–34.   (Column).   ISSN: 0162-4105.
BUNTROCK, ROBERT E.   1979b.   The Effect of Searching Environment
on Search Performance.   Online.   1979 October; 3(4): 10–13.   ISSN:
0146-5422.
BURROWS, SUZETTA; KYLE, SYLVIA.   1979.   Searching the MEDLARS
file on NLM and BRS: A Comparative Study.   Bulletin of the Medical
Library Association.   1979 January; 67(1): 15–24.   ISSN: 0025-7338.
BUTLER, BRETT.   1979.   Beyond the Library—U.S. Online Trends.   In:
Proceedings of the 3rd International Online Information Meeting: 1979
December 4-6; London, England.   Oxford, England: Learned Informa-
tion, Ltd.; 1979.   385–392.   ISBN: 0-904933-21-0.
CALKINS, MARY L.   1980.   Free Text or Controlled Vocabulary? A Case
History Step-by-Step Analysis plus Other Aspects of Search Strategy.
Database.   1980 June; 3(2): 53–67.   ISSN: 0162-4105.
CARTER, G. C.   1980.   Numerical Data Retrieval in the U.S. and Abroad.
Journal of Chemical Information and Computer Sciences.   1980 August;
20(3): 146–152.   ISSN: 0095-2338.
CARUSO, ELAINE.   1981.   TRAINER.   Online.   1981 January; 5(1): 36–
38.   ISSN: 0146-5422.
CHRISTIAN, ROGER.   1978.   The Electronic Library: Bibliographic Data
Bases, 1978–79.   White Plains, NY: Knowledge Industry Publications,
Inc.; 1978.   105p.   ISBN: 0-914236-15-6; LC: 78-18408.

CLEVERDON, CYRIL R. 1980. On-Line vs. Manual—The Cost-Effectiveness Debate. Journal of Information Science Principles and Practice (England). 1979 October; 1(4): 237-238. (Letter to the Editor). ISSN: 0165-5515.

CLINTON, MARSHALL; GRENVILLE, SALLY. 1980. Using European Systems from a North American Library. Online. 1980 April; 4(2): 22-27. ISSN: 0146-5422.

COLBERT, ANTOINETTE WALTON. 1979. Document Delivery. Online. 1979 January; 3(1): 61. (Column). ISSN: 0146-5422.

COLLINGE, BRIAN. 1978. BLAISE—The British Library Automated Information Service. Aslib Proceedings (England). 1978 October/November; 30(10/11): 394-402. ISSN: 0001-253X.

CONGER, LUCINDA D. 1979. Bibliographic Data Bases: The Holes in the Swiss Cheese. In: Tally, Roy D.; Dueltgen, Ronald R., eds. Information Choices and Policies: Proceedings of the 42nd Annual Meeting of the American Society for Information Science; Volume 16; 1979 October 14-18; Minneapolis, MN. White Plains, NY: Knowledge Industry Publications, Inc.; 1979. 300p. (Abstract). ISBN: 0-914236-47-4; ISSN: 0044-7870; LC: 64-8303.

CONVEY, JOHN. 1979. Online Service in a Public Library—The Lancashire Experience. In: Proceedings of the 3rd International Online Information Meeting; 1979 December 4-6; London, England. Oxford, England: Learned Information, Ltd.; 1979. 99-107. ISBN: 0-904933-21-0.

COOPER, MICHAEL D. 1978. Charging Users for Library Services. Information Processing & Management. 1978; 14(6): 419-427. ISSN: 0306-4573.

COOPER, MICHAEL D.; DEWATH, NANCY A. 1977. Effect of User Fees on the Cost of Online Searching in Libraries. Journal of Library Automation. 1977 December; 10(4): 304-319. ISSN: 0022-2240.

CORSON, JANET E. 1979. Breaking the Language Barrier: A Sociolinguistic Perspective of Online Search Strategy. In: Proceedings of the 3rd International Online Information Meeting; 1979 December 4-6; London, England. Oxford, England: Learned Information, Ltd.; 1979. 123-137. ISBN: 0-904933-21-1.

CRAWFORD, PAULA J.; THOMPSON, JUDITH A. 1979. Free Online Searches are Feasible. Library Journal. 1979 April 1; 104(7): 793-795. ISSN: 0000-0027.

CRAWFORD, ROBERT G. 1979. Software Review. Computers and the Humanities. 1979; 13: 309-310. ISSN: 0010-4817.

CRAWFORD, SUSAN; REES, ALAN M., eds. 1980. Perspectives On... On-Line Systems in Science and Technology. Journal of the American Society for Information Science. 1980 May; 31(3): 153-200. ISSN: 0002-8231.

CUADRA, CARLOS A. 1978. U.S.-European Cooperation and Competition in the On-Line Retrieval Services Marketplace. The Information Scientist (England). 1978 June; 12(2): 43-52. ISSN: 0020-0263.

DOLAN, DONNA R. 1979. Offlines. Database. 1979 September; 2(3): 85-87. (Column). ISSN: 0162-4105.

DOLAN, DONNA R. 1980. The BRS CROSS Database. Database. 1980 December; 3(4): 50-55. ISSN: 0162-4105.

DOLAN, DONNA R.; KREMIN, MICHAEL. 1979. Quality Control of Search Analysts. Online. 1979 April; 3(2): 8-16. ISSN: 0146-5422.

DOSZKOCS, TAMAS E. 1978a. An Associative Interactive Dictionary for Online Bibliographic Searching. In: Moneta, Josef, ed. Information Technology: Proceedings of the 3rd Jerusalem Conference on Information Technology (JCIT3); 1978 August 6-9; Jerusalem, Israel. Amsterdam, The Netherlands: North-Holland; 1978. 489-492. ISBN: 0-444-85192-5.

DOSZKOCS, TAMAS E. 1978b. Natural Language Searching in Online Bibliographic Retrieval Systems. In: Piternick, A. B. ed. Proceedings of the 8th Mid-Year Meeting of the American Society for Information Science; 1979 May 16-19; Banff, Alberta, Canada; 1978. Paper H1. (Abstract only, full paper on microfiche). Available from: American Society for Information Science, 1010-16th Street N.W., Washington, DC 20036.

DOSZKOCS, TAMAS E.; RAPP, BARBARA A. 1979. Searching MEDLINE in English: A Prototype User Interface with Natural Language Query Ranked Output, and Relevance Feedback. In: Tally, Roy D.; Dueltgen, Ronald R., eds. Information Choices and Policies: Proceedings of the 42nd Annual Meeting of the American Society for Information Science: Volume 16; 1979 October 14-18; Minneapolis, MN. White Plains, NY: Knowledge Industry Publications, Inc.; 1979. 131-139. ISBN: 0-914236-47-4; ISSN: 0044-7870; LC: 64-8303.

DRINAN, HELEN. 1979. Financial Management of Online Services—A How-To Guide. Online. 1979 October; 3(4): 14-21. ISSN: 0146-5422.

DUNCAN, ELIZABETH E.; KLINGENSMITH, PATRICIA J.; ROSS, NINA M. 1980. An Exercise in Utility. Online. 1980 January; 4(1): 64-67. ISSN: 0146-5422.

EAST, H. 1980. Comparative Costs of Manual and On-Line Bibliographic Searching: A Review of the Literature. Journal of Information Science Principles and Practice (England). 1980 September; 2(2): 101-109. ISSN: 0165-5515.

EDSTRÖM, M. E.; WALLIN, MARIE A. 1977. Implementation of a New Interactive On-Line Information Retrieval System: 3RIP. In: Proceedings of the 1st International On-Line Information Meeting; 1979 December 13-15; London, England. Oxford, England: Learned Information, Ltd.; 1979. 83-93. ISBN: 0-904933-10-5.

ELCHESEN, DENNIS R. 1978. Cost-Effectiveness Comparison of Manual and On-Line Retrospective Bibliographic Searching. Journal of the American Society for Information Science. 1978 March; 29(2): 56-66. ISSN: 0002-8231.

FARMER, NICK A.; O'HARA, MICHAEL P. 1980. CAS Online: A New Source of Substance Information from Chemical Abstracts Service. Database. 1980 December; 3(4): 10-25. ISSN: 0162-4105.

FARRADANE, JASON. 1980. On-Line vs. Manual—The Cost-Effectiveness Debate. Journal of Information Science Principles and Practice (England). 1979 October; 1(4): 235-236. (Letter to the Editor). ISSN: 0165-5515.

FENICHEL, CAROL HANSEN. 1978. Online Information Retrieval: Identification of Measures That Discriminate among Users with Different Levels and Types of Experience. Philadelphia, PA: Drexel University; 1979 July. 258p. (Ph.D. dissertation). Available from: University Microfilms International (UMI), 300 N. Zeeb Rd., Ann Arbor, MI 48106. UMI: AAD79-26997.

FENICHEL, CAROL HANSEN. 1980. An Examination of the Relationship between Searching Behavior and Searcher Background. Online Review. 1980 December; 4(4): 341-347. ISSN: 0309-314x.
FENICHEL, CAROL HANSEN. 1981. Online Searching: Measures That Discriminate among Users with Different Types of Experience. Journal of the American Society for Information Science. 1981 January; 32(1): 23-32. ISSN: 0002-8231.
FLYNN, T.; HOLOHAN, P. A.; MAGSON, M. S.; MUNRO, J. D. 1979. Cost Effectiveness Comparison of Online and Manual Bibliographic Information Retrieval. Journal of Information Science Principles and Practice (England). 1979 May; 1(2): 77-84. ISSN: 0165-5515.
FOSDICK, HOWARD. 1977. An SDC-Based On-Line Search Service: A Patron Evaluation Survey and Implications. Special Libraries. 1977 September; 68(9): 305-312. ISSN: 0038-6723.
GIBBS, MARY MARGARET; LASZLO, GEORGE A. 1980. Document Ordering through Lockheed's DIALOG and SDC's ORBIT—A User's Guide. Online. 1980 Online; 4(4): 31-38. ISSN: 0146-5422.
GONZALEZ, REBECCA A. 1980. Circuit News. Online. 1980 October; 4(4): 58-60. (Column). ISSN: 0146-5422.
GRAHAM, DEBORAH L. 1980. Simultaneous Remote Search: A Technique of Providing MEDLARS Services to Remote Locations. Bulletin of the Medical Library Association. 1980 October; 68(4): 370-371. ISSN: 0025-7338.
GREGORY, N. 1979. The U.S. Congress—Online Users as Policymakers. Online Review. 1979 December; 3(4): 355-360. ISSN: 0309-314X.
HALL, JAMES L. 1977. On-Line Information Retrieval Sourcebook. London, England: Aslib; 1977. 267p. ISBN: 0-85142-106-7.
HALL, JAMES L. 1979. On-Line Bibliographic Data Bases, 1979 Directory. London, England: Aslib; 1979. ISBN: 0-85142-115-6.
HARDY, NANCY F. 1979. Maximizing the Effectiveness of Online Searching—A Training and Education Model. In: Proceedings of the 3rd International Online Information Meeting; 1979 December 4-6; London, England. Oxford, England: Learned Information, Ltd.; 1979. 13-20. ISBN: 0-904933-21-0.
HAWKINS, DONALD T. 1978a. Bibliometrics of the Online Information Retrieval Literature. Online Review. 1978 December; 2(4): 345-352. ISSN: 0309-314X.
HAWKINS, DONALD T. 1978b. Multiple Database Searching: Techniques and Pitfalls. Online. 1978 April; 2(2): 9-15. ISSN: 0146-5422.
HAWKINS, DONALD T. 1979. The ManLabs-NPL Materials Data Bank. Online. 1979 April; 3(2): 40-55. ISSN: 0146-5422.
HAWKINS, DONALD T. 1980a. Machine-Readable Output from Online Searches. Journal of the American Society for Information Science. 1980; 32(4): 253-256. Available from: the author, Bell Laboratories, Murray Hill, NJ 07974. ISSN: 0002-8231.
HAWKINS, DONALD T. 1980b. Management of an Online Retrieval Service. 97-125. See reference: HOOVER, RYAN E., ed. 1980a.
HAWKINS, DONALD T. 1980c. Online Information Retrieval Bibliography, 1964-1979. Marlton, NJ: Learned Information, Inc.; 1980. 174p. ISBN: 0-938734-00-8.
HAWKINS, DONALD T. 1980d. Online Information Retrieval Bibliography. 3rd Update. Online Review. 1980 March; 4(1): 61-100. ISSN: 0309-314x.

200 DONALD T. HAWKINS

HAWKINS, DONALD T. 1980e. Problems in Physical Property Data Retrieval. Journal of Chemical Information and Computer Sciences. 1980 August; 20(3): 143-145. ISSN: 0095-2338.
HAWKINS, DONALD T. 1980f. Six Years of Online Searching in an Industrial Library Network. Science & Technology Libraries. 1980 Fall; 1(1): 57-67. ISSN: 0194-262x.
HAWKINS, DONALD T.; BROWN, CAROLYN P. 1980. What Is an Online Search? Online. 1980 January; 4(1): 12-18. ISSN: 0146-5422.
HAWKINS, DONALD T.; MENDENHALL, DONNA M. 1979. I Learned About Searching From That... Online. 1979 October; 3(4): 56-57. (Column). ISSN: 0146-5422.
HELLER, STEPHEN R.; MILNE, G. W. A. 1979. The NIH-EPA Chemical Information System. Environmental Science and Technology. 1979 July; 13(7): 798-803. ISSN: 0013-936x.
HELLER, STEPHEN R.; MILNE, G. W. A. 1980. Linking Scientific Databases—The NIH-EPA Chemical Information System. Online. 1980 October; 4(4): 45-57. ISSN: 0146-5422.
HELLER, STEPHEN R.; MILNE, G. W. A.; FELDMAN, R. J. 1979. A Computer-Based Chemical Information System. Science. 1979 January 21; 195(4275): 253-259. ISSN: 0036-8075.
HENRY, W. M.; LEIGH, J. A.; TEDD, L. A.; WILLIAMS, P. W. 1980. Online Searching: An Introduction. London, England: Butterworth & Co., Ltd.; 1980. ISBN: 0-408-10696-4; LC: 80-40242.
HEYER, JOHN. 1980. In-House Training for Online Searching at a Special Library. Online Review. 1980 December; 4(4): 367-374. ISSN: 0309-314x.
HLAVA, MARJORIE M. K. 1979. On-Line Systems. The Information Manager. 1979 September/October; 1(6): 26.
HOCK, RANDOLPH E. 1980. Publicly Available Online Bibliographic Databases for Humanities: The Dialog System. In: Raben, Joseph; Marks, Gregory, eds. Data Bases in the Humanities and Social Sciences: Proceedings of the IFIPS (International Federation of Information Processing Societies) Working Conference on Data Bases in the Humanities and Social Sciences; 1979 August 23-24; Hanover, NH. Amsterdam, The Netherlands: North-Holland; 1980. ISBN: 0-444-85499-1.
HOGAN, THOMAS H. 1979. News Retrieval Services—Growing but Where Are They Headed? Online Review. 1979 September; 3(3): 247-252. ISSN: 0309-314x.
HOLMES, P. 1979. The British Library Automated Information Service (BLAISE). Online Review. 1979 September; 3(3): 265-274. ISSN: 0309-314x.
HOOVER, RYAN E. 1979. Computer Aided Reference Service in the Academic Library. Experiences in Organizing and Operating an Online Reference Service. Online. 1979 October; 3(4): 28-41. ISSN: 0146-5422.
HOOVER, RYAN E., ed. 1980a. The Library and Information Manager's Guide to Online Services. White Plains, NY: Knowledge Industry Publications Inc.; 1980. 270p. ISBN: 0-914236-60-1; LC: 80-21602.
HOOVER, RYAN E. 1980b. The Mechanics of Online Searching. 197-232. See reference: HOOVER, RYAN E., ed. 1980a.
HULEATT, RICHARD S. 1979a. Finishing the Online Search. Online. 1979 April; 3(2): 24-31. ISSN: 0146-5422.

HULEATT, RICHARD S. 1979b. Online Use of Chemical Abstracts: A Primer for Beginning Chemical Searchers. Database. 1979 December; 2(4): 11-21. ISSN: 0162-4105.

HUNTER, J. A. 1979. Online Benutzergruppen, Ihre Zielsetzungen und Möglichkeiten [Online User Groups: Their Aims and Chances]. Nachrichten für Dokumentation (Germany). 1979; 30(4/5): 179-183. ISSN: 0027-7436.

HUTSON, MARY M. 1979. Fee or Free: The Effect of Charging on Information Demand. Library Journal. 1979 September 15; 104(16): 1811-1814. ISSN: 0000-0027.

INFORMATION MANAGER. 1979. Spreading the Word on Non-Bibliographic Databases. Cuadra Associates Works to Close the Knowledge Gap. Information Manager. 1979 May/June; 1(4): 28-31.

JAHODA, GERALD; BAYER, ALAN; NEEDHAM, WILLIAM L. 1978. A Comparison of On-Line Bibliographic Searches in One Academic and One Industrial Organization. RQ. 1978 Fall; 18(1): 42-49. ISSN: 0033-7072.

JOHNSON, ROBERT A. 1980. Planning for Online Searching at San Jose: A Design for Public Libraries of the 1980s. Science & Technology Libraries. 1980 Fall; 1(1): 117-132. ISSN: 0194-262x.

JONES, COLIN. 1977. Technotec Database and Technology Exchange Service of Control Data. Program (England). 1979 July; 11(3): 94-100. ISSN: 0033-0337.

JOSEPHINE, HELEN B. 1980. Electronic Mail: The Future is Now. Online. 1980 October; 4(4): 41-43. ISSN: 0146-5422.

KABACK, STUART M. 1978. Retrieving Patent Information Online. Online. 1978 January; 2(1): 16-25. ISSN: 0146-5422.

KABACK, STUART M.; LANDSBERG, M. KAREN; GIRARD, A. 1978. APILIT and APIPAT: Petroleum Information Online. Database. 1978 December; 1(2): 46-67. ISSN: 0162-4105.

KADEC, SARAH T.; MANCHER, RHODA. 1979. Online Services in the Executive Office of the President. Online Review. 1979 December; 3(4): 361-366. ISSN: 0309-314X.

KAUFMAN LARRY; NESOR, HARVEY. 1974. Calculation of Superalloy Phase Diagrams. Part I. Metallurgical Transactions. 1974 July; 5(7): 1617-1621. Coden: MTGTBF.

KENT, ALLEN; GALVIN, T. J. 1978. The On-Line Revolution in Libraries: [Proceedings of a conference]; 1977 November 14-16; Pittsburgh, PA. New York, NY: Marcel Dekker, Inc.; 1978. 303p. ISBN: 0-8247-6754-3; LC: 78-15800.

KIDD, J. S. 1977. Toward Cost-Effective Procedures in On-Line Bibliographic Searches. College and Research Libraries. 1977 March; 38(2): 153-159. ISSN: 0010-0870.

KIECHEL, WALTER, III. 1980. Everything You Always Wanted to Know May Soon be On-Line. Fortune. 1980 May 5; 101(9): 226-228, 233, 236, 240. ISSN: 0015-8259.

KLUGMAN, SIMONE. 1980. Online Information Retrieval Interface with Traditional Reference Services. Online Review. 1980 September; 4(3): 263-272. ISSN: 0309-314X.

KNAPP, SARA D. 1978. The Reference Interview in a Computer-Based Setting. RQ. 1978 Summer; 17(4): 320-324. ISSN: 0033-7072.

KRENTZ, DAVID M. 1978. Online Searching—Specialist Required? Journal of Chemical Information and Computer Sciences. 1978 February; 18(1): 4-9. ISSN: 0095-2338.

KUROKI, KRISTYN. 1980. Training the Searchers. 181-195. See reference: HOOVER, RYAN E., ed. 1980a.

KUSACK, JAMES M. 1979. Integration of Online Reference Service. RQ. 1979 Fall; 19(1): 64-69. ISSN: 0033-7072.

LANDAU, RUTH N.; ABELS, DAVID M.; WANGER, JUDITH. 1980. Directory of Online Databases. Santa Monica, CA: Cuadra Associates, Inc., 1523 Sixth St., Suite 12, Santa Monica, CA 90401; 1980. 154p. (Issued quarterly). ISSN: 0193-6840; LC: 79-54776.

LARSON, SIGNE E.; WILLIAMS, MARTHA E. 1980. Computer Assisted Legal Research. In: Williams, Martha E., ed. Annual Review of Information Science and Technology: Volume 15. White Plains, NY: Knowledge Industry Publications, Inc.; 1980. 251-286. ISBN: 0-914236-65-2; ISSN: 0066-4200; LC: 66-25096.

LEBLANC, ERIC S. 1978. CAN/OLE's On-Line Document Ordering Facility. In: Proceedings of the 6th Canadian Conference on Information Science; 1978 May 10-13; Montreal, Canada. Ottawa, Canada: Canadian Association for Information Science; 1978. 168-177. ISSN: 0703-3247; ISBN: 0-920420-010X.

LÖFSTRÖM, MATS. 1979. 3RIP: A Text Data Base System. In: Proceedings of the Digital Equipment Computer Users Society: Volume 6, Number 1; 1979 September 4-6; Monte Carlo, Monaco. Maynard, MA: Digital Equipment Corporation; 1979. 335-336. ISSN: 0095-2095.

LOWRY, GLENN R. 1980. Online Document Retrieval System Education for Undergraduates: Rationale, Content and Observations. Online Review. 1980 December; 4(4): 349-356. ISSN: 0309-314x.

LUEDKE, JAMES A., JR.; KOVACS, GABOR J.; FRIED, JOHN B. 1977. Numeric Data Bases and Systems. In: Williams, Martha E., ed. Annual Review of Information Science and Technology: Volume 12. White Plains, NY: Knowledge Industry Publications, Inc.; 1977. 119-181. ISBN: 0-914236-11-3; ISSN: 0066-4200; LC: 66-25096.

MACKESY, EILEEN M. 1979. MLA Bibliography Online Provides Access to Language, Literature, and Folklore. Database. 1979 September; 2(3): 36-43. ISSN: 0162-4105.

MAGSON, M. S. 1980. Modelling On-Line Cost-Effectiveness. Aslib Proceedings (England). 1980 January; 32(1): 35-41. ISSN: 0001-253x.

MAHON, F. V. 1978a. Euronet and You. Aslib Proceedings (England). 1978 December; 30(12): 416-419. ISSN: 0001-253x.

MAHON, F. V. 1978b. Online STI in 1979: A Better Chance via Euronet. In: Proceedings of the 2nd International Online Information Meeting; 1978 December 5-7; London, England. Oxford, England: Learned Information, Ltd.; 1978. 235-242. ISBN: 0-904933-15-6.

MARCUS, RICHARD S.; REINTJES, J. FRANCIS. 1979. Experiments and Analysis on a Computer Interface to an Information Retrieval Network. Cambridge, MA: Massachusetts Institute of Technology; 1979 April. 127p. Available from: the authors, Laboratory for Information and Decision Systems, Massachusetts Institute of Technology, Cambridge, MA 02139. (MIT: LIDS-R-900).

MARKEY, KAREN; ATHERTON, PAULINE. 1978. ONTAP: Online Training and Practice Manual for ERIC Database Searchers. Syracuse,

NY: Syracuse University; 1978. 182p. Available from: Syracuse University Printing Service, 125 College Place, Syracuse, NY 13210. ERIC: ED 160109.

MARKEY, KAREN; ATHERTON, PAULINE; NEWTON, CLAUDIA. 1980. An Analysis of Controlled Vocabulary and Free Text Search Statements in Online Searches. Online Review. 1980 September; 4(3): 225-236. ISSN: 0309-314X.

MARSHALL, DORIS B. 1980. To Improve Searching, Check Search Results. Online. 1980 July; 4(3): 32-47. ISSN: 0146-5422.

MARTIN, JEAN K. 1980. Preparation of Proposals for Online Bibliographic Services in Academic, Government, and Industrial Libraries. Science & Technology Libraries. 1980 Fall; 1(1): 7-15. ISSN: 0194-262x.

MCCARN, DAVIS B. 1978. Online Systems—Techniques and Services. In: Williams, Martha E., ed. Annual Review of Information Science and Technology: Volume 13. White Plains, NY: Knowledge Industry Publications, Inc.; 1978. 85-124. ISBN: 0-914236-21-0; ISSN: 0066-4200; LC: 66-25096.

MCCARN, DAVIS B. 1979a. National Library of Medicine—MEDLARS and MEDLINE. In: Belzer, Jack; Holzman, Albert; Kent, Allen, eds. Encyclopedia of Computer Science and Technology: Volume 11. New York, NY: Dekker; 1978. 116-151. ISBN: 0-8247-2261-2; LC: 74-29436.

MCCARN, DAVIS B. 1979b. Online Services of the National Library of Medicine. In: Proceedings of the 17th International Institute of Electrical and Electronics Engineers (IEEE) Computer Conference (COMPCON-78 Fall); 1978 September 5-8; Washington, DC. New York, NY: IEEE; 1978. 48-53. LC: 68-1628.

MCCARN, DAVIS B.; LEITER, JOSEPH P. 1973. On-Line Services in Medicine and Beyond. Science. 1973 July 27; 181: 318-324. ISSN: 0036-8075.

MCKEE, ANNA MARIE KECK; WILLIAMS, JANET. 1978. Computer Searching and Interlibrary Loans: Where's the Connection? Paper presented at: Special Libraries Association Conference; 1978; Kansas City, MO. 12p. ERIC: ED 157559.

MEADOW, CHARLES T. 1979a. Online Searching and Computer Programming: Some Behavioral Similarities (Or Why End Users Will Eventually Take Over the Terminal). Online. 1979 January; 3(1): 49-52. ISSN: 0146-5422.

MEADOW, CHARLES T. 1979b. The Computer as a Search Intermediary. Online. 1979 July; 3(3): 54-59. ISSN: 0146-5422.

MENDELSSOHN, RUDOLPH C. 1978. LABSTAT: The BLS Data Base and Information System. Statistical Reporter. 1978 September: 395-397. ISSN: 0038-6723.

MILNE, G. W. A.; HELLER, STEPHEN R. 1977. The NIH-EPA Chemical Information System. In: Smith, Dennis H., ed. Computer-Assisted Structure Elucidation: Synposium held at the 173rd Meeting of the American Chemical Society (ACS); 1977 March 23; New Orleans, LA. Washington, DC: ACS; 1977. 26-45. (ACS Symposium Series no. 54). ISSN: 0097-6156; ISBN: 0-8412-0384-9.

MOLSTER, H. C. 1979. Restrictions on Database Use: Are They Necessary? Online Review. 1979 March; 3(1): 85-93. ISSN: 0309-314x.

MOORE, J. M. 1979. Online Users Groups: Five Years Experience. In: Piternick, Anne B., ed. Proceedings of the 8th Mid-Year Meeting of the

204 DONALD T. HAWKINS

American Society for Information Science (ASIS); 1979 May 16-19; Banff, Alberta, Canada; 1979. Paper I2. (Abstract only, full text on microfiche). Available from: ASIS, 1010-16th Street N.W., Washington, DC 20036.

MOULTON, JAMES C. 1979. Dow Jones News/Retrieval. Database. 1979 March; 2(1): 54-64. ISSN: 0162-4105.

NASH, MARY M. 1979. The Globe and Mail Database—A Canadian First. Online Review. 1979 December; 3(4): 367-371. ISSN: 0309-314X.

NIEHOFF, ROBERT T.; KWASNY, STANLEY. 1979. The Role of Automated Subject Switching in a Distributed Information Network. Online Review. 1979 June; 3(2): 181-194. ISSN: 0309-314x.

NIEHOFF, ROBERT T.; KWASNY, STANLEY; WESSELLS, MICHAEL. 1979. Overcoming the Database Vocabulary Barrier: A Solution. Online. 1979 October; 3(4): 43-54. ISSN: 0146-5422.

NIELSEN, BRIAN. 1980. Online Bibliographic Searching and the Deprofessionalization of Librarianship. Online Review. 1980 September; 4(3): 215-224. ISSN: 0309-314x.

NORTON, NANCY PROTHRO. 1981. "Dirty Data"—A Call for Quality Control. Online. 1981 January; 5(1): 40-41. ISSN: 0146-5422.

ONLINE REVIEW. 1979. Free Enterprise vs. Government Control. Online Review. 1979 September; 3(3): 234-235. ISSN: 0309-314x.

OPPENHEIM, CHARLES. 1979. Methods for Chemical Substance Online. I. The Basics. Online Review. 1979 December; 3(4): 381-387. ISSN: 0309-314X.

PADIN, MARY ELLEN, ed. 1979. Computer Ease. Online. 1979 January; 3(1): 83-4. (Column). ISSN: 0146-5422.

PEMBERTON, JEFFEREY K. 1980. Welcome to Online-'80. In: Online-'80 Conference Program; 1980 November 12-14; San Francisco, CA. Weston, CT: Online, Inc.; 1980. 1p. Available from: Online, Inc., 11 Tannery Lane, Weston, CT.

PENSYL, MARY E.; WOODFORD, SUSAN E. 1980. Planning and Implementation Guidelines for an Academic Online Service: The M.I.T. Experience. Science & Technology Libraries. 1980 Fall; 1(1): 17-45. ISSN: 0194-262x.

PESTEL, HELEN C.; RUBIN, STEPHEN. 1977. Electronic Handbook—Fact or Fiction. Online. 1977 October; 1(4): 84-87. ISSN: 0146-5422.

PFAFFENBERGER, ANN; ECHT, SANDY. 1980. Substitution of SciSearch and Social SciSearch for their Print Versions in an Academic Library. Database. 1980 March; 3(1): 63-71. ISSN: 0162-4105.

PIERMATTI, PATRICIA ANN; BOLLES, SHIRLEY W. 1980. Planning Online Search Service in a State University. Science & Technology Libraries. 1980 Fall; 1(1): 47-50. ISSN: 0194-262x.

PILACHOWSKI, DAVID M. 1979. USPSD—United States Political Science Documents. Database. 1979 December; 2(4): 68-77. ISSN: 0162-4105.

PLOSKER, GEORGE R.; SUMMIT, ROGER K. 1980. Management of Vendor Services: How to Choose an Online Vendor. Special Libraries. 1980 August; 71: 354-357. ISSN: 0038-6723.

POWELL, JAMES R., JR. 1980. Excerpta Medica (EMBASE) Online: A Reacquaintance. Online. 1980 January; 4(1): 36-41. ISSN: 0146-5422.

RHYDEN, D. A. 1977. Computerized Storage and Retrieval of Newspaper Stories at the Globe and Mail Libraries. Special Libraries. 1977 February; 68(2): 57-61. ISSN: 0038-6723.

RIGG, P. 1980. The New Data Networks—Now and in the Near Future. Program (England). 1980 April; 14(2): 62-68. ISSN: 0033-0237.

ROBBIN, ALICE. 1979. Numeric Data Bases: Finding the Swiss Cheese. In: Tally, Roy D.; Dueltgen, Ronald R., eds. Information Choices and Policies: Proceedings of the 42nd Annual Meeting of the American Society for Information Science: Volume 18; 1979 October 14-18; Minneapolis, MN. White Plains, NY: Knowledge Industry Publications, Inc.; 1979. 299. (Abstract). ISBN: 0-914236-47-4; ISSN: 0044-7870; LC: 64-8303.

ROBINSON, JO. 1980. Education and Training for Computer-Based Reference Services: A Case Study. Journal of the American Society for Information Science. 1980 March; 31(2): 97-104. ISSN: 0002-8231.

SAFFADY, WILLIAM. 1979. The Economics of Online Bibliographic Searching: Costs and Cost Justification. Library Technology Reports. 1979 September/October; 15(5): 567-653. ISSN: 0024-2586.

SALTON, GERARD. 1980. Automatic Information Retrieval. Computer. 1980 September; 13(9): 41-56. ISSN: 0018-9162.

SCIENCE & TECHNOLOGY LIBRARIES. 1980. Planning for Online Search Service in Sci-Tech Libraries. Science & Technology Libraries. 1980 Fall; 1(1): 143p. ISSN: 0194-262x.

SEBA, DOUGLAS B. ed. 1979. Management Outpost. Online. 1979 January; 3(1): 62-63. (Column). ISSN: 0146-5422.

SHAPIRO, STANLEY J. 1980. Marketing and the Information Professional. Odd Couple or Meaningful Relationship? Special Libraries. 1980 November; 71: 469-474. ISSN: 0038-6723.

SHENG, KATHARINE K. 1979. Art Modern/DIALOG. Database. 1979 June; 2(2): 19-33. ISSN: 0162-4105.

SHENTON, KATHLEEN E. 1980. Types of Databases Available. 31-64. See reference: HOOVER, RYAN E., ed. 1980a.

SHENTON, KATHLEEN E.; LANDSBERG, M. KAREN. 1981. Conference Searching at 1200 Baud. Online. 1981 January; 5(1): 42-43. ISSN: 0146-5422.

SILCOFF, BRIAN. 1978. Databases Available to Canadian Users through Six Computer Citation Retrieval Network Centers—As of March, 1978. Canadian Journal of Information Science. 1978; 3: 110-122.

SIMMONS, PETER. 1979. Satellite Television and Training for Online Computer Searching. Journal of Education for Librarianship. 1979; 19(4): 312-317. ISSN: 0022-0604.

SLADE, ROD; KELLY, ALEX M. 1979. Sources of Popular Literature Online: New York Times Information Bank and the Magazine Index. Database. 1979 March; 2(1): 70-83. ISSN: 0162-4105.

STEWART, ALAN K. 1978. The 1200 Baud Experience. Online. 1978 July; 2(3): 13-18. ISSN: 0146-5422.

STUKENBROKER, B. 1979. IUD—Informationsvermittlung aus Online-System in Unternehmen—Eine neue Organisationsaufgabe [Online Searching Intermediation within Corporations: A New Organizational Task]. Nachrichten für Dokumentation (Germany). 1979 February; 30(1): 12-16. (In German). ISSN: 0027-7436.

SUMMIT, ROGER K. 1980a. Online Perspectives: Online-'80 Keynote Address; 1980 November 12-14; San Francisco, CA; 1980. Available from: the author, Lockheed Information Systems, 3460 Hillview Ave., Palo Alto, CA 94304.

SUMMIT, ROGER K. 1980b. The Dynamics of Cost and Finances of On-Line Computer Searching. RQ. 1980 Fall; 20(1): 60-63. ISSN: 0033-7072.

SWANSON, ROWENA WEISS. 1980. Probing Private Files. Database. 1980 June; 3(2): 70-76. ISSN: 0162-4105.

SWEETLAND, JAMES H. 1979. Using Online Systems in Reference Work. Online. 1979 July; 3(3): 10-19. ISSN: 0146-5422.

TEITELBAUM, HENRY H.; HAWKINS, DONALD T. 1978. Database Subject Index. Online. 1978 July; 2(2): 16-21. ISSN: 0146-5422.

TEITELBAUM-KRONISH, PRISCILLA. 1980. Online Services in Academic Libraries: Fee or Free? Science & Technology Libraries. 1980 Fall; 1(1): 51-56. ISSN: 0194-262x.

TOMBERG, ALEX. 1978. Networks in Europe. In: The On-Line Revolution in Information: Implications for the Users; 1978 July 6-7 Paris, France. Paris, France: International Council of Scientific Unions Abstracting Board (ICSU AB), 51 Boulevard de Montmorency, 75016 Paris, France; 1978. 59-66. ISBN: 92-9027-005-5.

TOMBERG, ALEX. 1979. The Development of Commercially Available Databases in Europe. Online Review. 1979 December; 3(4): 343-353. ISSN: 0309-314x.

TRIMBLE, J. HARVEY, JR. 1978. LABSTAT—The Bureau of Labor Statistics System for Storage and Analysis of Time Series Data. In: Proceedings of the 2nd International Online Information Meeting; 1978 December 5-7; London, England. Oxford, England: Learned Information, Ltd.; 1978. 139-144. ISBN: 0-904933-15-6.

TRUBKIN, LOENE. 1979. The Copyright Quandary for Database Publishers. In: Proceedings of the 3rd International Online Information Meeting; 1979 December 4-6; London, England. Oxford, England: Learned Information, Ltd.; 1979. 25-34. ISBN: 0-904933-21-0.

TRUBKIN, LOENE. 1980. Migration from Print to Online Use. Online Review. 1980 March; 4(1): 5-12. ISSN: 0309-314x.

VAN CAMP, ANN. 1979. Effective Search Analysts. Online. 1979 April; 3(2): 18-20. ISSN: 0146-5422.

WALKER, RICHARD D.; LUEDKE, JOHN R. 1979. DOE/RECON and the Energy Files: Some Files That May Soon "Go Public". Database. 1979 December; 2(4): 54-67. ISSN: 0162-4105.

WANGER, JUDITH. 1979a. Education and Training for Online Systems. In: Williams, Martha E., ed. Annual Review of Information Science and Technology: Volume 14. White Plains, NY: Knowledge Industry Publications, Inc.; 1979. 219-245. LC: 66-25096; ISBN: 0-914236-44-x; ISSN: 0066-4200.

WANGER, JUDITH. 1979b. Evaluation of the Online Search Process: A Preliminary Report. In: Proceedings of the 3rd International Online Information Meeting; 1979 December 4-6; London, England. Oxford, England: Learned Information, Ltd.; 1979. 1-11. ISBN: 0-904933-21-0.

WANGER, JUDITH; LANDAU, RUTH N. 1980. Nonbibliographic Online Database Services. Journal of the American Society for Information Science. 1980 May; 31(3): 171-180. ISSN: 0002-8231.

WATERS, RICHARD L.; MANN, JANE. 1980. Online Search Service at the Dallas Public Library. Science & Technology Libraries. 1980 Fall; 1(1): 109-115. ISSN: 0194-262x.

WERNER, GLORIA. 1979. Use of On-Line Bibliographic Retrieval Services in Health Sciences Libraries in the United States and Canada. Bulletin of the Medical Library Association. 1979 January; 67(1): 1-14. ISSN: 0025-7338.

WILLIAMS, MARTHA E. 1977. The Impact of Machine-Readable Data Bases on Library and Information Services. Information Processing & Management. 1977; 13: 95-107. ISSN: 0306-4573.

WILLIAMS, MARTHA E. 1978. Online Retrieval—Today and Tomorrow. Online Review. 1978 December; 2(4): 353-366. ISSN: 0309-314X.

WILLIAMS, MARTHA E. 1980. Database and Online Statistics for 1979. Bulletin of the American Society for Information Science. 1980 December; 7(2): 27-29. ISSN: 0095-4403.

WILLIAMS, MARTHA E. 1981a. Relative Impact of Print and Database Products on Database Producer Expenses and Income—Trends for Database Producer Organizations Based on a Thirteen Year Financial Analysis. Information Processing & Management. 1981; 17. (In press). ISSN: 0306-4573.

WILLIAMS, MARTHA E. 1981b. Databases, Computer Readable. In: Wedgeworth, Robert, ed. The ALA Yearbook—A Review of Library Events 1980: Volume 6: 128-131. Chicago, IL: American Library Association.

WILLIAMS, MARTHA E.; BRANDHORST, TED. 1977. Databases Online at LIS, SDC, and BRS. Bulletin of the American Society for Information Science. 1977; 3(5): 18-24. ISSN: 0095-4403.

WILLIAMS, MARTHA E.; BRANDHORST, TED. 1978. Databases Online in 1978. Bulletin of the American Society for Information Science. 1978 June; 4(6): 20-26. ISSN: 0095-4403.

WILLIAMS, MARTHA E.; BRANDHORST, TED. 1979. Changes vs. Stability in Databases. Bulletin of the American Society for Information Science. 1979 August; 5(6): 25-26. ISSN: 0095-4403.

WILLIAMS, MARTHA E.; LANNOM, LAURENCE; O'DONNELL, ROSEMARY; BARTH, STEPHEN H. 1979. Computer-Readable Data Bases: A Directory and Data Sourcebook. Washington, DC: American Society for Information Science; 1979. 1367p. Available from: Knowledge Industry Publications, Inc., White Plains, NY. ISBN: 0-914236-45-8; LC: 76-46249.

WILLIAMS, P. W. 1977. The Role and Cost Effectiveness of the Intermediary. In: Proceedings of the 1st International On-Line Information Meeting; 1977 December 13-15; London, England. Oxford, England: Learned Information, Ltd.; 1977. 53-63. ISBN: 0-904933-10-5.

WILLIAMS, P. W. 1979. Microprocessor Assisted Terminals for Online Information Systems. In: Proceedings of the 3rd International Online Information Meeting; 1979 December 4-6; London, England. Oxford, England: Learned Information, Ltd.; 1979. 139-146. ISBN: 0-904933-21-0.

WILLIAMS, P. W. 1980. The Use of Microelectronics to Assist Online Information Retrieval. Online Review. 1980 December; 4(4): 393-399. ISSN: 0309-314x.

WITIAK, JOANNE L.; PREWITT, BARBARA G.; DESCHERE, ALLEN R.
1980. Online Database Searching via Telephone Conferencing. Online.
1979 April; 3(2): 21-33. ISSN: 0146-5422.
ZAMORA, ANTONIO. 1980. Automatic Detection and Correction of Spelling Errors in a Large Database. Journal of Chemical Information and
Computer Sciences. 1980 January; 31(1): 51-57. ISSN: 0002-8231.

III

Applications

The basic tools and techniques of information science and technology are applied in many areas. Three of these application areas are treated in this volume of *ARIST*: 1) library networks, 2) information systems and services in the life sciences; and 3) information systems and services in the arts and humanities. In his chapter, "Library Networks," Glyn T. Evans observes that networks are accepted as a normal part of information storage and transfer. He describes the four major bibliographic utilities—OCLC, RLIN (Research Libraries Information Network), WLN (Washington Library Network), and UTLAS (University of Toronto Library Automation System)—and notes that they not only meet their intended objectives but have become excellent vehicles for carrying out both fundamental and applied research in information science. Evans reviews developments and plans for library networks on the regional, state, national, and international levels. He sees technical developments as enhancing the opportunities for network development and notes that the liberal arts are beginning to represent a market strong enough to justify hardware developments for bibliographic data processing. Evans observes that online library networks are growing and evolving but that some of the new services are revolutionary in their use of technical and social opportunity. While networks are growing and visions of national networks are exciting, Evans warns that failure to recognize and accommodate the essential differences in structure, funding, purpose, and goals between utilities and networks could lead to frustration.

In their chapter, "Information Systems and Services in the Life Sciences," Nancy Vaupel and Arthur W. Elias have reviewed the relevant literature and show that systems and services exist to promote information utilization in nearly every area of the life sciences. They observe that literature about systems and services for the medical and agricultural sciences predominates. Since their chapter specifically excludes the medical sciences, there is considerable attention given to the systems and services of agriculture. With regard to the disciplines of veterinary science, toxicology, pharmacology, and forestry, four themes are found to concern many authors, both information professionals and scientist end users. The information literature concentrates on: 1) comparing the life science information resources available; 2) reporting on the development of highly specialized information systems (or databases) and services, 3) describing the overall characteristics of particular databases, and 4) analyzing or recommending indexing structures for databases. The literature of the past five years shows that progress has taken place in the handling of life science information, especially with the help of the computer. The future holds promise for better communication about systems and services, more innovative system improvements on the part of database suppliers to meet the needs of end users, and more cooperation among systems and services to give the best service possible.

Joseph Raben and Sarah K. Burton review activities related to "Information Systems and Services in the Arts and Humanities" since the topic was covered in *ARIST* in 1972. Raben and Burton find that rather than creating new techniques or applications, computer-oriented humanists have devoted their energies to polishing those that were developed in the previous decade, to communicating their skills and knowledge among themselves and to newcomers, and to assimilating the new hardware. Their chief means have been those available to all scholars: conferences, conference proceedings, and specialized journals. All these avenues are now flourishing in the humanities and are often conjoined with parallel activities in the social sciences, thereby providing opportunities for mutual support and the exchange of information. The volume of material being produced, particularly dictionaries and concordances, implies that the use of computers in at least this area of humanities research is well established. Less widely recognized is the use of statistics in resolving humanistic problems, such as the dating of manuscripts. Other experimental areas include historical research, musical analysis, and the study of art objects. In all these fields, however, databases are being constructed, at least for bibliographic information, and from these may come more penetrating changes in the techniques of analysis.

7 Library Networks

GLYN T. EVANS
State University of New York,
Central Administration, Albany

INTRODUCTION

Library networks are now an accepted part of the process of information storage, retrieval, and transfer. A decade of effort since OCLC, Inc. (now OCLC Online Computer Library Center) went online in 1971 has given the four major utilities—OCLC, RLIN (Research Libraries Information Network), WLN (Washington Library Network), and UTLAS (University of Toronto Library Automation System)—and some regional networks a stability that is as remarkable as it is necessary. The literature reflects this. Such major journals as *JOURNAL OF THE AMERICAN SOCIETY FOR INFORMATION SCIENCE* (ASIS), *AMERICAN LIBRARIES*, and *BULLETIN OF THE AMERICAN SOCIETY FOR INFORMATION SCIENCE* (1979; 1980) devote large areas to reviews and perspectives on networks.

In 1980 the speculative literature on networks was a small part of the published record, and it still is (VENEZIANO). Reports of the acceptance, use, and expansion of network services outnumber theoretical articles, reflecting the general widening of interest and participation in library networks. Through growth and in response to members' needs the networks have stimulated fundamental and applied research in information science in areas such as the computer representation of non-Roman scripts and online public access to massive subject files.

The sociology of networks is the most important aspect of this literature now and for the near future. The reasons for this are: the White House Conference on Library and Information Services (WHCLIS), the changing patterns of governance, the activities and ambitions of national organizations, the Anglo-American Cataloging Rules, 2nd edition (AACR2), international developments, and shifting social and political perspectives. The increased strength of the networks has resulted in greater interest in their development and control.

Carol Bekar, Senior Administrator, Library, Sterling-Winthrop Research Institute, Rensselaer, New York, NY, prepared the bibliography and collaborated with the author in editing this chapter. The author acknowledges her skillful contribution with gratitude.

BIBLIOGRAPHIC UTILITIES

Many of the major utilities have continued to expand their range of services and the number and variety of their users. OCLC is still the giant in the field and continues to consolidate its position. SCHIEBER reports an increase of more than two million titles per year of catalog transactions (from 10.6 million in 1977–1978 OCLC fiscal year to 12.8 million in 1978–1979) and growth in numbers of libraries and terminals using OCLC. More than two million catalog cards per week are printed by OCLC; in the light of current technology, that is about two million too many. OCLC's acceptance, however, is better reflected by the success of its industrial revenue bond for $38.5 million to finance its new building and equipment and to extend its research and development (R&D) program. The new building is scheduled for occupancy in 1981. OCLC's growth is being maintained (OCLC, INCORPORATED, 1980a), although its annual *rate* of growth of catalog transactions is slowing (the increase is being reduced by 0.7 million to 1.3 million a year, to a 1979–1980 total of 14.1 million transactions). The causes for this decrease are puzzling. Does it reflect tightening acquisitions budgets, eradication of processing backlogs, completion of retrospective conversion projects that occupy 45% of shared cataloging effort, or the number of smaller libraries that are joining the system? OCLC made a significant policy decision in March 1980 when, after a special Board Committee held a series of public hearings throughout the nation, it decided not to restrict third-party use of machine-readable records as long as it is for the benefit of participating libraries, regional networks, or OCLC. However, use of such records by for-profit commercial entities will be "coordinated by OCLC management" (OCLC, INCORPORATED, 1980a).

RLIN, a member of Research Library Group (RLG), has continued to expand its membership, which doubled to 22 in 1980, and to develop new services.[1] The number of formats available for processing increased to include serials, maps, films, and music. Work on authority control, terminal developments, and reconfiguration of the database is continuing. Special projects in music and theology are being planned as well as an interlibrary loan (ILL) module. In addition, the earlier programs for RLG non-online network activities, such as document preservation, are being reexamined. RLIN continues to be successful in attracting private grants and foundation loans. More than $5.4 million in grants and loans were announced in *RESEARCH LIBRARIES GROUP NEWS* (1980b), and *ADVANCED TECHNOLOGY LIBRARIES* (1981b) reports another $1 million grant.

Whether RLIN can achieve the market acceptance of OCLC, Inc. remains to be seen. In April 1980 RLG and WLN were jointly awarded a grant of $300,000 to develop and to implement a shared authority file facility with Library of Congress (LC) participation (*INFORMATION HOTLINE*, 1980e). The first stage will be to develop a telecommunications link between the

---

[1] Much of the description of RLIN systems development is drawn from a personal communication from Lois Kershner, Director of Library Services, Research Libraries Group, Inc., November 20, 1980.

authority files of each network and to develop the software required to maintain jointly accessible files even though each system will continue to use its own authority files. Extension of this work into a common authority file would be a considerable and significant achievement. RLG has also agreed to cooperate in some areas with UTLAS (*ADVANCED TECHNOLOGY LIBRARIES*, 1981b).

In Canada, UTLAS has undergone a major administrative and structural change, following the dissolution of the Union Catalogue/Telecommunications Catalogue (UNICAT/TELECAT) Consortium. STIERWALT, in reviewing the development of UNICAT/TELECAT and the UTLAS network, reports that as large utilities grow and evolve into commercial facilities, they cannot respond rapidly enough to local needs to satisfy individual requirements for system changes, services, and information. Stierwalt suggests that computer-to-computer communication packages will be available at reasonable cost, permitting local systems to communicate with each other and with larger regional systems. His paper includes an important bibliography of all published and unpublished papers developed by the consortium.

UTLAS has also continued to expand its services. It now offers a current-awareness project (New Publications Awareness List), an alerting mechanism by subject field based on current catalog input (*UTLAS NEWSLETTER*, 1979). The Acquisition and Serials Control (ASC) system is being tested in a pilot project. It is designed with the support of the central bibliographic file. The interesting developments in UTLAS file design, in which purely local functions are expected to be devolved from the central facility to local mini-computers, indicate one of the options regarding the distribution of network services that are available to network planners. As shown later, the debate is as much tinged by social concerns as by technical or economic arguments.

EXTENSION OF NETWORK SERVICES

The networks have significant R&D programs, and new systems, generally based on existing databases and telecommunications facilities, are constantly being introduced.

The Online Union List of Serials system, developed by OCLC jointly with Indiana University, was implemented in fall 1980 (*OCLC NEWSLETTER*, 1981c). The strength of the serials database, the availability of American National Standards Institute (ANSI) Standard Z39.42 for Summary Serials Holdings, and the use of the OCLC serials control system combined to produce a unique opportunity for imaginative development and provide an important service for network members. An interesting facet of the design is the ability to designate OCLC members as input or union list processing centers for non-OCLC members.

Far less successful was OCLC's attempt at a library circulation system (*JOURNAL OF LIBRARY AUTOMATION*). After review, OCLC attempted to develop a system based on an original-equipment manufacturer (OEM) agreement with GEAC Computer Corp., Ltd. Talks were discontinued early in 1980, and OCLC decided to develop its own system linked to its telecommunication network; it is due for test demonstration by summer 1981. Again, the system would rely on the existing database of library holdings. OCLC cited financing and uncertain economic conditions as causes of withdrawal.

The above developments are evolutionary and were OCLC's stated goals as early as 1967. The revolutionary development for OCLC is the Channel 2000 experiment with the QUBE interactive cable TV system in Columbus, Ohio, in which OCLC makes available to users with a decoder the holdings of the local public library system along with the text of the *American Academic Encyclopedia* (OCLC, INCORPORATED. RESEARCH DEPARTMENT). Also available to users are an interactive home banking system, regional information, beginning reader and math programs, and a community bulletin board for the deaf. Using a touch pad keyboard and a menu card system users can search the public library catalogs by author, title, and subject. For example, the sequence of screens required to find the book [The] *Third Wave* by A. Toffler, searching by title, is:

- Select video catalog
- Select title index
- Select titles beginning with T
- Select titles in range Text–Those
- Select titles in range Thick–Thirty
- Select *Third Wave*

Through the system the book can be ordered for home delivery. The text of encyclopedia articles can be retrieved by similar procedures.

It is difficult to overestimate the significance of this development. In terms of theory, does the system of indexing—i.e., precoordinate rather than postcoordinate—demonstrate recall and retrieval advantages? Does it overthrow rather than challenge the elaborate structures and investment in postcoordinate retrieval, much of which was developed in response to the need to access existing databases that were not designed for online retrieval? What are the practical limitations of precoordinate searching? What precision can be achieved as a function of file size and in how many steps? What is the economic structure of such a system, whether accessed through home cable TV or via a direct terminal to computer link? How does or can the system cope with the unexpected—i.e., is there a need for an escape mechanism to postcoordinate strategy; if so, what will it be and how will it be used? How skilled does the user need to be? What are the requirements for vocabulary control and a syndetic structure in such a system, at least for subject access and perhaps for names too? Is the procedure limited to certain types of literature?

The social challenge of Channel 2000 is clear. Text, citations, and indices as well as document request and delivery procedures are harnessed in a link among a major computer resource, a local document store, and widespread communication access from the home or business site. Will technology and economics force developments, such as electronic publishing, inexpensive home printers, and massive text stores, to create at last the information source that is independent of time and distance?

LIBRARY NETWORKS   215

Changing technology and associated costs do affect optimal file design. Precoordinated searching was established in 1968 as the best technique for the online needs of OCLC. OCLC's success is partly derived from its selection of search keys, coupled with an established purpose that separated online file creation and maintenance from the demands of Boolean information retrieval searching. In discussing the development of multiple access storage devices MALINCONICO (1980c) points out that the cost of storage is the least important factor and that the required number of accesses is very important. In other words, at present, addition of more indexes to reduce accesses is probably cheaper; however, addition of an additional index to bridge access files and target records increases the number of needed accesses and hence cost and response time. A radically new storage device will be needed to resolve this contradiction.

The Council on Library Resources (CLR) commissioned a study from Battelle Columbus Laboratories on the benefits and costs of linking the bibliographic utilities (SMALLEY ET AL.). The report reviews the difficulties that are inherent in effecting linkage, including disparate organizational goals, overlapping interests, and the absence of communication protocols. The differing levels of achievement and the range of services among the utilities constrained the study. For example, limiting the hit rate study to monographs, excluding the ILL system of OCLC, and excluding corporate and special libraries, reduced the scope of the study drastically enough to make its conclusions questionable. The study found that OCLC had the highest hit (or database find) rate at 93%, with 87% found on RLIN or WLN. This example, however, is limited to current cataloging and fails to reflect the relative sizes of the databases—viz., OCLC holds more than seven million records, and RLIN holds less than two million. Searchers of the OCLC database would have gained about 3% more hits for current material with access to other utilities; others about 10% given access to OCLC. Battelle developed a computer planning model called BIBLINK during this study and recommended its continued use by the utilities (SMALLEY ET AL.).

CLR issued a discussion paper as a companion document that recommended continued study of the options and the use of BIBLINK (C. L. JONES). Both the report and the CLR document were criticized on methodology, results, interpretation, and future planning suggestions. Rowland Brown (*OCLC NEWSLETTER*, 1981b), president of OCLC stated that the networks are already committed to and participating in discussions of linking but that the report and CLR commentary contain suggestions that may not be in the best interests of libraries or the utilities.

DATABASE USAGE

The massive size and relative accessibility of databases are encouraging a wider range of users to test them for specific purposes and to report the results. KILTON commends the OCLC database for pre-order verification of serials orders. NIETMANN & HIRST (who study the cataloging of law materials) grant the superiority of the OCLC database but prefer RLIN anyway. Perhaps the most startling study, because of its implications, was the online searching of the OCLC database for research material from New South Wales, Australia, by DOBROVITS & O'MARA. They reported at least 50% success regardless of age, language, subject matter, or place of publication. However, a low hit rate can indicate the uniqueness of a special library collection, and hence its value to scholars, both online and through the offline production of special catalogs and bibliographies (BEASLEY).

The size and variety of the databases and their related services have interested special constituencies. Perhaps the first to organize formally were the medical librarians who were using OCLC (*START OF MESSAGE*). Special libraries as a group have not participated widely in the online library networks, although some libraries have been members. There have been some legal and fiscal impediments to the participation of for-profit institutional libraries, including the preservation of the tax status of the online utilities and the regional networks. Present rulings allow a minimal level of participation by that group. On the other hand, FEDLINK is comprised almost entirely of special libraries and has 270 members [U. S. FEDERAL LIBRARY COMMITTEE (FLC)]. Special libraries have felt excluded from participation and influence and are trying to change this situation. The National Commission on Libraries and Information Science (NCLIS) and the Special Libraries Association (SLA) created a joint task force on the Role of Special Libraries in a National Network (*LJ/SLJ HOTLINE*, 1980a). An important invitational conference on the Special Library Role in Networks was held in May 1980 (GIBSON). STRABLE posed the fundamental dilemmas: are networks ready for special libraries and are special libraries ready for networks? Although the conference reached no conclusion, it seems clear that technically, bibliographically, and fiscally, both will benefit. However, social issues such as the tax status of networks and participation in governance may present problems.

NCLIS has also been concerned that school libraries have not become major participants in networking, although superficially online networking seems an attractive economic proposition for them, particularly processing centers. However, one of the major hurdles is resistance to the idea by school librarians themselves (U. S. NATIONAL COMMISSION ON LIBRARIES AND INFORMATION SCIENCE).

As in the special library field, some school library processing centers have participated in library networks for years, have benefited, and have contributed to databases. The contribution has been a strong one since the ability to catalog educational materials has been available. In addition, online access to bibliographic networks provides an educational opportunity for school librarians to train children in library use.

Some states are using legislation and funding to foster closer regional and national cooperation by school libraries—e.g., New York (NEW YORK). As a result of legislation several pilot school processing systems are participating in OCLC or the Metro/New York Public Library Network but not without difficulty (MAUTINO; NEUMANN).

The databases of the major utilities are more than repositories of cataloging information. They are inventories of the usually partial holdings of participating libraries and can be copy specific depending how well the libraries maintain that inventory. The inventory is accessible, to varying degrees, both online and on archival tapes. Those libraries that maintained inventory did so in anticipation of using ILL and circulation systems as well as an online catalog. Developments by utilities in ILL and circulation systems are justifying that faith, and libraries are now mounting retrospective conversion projects through the utilities to build inventories. Forty-five percent of the activity on the OCLC system was devoted to retrospective conversion (OCLC INCORPORATED, 1980a). In June 1980, OCLC reorganized its holding symbols into an easier, locality driven hierarchic display, facilitating ILL access, and installed its ILL system (*OCLC NEWSLETTER*, 1981c). Studies show that use of databases, such as OCLC and the Ohio State University Library Circulation System (LCS) system, increases accessibility and improves ILL services. OCLC implemented its ILL subsystem in April 1979, and more than one million loans had been transacted by fall 1980 (OCLC INCORPORATED, 1980b). The logic of using a seven-million title, 70-million holdings database and a telecommunication system linking 2,300 libraries for ILL is inescapable. Early use studies show reduced processing and delivery times.

PLOTNIK (1979) greeted the news as "a new age unleashed" and described it as a "giant step closer to a national resources sharing system, the second phase of the Great American Online Library Dream." For many observers, the international implications are even more attractive. DOUGHERTY recognizes the link between universal bibliographic control (UBC) and universal availability of publications (UAP) and advocates the building of an international database.

Growth of ILL via networks, which is perceived by libraries as valuable, is not viewed by all as a boon. RAYMAN, reports considerable satisfaction in the use of the OCLC subsystem but indicates that ILL workload has increased in comparison with his 1978 study, probably through the Western Illinois University library's increased holdings symbols. Rayman is particularly concerned about the lending of books in print and its effect on publishing revenues. WHITE studied factors in the decision of libraries to acquire journals and found that consortium and network policies and knowledge of the availability of titles do affect library acquisitions. ROUSE & ROUSE (1979a), using ILL statistics from the Illinois State Library Network (ILLINET) management information base, report different periods of monograph obsolescence for different levels within networks in Illinois; at the regional level the period was 10 years, but at the state level the period was more than 15 years. The results presumably record the effect of hierarchic upward-referral systems searching for scarcer literature and have implications for library document retention policies. Findings may alter as hierarchical systems are replaced by the point-to-point technology of OCLC-like or circulation-network systems.

Online circulation systems that maintain both a database and an inventory are seen as becoming networks. The technical developments on mini- and microcomputers mean that modest library systems can now afford to build a network. Urban public library systems, small groups of community colleges, and gatherings of large academic libraries are forming into online circulation networks. The impetus for this development has come from the private sector, which began to develop in-house systems some years ago. BAHR describes 12 systems in a 1979 overview, and MATTHEWS, in a report that is deliberately complementary to that of Bahr and that of BOSS (1979), presents matrices of actual capabilities as they exist on installed customer circulation systems as of spring 1980. In addition to expected functions, Matthews reports Computer Library Systems, Inc.'s (CLSI) interface to Brodart Industries as a book jobber; three companies report interface to bibliographic utilities, and Kamen Sciences Co. report interfacing to online search systems. Bahr notes the economic advantages of circulation networks for smaller libraries: improved internal cost efficiencies and service expansions are improvements that are achieved easily. The cooperative ventures of networks are facilitated when member libraries have holdings in machine-readable form. CHERRY reports on public library use of CLSI's Public Access Catalog, a touch-sensitive online alternative to the card catalog, in which the human searcher touches a screen to indicate a choice from a screen display of data. Some operational problems have occurred, but they are easily corrected. The public did respond favorably to the terminal, particularly young readers; the skeptics were middle aged or older. However, patrons continue to use the card catalog. After the novelty of the terminal has worn off, the screen is used as a catalog, not as a toy.

DOWLIN surveyed library users for their preference for terminal access or catalog card access and found that 85% preferred terminal access. If direct subject access were available on the system tested, 94% would prefer terminals. Ease or speed of use were cited as reasons; 17% preferred the terminal because the screen showed location and inventory information. MILLER suggests that the managers of the Ohio State LCS system, after a decade of use, may now prefer a full bibliographic record and that they would consider incorporating Boolean logic with its search strategy. KASKE & SANDERS report that users consistently wish for features in a subject access system that cannot now be supplied by the bibliographic record—e.g., author credentials, book status, additional access points such as contents page, or chronological date coverage.

The conceptual boundary that separates online circulation from the online catalog has disappeared. ROCKMAN introduces a group of papers devoted to the potential of online circulation systems as public catalogs and suggests that circulation and cataloging information may merge into one file for convenience of the user. However, the operational problems of database selection, dispersal, and access remain. Should the major bibliographic utilities be linked to local circulation systems to build and feed the circulation database as OCLC is planning? Should local circulation systems support and relieve the demands on the big utilities for subject access? What proportion of information demands on a local circulation system can be satisfied by that data resource or need to be routed elsewhere? Automated circulation systems are becoming the hub of automation activities, an observation that challenges the view of the catalog as the primary focus of the library.

Studies of known-item searching of the University of Illinois circulation file by patrons showed that 56% of the searches that failed at the card catalog were successful online (SPECHT). Also graduate students used the system significantly differently from undergraduates—i.e., they were more likely to search for citations than for known-item location or availability of information. Patron access to catalog databases is discussed later.

Libraries that acquire a turnkey system are responsible for selecting and maintaining computer and communications equipment (FROST). The Austin Public Library is withdrawing in-house CLSI equipment in favor of IBM's Dortmund Bibliographic System (DOBIS), to be operated on the city's data processing computer (*ADVANCED TECHNOLOGY LIBRARIES*, 1981a; *LJ/SLJ HOTLINE*, 1981).

Some problems remain. The turnkey systems are tending to use full bibliographic records, while GORMAN (1979) argues for a shorter record, pointing to its economic and operational advantages. He speculates that the most significant impact of short records may be on traditional cataloging theory, noting the need for a short record catalog code; only a few very large libraries may need traditional full catalogs in machine-readable form as long as other libraries have online access to such full databases.

Some of the major utilities—WLN, UTLAS, and OCLC—perceive circulation as a decentralized module for local activity that is based on and linked to the master file. Turnkey circulation systems provide catalogs that tend to be self-contained or of limited linkage. No turnkey circulation system vendor provides online linkage to another vendor's turnkey circulation system (MATTHEWS).

The technical problems may take some time to resolve because turnkey systems tend to be developed by the private sector, and the utilities are not-for-profit groups. CUADRA discusses the public/private roles in the provision of library services and reports the establishment of a NCLIS Public/Private Task Force. Although the task force may not even identify all the problems that exist in this area, Cuadra hopes that it will mark the end of adversarial discussion in favor of a common good seen from a common perspective. The melding of circulation and bibliographic systems would be a good place to start.

Database use requires trained searchers and sites that are hospitable to access; in the shared cataloging environment, it requires people and sites that are dedicated to database creation. The installation of terminals to any library network requires careful planning and a sensitivity to human relations. Seldom is the installation of the first online terminal easy. PURNELL describes the integration and documentation that were required before the adoption of OCLC at Indiana University Regional Campus Libraries Technical Services Center and the development of an interface between OCLC and the internal automated acquisitions system. D. NEWMAN describes work done by Barkey at Claremont Colleges to interface OCLC with a Hewlett Packard 3000 Series II computer and to capture catalog data for local acquisitions, bookkeeping, and circulation systems. These systems had been developed internally, and the interface has created a "total library system." The system was financed through savings realized by improved cost efficiency after OCLC linkage.

BRADEN ET AL. surveyed 121 academic libraries after they adopted OCLC and provides quantitative information on current catalog production, staff size and utilization, and cataloging practices. Traditional policies and practices have been modified, in part because of varying practices by other participating libraries. Because cataloging standards are not uniformly applied by libraries that are entering data, the full potential of the system is not being realized. Braden et al. report the establishment by OCLC of its Internetwork Quality Control Council (IQCC) and the council's recognition that the final quality of the database rests with the members of the network and the regional networks. The utility is only the vehicle. The regional network staffs are responsible for training the personnel of their new member libraries. MELIN discusses the roles, functions, and characteristics of network staff librarians who provide vital, human links between the network utility and the local library.

DATABASE CONTENT AND QUALITY

Quality control of databases is difficult enough under the controlled environment of major producers such as Chemical Abstracts Service (CAS), R. R. Bowker Co., or LC. Uncertainty increases with every new member of any shared network. WLN addressed this problem in its basic design, and as its software is adopted elsewhere [e.g., at the Southeastern Library Network (SOLINET)] may find its work in this field widely accepted. THOMSON discusses the potential use of WLN software in Australia. Other networks and LC rely largely on reports from the field and subsequent correction—a remedial and expensive procedure—coupled with extensive education and awareness among participants. OCLC reports that more than 45,000 error report corrections were made by its central quality control group in 1980.[2]

ROUGHTON reviewed 612 serials records and found that about 25% contained an error while 68% lacked at least one of six fields considered basic to a serial record; about 33% had been authenticated by LC. Roughton suggests that although it may be reasonable to lock monographic records, serials records are so dynamic that the ability to amend them should be more widely available—i.e., to more libraries than the 18 Conversion of Serials (CONSER) participants. Where should such unlocking stop when the evidence is that even highly skilled and motivated CONSER libraries create a high proportion of errors? MARTINELLI describes a fundamental disagreement between LC and the National Library of Medicine (NLM) over the descriptive cataloging of serials and stresses the need for standardization, although NLM has now agreed to follow LC interpretation under AACR2. Both are CONSER participants; what chance for poor mortals?

Unfortunately, there is no coherent theory of the economic or bibliographic aspects of maintaining quality control in a decentralized bibliographic

---

[2] Personal communication to the author from Philip Scheiber, OCLC Inc., December 1980.

database. EVANS posed 11 fundamental questions touching economics, investment patterns, authority, error correction, personnel, assignment of roles among agencies, standardization, and sanction and reward procedures, but they are barely addressed under the pressure of remediation, let alone answered. Theoretical work is proceeding, however, in the development of computer correction routines for spelling errors. ZAMORA describes the evolution of the computer techniques used at CAS, in which a hashing technique for dictionary look-up and data compression extends the automated editing procedure and increases the proportion of misspelled words found and subsequently corrected. Manual editing is still used in cases of uncertainty. Can and should similar automated editing procedures be adopted online by the bibliographic utilities? What are the economic advantages of such a system, and what are the tradeoffs in costs and response time? O'NEILL & ALURI proposed a method for correcting typographical errors in subject headings in OCLC records. The method consists of deriving forward and reverse search codes from both the authority file and the incoming heading and then comparing for exact matches, correctable headings, and questionable entries that will need manual editing. Under test, all omissions, additions, substitutions, and transpositions were corrected, as were subdivisions containing abbreviations. Form subdivisions (form of item, e.g., essays, addresses) that contain errors are troublesome; many were identified but not corrected.

The work of both Zamora and O'Neill and Aluri depends on the availability of authority files, the consistent need for quality control. OCLC made the LC name authority file of 180,000 names available online to users in January 1980, but no studies are available on how this file affects data quality (*OCLC NEWSLETTER*, 1981c). MALINCONICO (1979) reasserts the centrality of authority files in a computer database environment as long as their logical structure is maintained and the files are used to control the evolving database. The development of machine interpretable links and the establishment of a syndetic structure allows words and names to be used consistently for different purposes. In this way, the database can become a catalog or rather has the potential of becoming an infinity of catalogs.

CLR's Bibliographic Service Development Program (BSDP) proposed an integrated consistent authority file service for nationwide use (*LC INFORMA-TION BULLETIN*, 1980a). Their document describes the problems of authority file development, reviews the present environment, reports the project under the grant to RLG and WLN cited above, and proposes an administrative structure for building and maintaining the file. Their definition of nationwide, however, means for now at least those who participate in the file's creation, members of RLIN and WLN and others who have access to RLIN, even though LC has prime authority over file content. CLEMENT reports on the automated file at the National Library of Canada (NLC), making the welcome suggestion that the use of authority files will allow local or national flexibility while ensuring network compatibility and facilitating national and international bibliographic data exchange.

AACR2 may give us a fresh start, following its adoption on January 2, 1981. The OCLC network pulled off a remarkable feat when it closed its system for 12 days to convert its online seven-million record file to AACR2. In the process 3.7 million changes were made to 2.7 million records; 39% of the file was changed, and most of the remaining 61% was either in AACR2 form or was compatible with it. The costs of doing this may never be computed; even the revenue lost for 12 days is considerable. The result is a consistent but not perfect file; certainly some of the conversions are not totally correct (*OCLC NEWSLETTER*, 1981a).

Nevertheless, as AVRAM (1979) notes, "every machine-readable record which does not conform to AACR2 by January 1981 will be a retrospective record." These records will need conversion; what about the databases of those networks that have not automatically converted to AACR2?

AACR2 is expected to provide better standards and to produce records that are more amenable to computer manipulation and maintenance. However, FASANA points out that: 1) the latitude given to local decision is anathema for a shared cataloging database; 2) the continuation of International Standard Bibliographic Description (ISBD) punctuation is already backward-looking from the users' viewpoint; 3) to link adoption of AACR2 with closing the card catalog is erroneous because of the problems of synchronization and substitution; 4) retrospective conversions are not complete; and 5) although the fully online catalog may be desirable, it is not yet here, and it may be late. Nine years after the New York Public Library card catalog was closed in 1972, problems that were created then are still being resolved.

THE ONLINE CATALOG

The vision of the online catalog is shared by many and is a recurrent theme in the literature. To many it is already here or is at least in part; online circulation systems and shared catalog databases are frequently viewed as online catalogs.

There are thoughtful reports and debates about the content and appearance of the online catalog. GORMAN & HOTSINPILLER, responding to charges that ISBD punctuation and conventions baffle the user, built a small file that was a mixture of cards with and without ISBD and then tested the comprehension and response time of 48 students to the file. Their study showed that ISBD aided rather than hindered reader understanding. SMITH (1980b) reports a meeting at which display systems for nuclear power plant controls and flight cockpit information were described along with legibility criteria for data display in command systems. BORRELL briefly reviews the technological developments in information display, carefully defining information display in terms of three common facets: 1) a cathode ray tube (CRT) is the display medium, 2) data are stored and processed by computers, and 3) data are transmitted. Various groups, including producers of videotex systems, producers of computer graphics, and communication related industries have an interest in the field. These developments must affect the services offered by library networks. SMITH (1980a) reviewed another meeting that dealt with design principles, user dialog and performance, terminal allocation and dispersal, home delivery of library service, and access for the handicapped.

Display formats are also considered by BOSS & MARCUM. They predict that online catalogs will be cheaper than card catalogs in five years—even including conversion costs—and suggest that computer output microform (COM) can be an interim step toward an online catalog. They caution however, against an interim change of only two years because of disruption of processes.

As terminal time becomes available, as OCLC's database grows, and as searching becomes more precise, libraries are experimenting with OCLC and other network terminals for public access. One stumbling block has been the limitation in the OCLC system of 256 responses to one search; that limitation was eliminated in September 1980 when search enhancements were introduced (*OCLC NEWSLETTER*, 1981c). Again using OCLC's path of precoordination and remembering the comments of MALINCONICO (1980b), it is expected that less than 1% of the seven-million record file will result in a "dead-end search" after the addition of qualifiers such as date and format, the increase in the number of fields indexed to include such elements as performer [Machine Readable Cataloging (MARC) Tag 705], and expansion of the number of responses to 1,500. Some aspects of the enhancements—e.g., the performer search—are very attractive to library patrons and special groups such as music librarians. The frustration of the dead-end search, and the mechanism that grew up among regional networks as they publicly recognized it and began to swap dead-end search codes among themselves, eventually resulted in SCOTT's newsletter, *Dead End Searches;* it is now happily in demise after installation of the search enhancements.

The search code approach also tends to permit a searcher to find an item even if the patron has a faulty citation because it does not require full textual correspondence during the search. At the University of Michigan, a study of public use by FRIEDMAN found that patrons used author/title code 1,922 times out of 3,978 searches, title 1,713 times, author 218 times, and CODEN only once. She concludes that public access to the utility databases in large academic libraries is useful and encourages libraries to examine the potential of the databases for public service.

Clearly, present online patron access raises more questions than it answers, even though there is great potential for cost-effective library service. A welcome start to clarification of the issues is the small grant made by CLR jointly to OCLC and RLIN (itself a welcome sign) to study online patron access to bibliographic databases.

TECHNOLOGICAL DEVELOPMENTS

Technical evolution continues to enhance the opportunities for network development. Networks are beginning to have a market strong enough to justify technical and hardware development for purely bibliographic data processing. This is not new—the American Library Association (ALA) computer print train and the OCLC Model 100 terminal are early examples—but new levels of innovation are being attained. Examples of new peripherals that are visible to the user are the OCLC Model 110 terminal (capable of multifonts, multiscripts, and right-to-left, through the downline loading of pro-

224   GLYN T. EVANS

grams from computer to terminal), the decoder for Channel 2000, and CLSI's touch terminals.

Less visible are the innovations in telecommunications and database system design. RUSH describes what is needed for the user to perform known and unknown item searches, to add, alter, or delete data, and to arrange data in a massive online bibliographic system. Present computer architecture does not provide an efficient system for these functions. Rush then describes the OCLC hardware structure of the network supervisor to control communications, the application processors (presently Xerox Sigma 9 machines), and the database processor (both network supervisor and database processor are Tandem T16 computers). System use, files, file access procedures, and the size of the database are reported. Finally, he recounts the growth of the database and the continuing demands on it. The remote communications processor that is allowing SOLINET (and other regional networks) to develop regional systems linked to and devolved from the main OCLC system is an integral component of the design developed by OCLC.

Such an online system requires constant automatic monitoring (which is the process of collecting data associated with the functioning and use of a system) and evaluation (which is the process of analyzing the function and use of a system) so that decisions can be made concerning the effectiveness of the system (both hardware and software) in satisfying its design objectives. PENNIMAN & DOMINICK report generally on the problem and collaborate with Rush (DOMINICK ET AL.) in proposing a monitoring system for the OCLC system.

One example of system monitoring at OCLC is reported by RASTOGI. He studied the retrieval behavior of derived search keys from the name/title files for effectiveness (i.e., the ability of the key to find all and only those entries in the file of interest) and efficiency (i.e., the minimal expenditure of time, money, and energy). Models of search key behavior were compared with actual performance of the system with a large file when the OCLC database had 4.4 million records. Rastogi proposed that the high-response keys be split into a separate file and that the user be asked for more information. This work influenced the search enhancements established by OCLC in 1980.

Theoretical work on library network design and modeling continues to appear. W. ROUSE has prepared a tutorial on the mathematical modeling of library systems, in which he considers book use, resource allocation, and library networks. He reports that so far modeling can only be credited with very limited practical accomplishments although it may be gaining increased attention and use. KANG & ROUSE reviewed the applicability of forecasting methods in predicting demand for library network services, using data from ILLINET. Regression methods were appropriate for analyzing ILL statistics. Interactive analysis is discussed, and Kang reports that the programs are being used regularly to provide forecasts to the Illinois State Library, which operates ILLINET.

Game theory has been used to study library networks by COHEN & VIJVERBERG. They found that users tend to cluster into a coalition around common use of a single function, e.g., cataloging in OCLC. The analyses were performed before the rapid expansion of network services in the past two years. The theory may help to identify constituencies within the multipurpose networks and may help to develop charging algorithms for different services and clusters of users.

Changing telecommunications technology may affect library networks. The Public Services Satellite Consortium (PSSC) surveyed 118 academic libraries in 38 states (selected because of their proximity to a narrow band telecommunication facility) to assess how and which library services might be facilitated through the use of satellite communications (*PUBLIC SERVICE SATELLITE CONSORTIUM NEWSLETTER*). The studies found that 99% of libraries engaged in ILL, 82% in OCLC, 73% in literature searching, and 34% in automated circulation.[3] It is too early to assess how satellite transmission will affect networks other than perhaps reducing costs. Will there ever be sufficient library network telecommunications traffic to justify a portion of a satellite channel? Clearly, industry expects the market for the home delivery of information to expand, with interactive terminals becoming a major growth area; one in four U. S. households is expected to have video terminals by the end of the 1980s (*INFORMATION HOTLINE*, 1980c). If technology takes the path of OCLC's Channel 2000, however, saturation may be even higher much sooner.

The international aspects of library networking are also demonstrated in the work to establish computer manipulation of non-Roman texts. RLIN is working on East Asian scripts (*RESEARCH LIBRARIES GROUP NEWS*, 1980a), and OCLC's work on its Model 110 terminal has been noted. AGENBROAD reviews the current status of character sets, and WELLISCH discusses the exchange of bibliographic data in non-Roman scripts. Romanization and the development of ANSI standards for romanization are discussed by BRANDHORST, who stresses the importance of "reversibility" as a fundamental requirement.

REGIONAL LIBRARY NETWORKS

The regional networks provide local training, implementation, documentation, and liaison support to the major utilities. Their relationships with the utilities are symbiotic. Through their advocacy and marketing, they stimulated the utilities' growth and thus grew themselves. They had disparate beginnings and have different roots and accountabilities. The combination of new technological opportunity, original development, and local needs is stimulating the reassessment of regional missions and the creation of new, semi-independent paths.

SOLINET is developing a regional support system in which the WLN software originally written for IBM equipment is being adapted for a Burroughs B7805 computer (*SOLINEWS*, 1980a; 1980b). The system will be demonstrated with ten test libraries in May 1981. SOLINET acquired the WLN

---

[3] Personal communication from Mary Diebler, Service Development Specialist, Public Service Satellite Consortium. January 21, 1981.

software under license. OCLC is participating and completed the first stage of the devolution of its own telecommunications network when it installed the first regional communications processor, using Tandem Computers, Inc. equipment to concentrate telecommunications between Atlanta and Columbus. This technical development required a new contractual relationship between SOLINET and OCLC, a development away from the vendor/ broker relationships heretofore established in network contracts. This development has considerable significance for the future of networking.

The Pittsburgh Regional Library Center (PRLC) (*PRLC NEWSLETTER*) has performed a Delphi study to help it plan its own future. The study recommended that PRLC concentrate in five areas: 1) union listing, 2) continuing education, 3) cooperation with other networks, 4) acting as an information clearinghouse, and 5) cooperative purchasing. OHIONET, which evolved as the regional network supporting libraries in Ohio when OCLC changed its structure in 1977, seems to be coming full circle as it begins preliminary discussions about developing its own circulation system (*LIBRARY JOURNAL*, 1981; OHIONETWORK). Network territorial boundaries are beginning to shift as PALINET began to provide service to Maryland libraries previously served by Capital Consortium Network (CAPCON) in Washington, DC (*PALINET NEWS*). Smith addressed the question of unity of network services in the Midwest, served presently by OCLC, RLIN, Midwest Regional Library Network (MIDLNET), and state networks (*MIDLNET NEWS-LETTER*).

R. JONES reports on the adoption of the UTLAS system by the Tri-Regional Catalogue in Northeastern Ontario. Adoption and use of UTLAS for the production of regional union catalogs have not significantly affected costs, but they have led to increased productivity and service.

STATE ACTIVITIES

WLN is operated by the Washington State Library. ILLINET is the only regional network tied to a major utility to be operated by a state's library. Indiana Cooperative Library Services Authority (INCOLSA) was established as a state agency outside the Indiana State Library. Minnesota Interlibrary Telecommunications Exchange (MINITEX), California Library Authority for Systems and Services (CLASS), which as a regional network provides RLIN services in California, and the State University of New York/OCLC network are the only other regional networks with state agency relationships. The rapid growth of networks has not been generally fostered by state library activities although many state libraries are members of networks. Many state library agencies are now developing plans for statewide network services that rely on and interface with regional networks and the bibliographic utilities and that capitalize on past system investment. Examples are the LOUISIANA STATE LIBRARY, which is developing a statewide union list based on the Louisiana Numerical Register and the holdings of OCLC libraries in AMIGOS and SOLINET; the Ohio Regional Library and Information System (ORLIS) (OHIO STATE LIBRARY); the State Library Commission of Iowa, which is to build a statewide library network called IOWANET (IOWA STATE LIBRARY); the Rhode Island Interrelated Library Network proposal (RHODE ISLAND DEPARTMENT OF STATE LIBRARY SERVICES); the Alabama Public Service pilot projects for multitype library cooperatives, which will join OCLC for ILL and COM catalog production (ALABAMA PUBLIC LIBRARY SERVICE); the proposal of the Oklahoma Department of Libraries for the Oklahoma Library Network (OKLAHOMA DEPARTMENT OF LIBRARIES), which will use OCLC as one mechanism; and the New Hampshire Centralized Catalog Card Service, which phased out its own system in favor of OCLC.[4] BECKER & HAYES proposed a Statewide DataBase for Missouri in 1978, and PALMOUR & DEWATH surveyed statewide Missouri library holdings in 1980.

EPSTEIN & EPSTEIN, in a proposed five-year plan prepared for the Wisconsin Department of Public Instruction, offer a comprehensive review of current development opportunities; they recognize the varied stages of developments of libraries within a single state. The plan takes careful cognizance of the current network environment and the history of individual investment in library network membership.

The guiding principle behind these efforts is that there are many small public and school libraries that have not and may never join a regional network but will nonetheless need access to bibliographic services. COM catalogs and regional ILL processing centers, both relying in part on the products of the utilities, are the general answer. It will be interesting to see how these state-based networks develop as telecommunications technology evolves.

Some regions within states are displaying interesting initiatives and sensitive awareness to the opportunities presented by technology. For example, FORD & MEYER prepared a technical proposal for a library automation network in south central New York. It drew attention to problems that remain unaddressed or unsolved on existing commercial minicomputer-based systems, including consolidation and maintenance of an online union data file for many libraries, ILL services, and external interfaces to other systems. KING ET AL. reviewed the feasibility of establishing an interlibrary telecommunications network in northern New York and proposed a local structure that would interface with existing bibliographic resource networks, a proposal that seems eminently sensible.

NATIONAL AND INTERNATIONAL DEVELOPMENTS

Two main areas of international development affect networks: the logical problems of the exchange of bibliographic data (i.e., standards, codes, character sets, transliterations, and formats) and technical problems (i.e., direct linkage possibilities, expansion of online services, and fiscal and political relationships). Direct linkage offers exciting opportunities. OCLC is planning an

---

[4] Personal communication from Avis M. Duckworth, State Librarian, Concord, New Hampshire, December 3, 1980.

online extension to the United Kingdom (UK) and Western Europe in 1981. GATENBY ET AL. report on an investigation to link OCLC online to Australia via the Australian Multi-mode International Data Acquisition Service (MIDAS). They concluded that as the MIDAS system becomes fully operational it would be worth continuing negotiations for online service from OCLC.

UTLAS announced a $1 million contract to provide services to librarians in Japan through the Maruzen Co., Ltd. of Japan, in which Maruzen will act as a node in the network. Long-range plans call for a joint program to develop a Japanese character set for printing various library products (*ADVANCED TECHNOLOGY LIBRARIES*, 1981c).

IFLA (INTERNATIONAL FEDERATION OF LIBRARY ASSOCIATIONS AND INSTITUTIONS) published a revised second edition of *UNIMARC: Universal MARC Format* in 1980. UNIMARC will provide an international format into and from which national agencies will translate records from the national system. The second edition includes eight data elements that are needed for the unique identification and description of a bibliographic item and that would therefore need to be included in each record.

In 1979 NLC completed a three-year project that examines its role, services, and objectives. The report proposes a five-year plan that calls for the creation of a Canadian library network and describes a policy framework for its implementation (CANADA. NATIONAL LIBRARY). The proposed structure is a decentralized network in which NLC would be a central node and would play a coordinating role but would also contract with other network libraries for such services as record creation and backup lending and referral.

DUCHESNE ET AL. (1979; 1980) report two of the studies of the Canadian Computerized Bibliographic Center Study, an overview of computerized library networking in Canada, and a final report that supplements the NLC report cited above. Nine recommendations are made, covering the need for promotion, establishment of priorities, online interconnection programs, funding, liaison and publicity, standards, and the establishment of a Canadian national bibliographic database. UTLAS, the largest Canadian online network, is treated as a library processing facility in the reports; its role will be to interconnect its communications network to other network nodes.

NLC has invested considerable effort in modifying and adopting IBM's DOBIS system for its own use and for its role as a node in the forthcoming national network. The English/French bilingual needs of Canada are added to the usual requirements of a bibliographic database system. DUNN, NEWMAN & CLYDE, and NEWMAN ET AL. report on the work to develop a Canadian government version of DOBIS based at NLC and the Canadian Institute for Scientific and Technical Information (CISTI). The *NATIONAL LIBRARY NEWS* reports on the use of DOBIS for the automation of the Canadian Union Catalogue.

In the United States, LC continues its difficult task of developing extensions to the MARC formats. In 1980 (U. S. LIBRARY OF CONGRESS, 1980), preliminary specifications for technical reports, an extension of *Books: a MARC Format*, were issued. Technical reports are defined as documents that formally present the results of scientific, technical, or management activities and that provide information of more than transient interest, usually with limited initial distribution but which are often placed in central repositories. The format is extended to provide for the Standard Technical Report Number (STRN) and other agency and project numbers, and a new field for enriched titles augmented by a cataloger is created. The MARC Format for Machine Readable Data Files (MRDF) has been revised in a preliminary edition to incorporate revisions of ANSI Z39.2-1979 (American National Standard for Bibliographic Information Interchange on Magnetic Tape) (U. S. LIBRARY OF CONGRESS. NETWORK DEVELOPMENT OFFICE). The format was designed to accommodate data elements specified in AACR2 but has been expanded to accept various products—e.g., a union catalog. A revision of codes in the legend is also proposed.

LONG prepared a summary study of message text formats for bibliographic search queries that reviews the access points and search keys used by LC, NLM, OCLC, University of Chicago, WLN, Northwestern University, and RLIN. This work is fundamental to an understanding of the technical problems of linking bibliographic utilities. VONDRAN reviews the experience of the National Union Catalog (NUC) and its implications for network planning. Emphasis is on the variations of catalog entries submitted to NUC and recommendations for resolving bibliographic conflicts (e.g., written guidelines and the establishment of an editorial staff). The diminished comprehensiveness of NUC is compared with the growth of the OCLC database. Both Long's and Vondran's papers were published in the Network Planning Paper series of LC's Network Development Office.

LC's Network Advisory Committee (NAC) (DOUGHERTY & MARUYAMA) met in March 1980 and identified six key issues in the creation, production, and utilization of a national bibliographic database: 1) ownership of bibliographic records; 2) ownership of machine-readable bibliographic records; 3) access to and use of bibliographic records; 4) the economic incentive for creating bibliographic records; 5) fair compensation for their use; and 6) the lack of a mechanism to share bibliographic data on a national scale.

Later, LC issued two Working Papers on the development, governance, and support of a nationwide network and the ownership and distribution of bibliographic data (WEBSTER & MARUYAMA). The papers are to be discussed in a series of Forums on Nationwide Network and Bibliographic Data (NEWS FROM THE LIBRARY OF CONGRESS), to be held throughout 1981 by NAC and professional organizations. The papers are significant because they acknowledge that bottom-up planning is essential in the development of a national library network, whatever form the network will take. The CONSER file was distributed by LC in 1980 after five years of cooperative effort (INFORMATION HOTLINE, 1980b). Over a quarter of a million records contributed by 15 participants, including those authenticated by LC and NLC, and built and maintained on the OCLC system, were made available in the MARC format. MARTIN (1980b) reviews the ambiguous goals of LC and makes a strong plea that its strength be restored and that it reassert its position as a major national resource, if not the official national library.

In making this plea, Martin is asserting a de facto role for LC. The bibliographic community continually looks to LC for records, authority, and service. As shared technology evolves, the need for an ultimate bibliographic authority becomes even more apparent. In discussing LC's role in national planning, AVRAM (1979) describes several bibliographic endeavors in which LC is cooperating with other institutions but notes that the original concept of distribution of MARC data principally from LC to others is no longer valid. The MARC format and procedures need a reexamination that recognizes the roles of the bibliographic utilities in a national network.

The success of the bibliographic utilities has given substance to the dream of a national library network. The concept of a national network is easy to grasp but difficult to define; even the act of definition becomes an act of advocacy. The national network and its structure and governance are the omnipresent topics of discussion. The fundamental debate is between advocates of "bottom-up" vs. "top-down" planning, although that statement masks the subtleties of the problem.

The WHITE HOUSE CONFERENCE ON LIBRARY AND INFORMA-TION SERVICES (WHCLIS) provided some resolutions on networking. Pre-conferences provided an opportunity for discussion and enunciation of the issues. The most interesting and important pre-conference was Networking for Networkers held in Indiana. A brochure (MARKUSON & WOOLLS, 1979), distributed to WHCLIS delegates, posed the question: Is a national library network desirable? The brochure points out that a national library network does not exist but that a viable and active network structure has been developed by librarians and library boards outside state and federal directives. MARKUSON & WOOLLS (1980) subsequently edited the complete pre-conference proceedings.

MALINCONICO (1980b) suggests that a national bibliographic network is a patrician pursuit, suitable only for research libraries that can afford it—a surprising view given the evidence of grant and foundation subsidies to entice research libraries into RLIN. E. COHEN criticizes this opinion, citing the telephone system to show that the greater the use, the lower the cost. GORMAN (1980a) discusses the development of RLIN and regrets the diversion and dilution of resources required by that effort. The Association of Research Libraries (ARL) (*INFORMATION HOTLINE*, 1980a) adopted eight principles for network development, which laid responsibilities on the bibliographic utilities that would be difficult to fulfill and in some cases may not be in their members' best interests. It is difficult to see, for example, why a utility should support the development of local systems that would encourage migration and loss of revenue. Would such an investment be in the best interests of all of its members, to whom it has a fiduciary and legal responsibility? The distribution of network services may be technically and fiscally desirable, but there is no evidence that ARL had devolution in mind as it framed its principles. MALINCONICO (1980a) also suggests that NCLIS modify its current charge and govern the national network. This is a top-down view.

SWANSON (1980b) carefully demonstrates that "libraries are woven into the social structure and so in some measure share the complexity and pluralism of society. Like society they cannot be redesigned in accord with an overall goal." He argues that the stated goals of national information policy: 1) do not identify the fundamental problems that libraries face, 2) disregard the need for correctability and evolutionary regulative mechanisms, and 3) specifically propose to dismantle present regulative mechanisms of the market. In another paper, SWANSON (1980a) warns against top-down planning when he argues that the "NCLIS/ALA goal of equal opportunity of access to information is unintelligible. That does not mean, however, that it is innocuous; obviously there are people who claim to understand what it means and will try to apply it. It poses therefore a direct threat to evolutionary mechanisms."

The fact is that networks are already governed. MARTIN (1980a), in reviewing *The Structure and Governance of Library Networks*, notes that the book is an answer that is seeking a question, "an expression of the desire to create a top-down governance structure rather than allowing the existing networks and their governances to evolve."

CARLILE and CARLILE & BURKLEY describe the diversity among legal structures of library networks. Almost without exception the national and regional networks are governed or advised by elected boards and committees drawn from their members. Thus, the networks express the needs of their members and constituents, who have a stake in their future. Network managements tread the path of leadership with a legal and fiduciary responsibility in their hands and a clear accountability. Further, librarians elected to serve their networks do so with sensitivity and responsibility and with increasing experience in the techniques and possibilities of network governance.

Much of the discussion of networking is stimulated by this shift in investment and influence on library and information services away from older organizations. The bibliographic community has yet to deal effectively with the new cooperative organism.

WEDGEWORTH states that the library community cannot control appointments to a statutory governance body and that a voluntary governance mechanism may be the next step. It is necessary to give greater scrutiny to services as opposed to needs, moving from the network as an "unanalyzed abstraction" to an operational entity defined in operational terms. He points out that shared expectations can lead to effective compromises in which different organizations can share interests and develop optimal solutions. Organizational response mechanisms, such as negotiation, compromise and tradeoffs, must not be disregarded but used effectively.

Wedgeworth writes: "Any governance mechanism we adopt must recognize that our world has become much more complex over the past two decades. . . . Increasingly such discussion will take place in international arenas like IFLA, FID, ICA, and Unesco. Who will speak for the U. S. in those arenas? We must move to answer that and other governance questions before the issues have left us in favor of less judicious solutions."

CONCLUSIONS

Online library networks continue to grow in numbers of participants and range of services offered. While many of the new services are evolutionary, others (e.g., OCLC's Channel 2000) are revolutionary in their use of technical

232 GLYN T. EVANS

and social opportunity. Significant progress is being made in the implementation of new systems and services, the definition of fundamental logical structures of data structure and format, and the technical and telecommunications facets of networking.

Networks will also expand, probably through linkage among themselves, through devolution from central sites by region and function, and through international expansion. The establishment of utilities and networks as viable cross-boundary social structures is causing some perturbation in the structure of information services, stimulating visions of a national library network and exciting ambitions to define and control such an entity. Failure to recognize and accommodate the essential differences of structure, funding, purpose, and goals among the utilities and networks may lead to the continued frustration of what may be laudable and valid targets for the linked evolution of independent networks and leave the targets foundering as pious hopes rather than as realizable entities.

BIBLIOGRAPHY

ADVANCED TECHNOLOGY LIBRARIES. 1981a. DOBIS/LEUVEN to Replace CLSI in Austin. Advanced Technology Libraries. 1981 January; 10(1): 1. ISSN: 0044-636X.
ADVANCED TECHNOLOGY LIBRARIES. 1981b. RLG Switches to Annual Program Fee, Forges Links with UTLAS. Advanced Technology Libraries. 1981 January; 10(1): 1,7. ISSN: 0044-636X.
ADVANCED TECHNOLOGY LIBRARIES. 1981c. UTLAS Sale Will Improve Library Services in Japan. Advanced Technology Libraries. 1981 January; 10(1): 2. ISSN: 0044-636X.
AGENBROAD, JAMES E. 1980. Character Sets: Current Status and East Asian Prospects. Journal of Library Automation. 1980 March; 13(1): 18-35. ISSN: 0022-2240.
ALABAMA PUBLIC LIBRARY SERVICE. 1980. Proposed Rules and Regulations for Pilot Project: Cooperative Multitype Library Systems. Montgomery, AL: Alabama Public Library Service; 1980 November 1. 13p. Available from: the authors, 6030 Monticello Drive, Montgomery, AL 36130.
AMERICAN LIBRARIES. 1980. Understanding the Utilities. American Libraries. 1980 May; 11(5): 262-279. ISSN: 0002-9769.
ARTHUR D. LITTLE, INCORPORATED. 1979. A Comparative Evaluation of Alternative Systems for the Provision of Effective Access to Periodical Literature. A Report to the National Commission on Libraries and Information Science (NCLIS). Washington, DC: NCLIS; 1979. 119p. Also available from: Superintendent of Documents, U.S. Government Printing Office, Washington, DC 20402. GPO: 052-003-00715-1.
AVRAM, HENRIETTE D. 1978. Recommendations toward the Establishment of a Common Exchange Format for Use by All Agencies in the Information Community. In: Diericks, H.; Hopkinson, A., eds. Towards a Common Bibliographic Exchange Format?: Proceedings of the International Symposium on Bibliographic Exchange Formats; 1978 April 27-29; Taormina, Sicily. London, England: UNIBID; 1978. 135-146.

(Contents page cites title as: Various Aspects of Exchange: ISO 2709, UNIMARC, the Reference Manual, ISBDS).

AVRAM, HENRIETTE D. 1979. The Role of the Library of Congress in National Planning for Bibliographic Control. In: National Planning for Bibliographic Control: Minutes of the Association of Research Libraries (ARL) 94th Meeting; 1979 May 10-11; Cambridge, MA. Washington, DC: ARL; 1979. 14-24. Available from: the publisher, 1527 New Hampshire Ave., N.W., Washington, DC 20036.

AVRAM, HENRIETTE; MCCALLUM, SALLY H. 1980. Directions in Library Networking. Journal of the American Society for Information Science. 1980 November; 31(6): 438-444. ISSN: 0002-8231.

BAHR, ALICE HARRISON. 1979. Automated Library Circulation Systems, 1979-80. 2nd edition. White Plains, NY: Knowledge Industry Publications, Inc.; 1979. 105p. (Professional Librarian Series). ISBN: 0-914236-34-2; LC: 79-16189.

BATTIN, PATRICIA. 1980. Research Libraries in the Network Environment: The Case for Cooperation. Journal of Academic Librarianship. 1980 May; 6(2): 68-73. ISSN: 0099-1333.

BEASLEY, RUTH ANN. 1980. Another Look at OCLC's Potential for Special Libraries. Journal of the American Society for Information Science. 1980 July; 31(4): 300-301. ISSN: 0002-8231.

BECKER, JOSEPH; HAYES, ROBERT M. 1979. A Statewide Data Base of Bibliographic Records for Missouri Libraries. Los Angeles, CA: Becker and Hayes, Inc.; 1979. 57p. Available from: the authors, 11661 San Vicente Blvd., Los Angeles, CA 90049.

BELL, C. MARGARET. 1980. The Applicability of OCLC and Inforonics in Special Libraries. Special Libraries. 1980 September; 71(9): 398-404. ISSN: 0038-6723.

BERGER, PATRICIA WILSON. 1980. Managing Revolutions: Coping with Evolving Information Technologies. Special Libraries. 1980 September; 71(9): 386-397. ISSN: 0038-6723.

BOISSONNAS, CHRISTIAN. 1979. The Quality of OCLC Bibliographic Records: The Cornell Law Library Experience. Law Library Journal. 1979 Winter; 72(1): 80-85. ISSN: 0023-9283.

BORRELL, JERRY. 1980. Information Display: Technology, Implementations, and the Future. Journal of Library Automation. 1980 December; 13(4): 277-281. ISSN: 0022-2240.

BOSS, RICHARD W. 1979. Circulation Systems: The Options. Library Technology Reports. 1979 January/February; 15(1): 7-105. ISSN: 0024-2586.

BOSS, RICHARD W. 1980. Turnkey Minicomputer Systems as On-Line Catalogs. RQ: Reference Quarterly. 1980 Fall; 20(1): 40-44. ISSN: 0033-7072.

BOSS, RICHARD W.; MARCUM, DEANNA B. 1980. The Library Catalog: COM and On-Line Options. Library Technology Reports. 1980 September-October; 16(5): 443-556. ISSN: 0024-2586.

BOURNE, CHARLES P. 1980. On-Line Systems: History, Technology, and Economics. Journal of the American Society for Information Science. 1980 May; 31(3): 155-160. ISSN: 0002-8231.

BRADEN, SALLY; HALL, JOHN D.; BRITTON, HELEN H. 1980. Utilization of Personnel and Bibliographic Resources for Cataloging by OCLC Participating Libraries. Library Resources & Technical Services. 1980 Spring; 24(2): 135-154. ISSN: 0024-2527.

BRANDHORST, TED. 1979. ANSI Z39 Romanization Standards and "Reversibility": A Dialog to Arrive at Policy. Journal of the American Society for Information Science. 1979 January; 30(1): 55–59. ISSN: 0002-8231.

BULLETIN OF THE AMERICAN SOCIETY FOR INFORMATION SCIENCE. 1979. Networking: North America. Bulletin of the American Society for Information Science. 1979 June; 5(5): 11–31. ISSN: 0095-4403.

BULLETIN OF THE AMERICAN SOCIETY FOR INFORMATION SCIENCE. 1980. Governance of Networks. Bulletin of the American Society for Information Science. 1980 June; 6(5): 10–20. ISSN: 0095-4403.

CANADA. NATIONAL LIBRARY. 1979. Toward a Canadian Library Network: The National Library's Five-Year Plan. Appendix I. In: National Library of Canada. The Future of the National Library of Canada. Ottawa, Ontario: National Library of Canada; 1979. 57–67. ISBN: 0-662-50628-6.

CARLILE, HUNTINGTON. 1980. The Diversity among Legal Structures of Library Networks. In: Markuson, Barbara Evans; Woolls, Blanche, eds. Networks for Networkers: Critical Issues in Cooperative Library Development: Proceedings of the Conference on Networks for Networkers; 1979; Indianapolis, IN. New York, NY: Neal-Schumann; 1980. 187–210. ISBN: 0-918212-22-7; LC: 79-24054.

CARLILE, HUNTINGTON; BURKLEY, JOHN H. 1980. Legal Aspects of Organizing a Library Network. Bulletin of the American Society for Information Science. 1980 June; 6(5): 16–18. ISSN: 0095-4403.

CHERRY, SUSAN SPAETH. 1981. The Moving Finger "Accesses." American Libraries. 1981 January; 12(1): 14–15. ISSN: 0002-9769.

CLEMENT, HOPE E. 1980. The Automated Authority File at the National Library of Canada. International Cataloging: Quarterly Bulletin of the IFLA International Office for UBC. 1980 October/December; 9(4): 45–48. ISSN: 0047-0635.

CLSI NEWSLETTER. 1979. CLSI: Serving the Automation Requirements of Libraries. CLSI Newsletter of Library Automation. 1979 Fall-Winter; (12): 10p. ISSN: 0363-9479.

CLSI NEWSLETTER. 1980. Public Access—The Next Phase of Library Automation—Becomes a Reality. CLSI Newsletter of Library Automation. 1980 Spring-Summer; (13): 8p. ISSN: 0363-9479.

COHEN, ELAINE. 1980. Sophomoric. Library Journal. 1980 December 15; 105(22): 2525. (Letter to the Editor). ISSN: 0363-0277.

COHEN, JACOB; VIJVERBERG, WIM. 1980. Applying Game Theory to Library Networks. Journal of the American Society for Information Science. 1980 September; 31(5): 369–374. ISSN: 0002-8231.

CUADRA, CARLOS A. 1980. The Role of the Private Sector in the Development and Improvement of Library and Information Services. Library Quarterly. 1980 January; 50(1): 94–111. ISSN: 0024-2519.

DINGLE-CLIFF, SUSAN; DAVIS, CHARLES H. 1981. Comparison of Recent Acquisitions and OCLC Find Rates for Three Canadian Special Libraries. Journal of the American Society for Information Science. 1981 January; 32(1): 65–69. ISSN: 0002-8231; CODEN: AISJB6.

DOBROVITS, P.; O'MARA, R. 1979. Searching the OCLC Database for Older Type Research Material. LASIE: Information Bulletin of the

Library Automated Systems Information Exchange (Australia). 1979 September/October; 10(2): 2–9. ISSN: 0047-3774.

DOMINICK, WAYNE D.; PENNIMAN, W. DAVID; RUSH, JAMES E. 1980. Research Report on an Overview of a Proposed Monitoring Facility for the Large-Scale, Network-Based OCLC On-Line System. Columbus, OH: OCLC, Inc. Office of Planning and Research, Research Department; 1980 January 23. 22p. (Report no.: OCLC/OPR/RR-80/1). Available from: the publisher, 1125 Kinnear Road, Columbus, OH 43212.

DOUGHERTY, RICHARD M. 1979. UAP and the United States. Unesco Journal of Information Science, Librarianship and Archives Administration. 1979 April-June; 1(2): 102–103. ISSN: 0379-122X.

DOUGHERTY, RICHARD M.; MARUYAMA, LENORE S. 1980. A Report of the Meeting of the Network Advisory Committee, March 4–5, 1980. Appendix II. Library of Congress Information Bulletin. 1980 May: 186–188. ISSN: 0041-7904.

DOWLIN, KENNETH. 1980. On-Line Catalog User Acceptance Survey. RQ: Reference Quarterly. 1980 Fall; 20(1): 44–47. ISSN: 0033-7072.

DUCHESNE, R. M.; GUENTER, D. A.; ISLAM, M. 1980. Towards More Effective Nationwide Library and Information Networking in Canada. Ottawa, Ontario: National Library of Canada; 1980 March. 85p. (Final Report of the Canadian Computerized Bibliographic Centre Study). ISBN: 0-662-10982-1.

DUCHESNE, R. M.; ISLAM, M.; GUENTER, D. A. 1979. Overview of Computerized Networking in Canada. Ottawa, Ontario: National Library of Canada; 1979 May. 86p. (Canadian Computerized Bibliographic Centre Study, Background Paper). ISBN: 0-662-10901-5.

DUNN, MARY JOAN. 1980. DOBIS. Argus. 1980 mai/juin; 9(3): 105–109. ISSN: 0315-9930. (Canada).

EPSTEIN, HANK. 1980. The Technology of Library and Information Networks. Journal of the American Society for Information Science. 1980 November; 31(6): 425–437. ISSN: 0002-8231.

EPSTEIN, HANK; EPSTEIN, SUSAN BAERG. 1980. The Effective Use of Automation in Wisconsin Libraries 1981–1985. Costa Mesa, CA: Information Transform Industries; 1980 October. 126p. (Bulletin no. 1204).

EVANS, GLYN T. 1979. Constituency Concerns in OCLC Management: User, Library, Network, OCLC. In: Gore, Daniel; Kimbrough, Joseph; Spyers-Duran, Peter, eds. Requiem for the Card Catalog; Management Issues in Automated Cataloging. Westport, CT: Greenwood Press; 1979. 141–155. (New Directions in Librarianship, no. 2). ISBN: 0-313-20608-2; LC: 78-7129.

FASANA, PAUL J. 1980. 1981 and Beyond: Visions and Decisions. Journal of Library Automation. 1980 June; 13(2): 96–107. ISSN: 0022-2240.

FORD, WILLIAM H.; MEYER, ALAN H. 1979. Technical Report for a Proposed Library Automation Network in the South Central Region of New York State. Gaithersburg, MD: ONLINE Computer Systems, Inc.; 1979 December 18. 80p. (Completed through a Contract with Finger Lakes Library System under LSCA Project 79-26). Available from: the authors, 4 Professional Drive, Suite 119, Gaithersburg, MD 20760.

FRIEDMAN, ELAINE S. 1980. Patron Access to Online Cataloging Systems: OCLC in the Public Service Environment. Journal of Academic Librarianship. 1980 July; 6(3): 132–139. ISSN: 0099-1333.

236

GLYN T. EVANS

FROST, KENNETH R. 1980. The Library Owned Computer. Ontario Library Review (Canada). 1980 June; 64(2): 92–97. ISSN: 0030-2996.
GATENBY, JANIFER; ROGERSON, MARY; PEAKE, DOROTHY. 1978. An Investigation into the Feasibility of Using OCLC in Australia, via the MIDAS Service. LASIE: Information Bulletin of the Library Automated Systems Information Exchange (Australia). 1978 September-October; 9(2): 2–9. ISSN: 0047-3774.
GIBSON, ROBERT W., ed. 1980. The Special Library Role in Networks: A Conference Held at the General Motors Research Laboratories: [Proceedings]; 1980 May 5–6; Warren, MI. New York, NY: Special Libraries Association; 1980. 296p. ISBN: 0-8711-279-5.
GORMAN, MICHAEL. 1979. Toward Bibliographic Control: Short Can Be Beautiful. American Libraries. 1979 November; 10(10): 607–608. ISSN: 0002-9769.
GORMAN, MICHAEL. 1980a. Network! or I'm Rational [Mad] as Hell and I'm Not Going to Take It Any More. American Libraries. 1980 January; 11(1): 48–50. ISSN: 0002-9769.
GORMAN, MICHAEL. 1980b. Toward Bibliographic Control: How the Machine May Yet Save LCSH. American Libraries. 1980 October; 11(9): 557–558. ISSN: 0002-9769.
GORMAN, MICHAEL; HOTSINPILLER, JAMI. 1979. ISBD: Aid or Barrier to Understanding? College & Research Libraries. 1979 November; 40(6): 519–526. ISSN: 0010-0870.
HAAS, WARREN J. 1980. Research Libraries and the Dynamics of Change. Scholarly Publishing (Canada). 1980 April; 11(3): 195–202. ISSN: 0036-634X.
INFORMATION HOTLINE. 1980a. ARL Adopts Principles on Network Development and Research Libraries. Information Hotline. 1980 November; 12(10): 5–6. ISSN: 0360-5817.
INFORMATION HOTLINE. 1980b. LC Makes CONSER File Available. Information Hotline. 1980 November; 12(10): 2. ISSN: 0360-5817.
INFORMATION HOTLINE. 1980c. One in Four U. S. Households to Have Video Terminals by End of '80s. Information Hotline. 1980 June; 12(6): 5. ISSN: 0360-5817.
INFORMATION HOTLINE. 1980d. Online Patron Access to Bibliographic Data Bases. Information Hotline. 1980 October; 12(9): 4. ISSN: 0360-5817.
INFORMATION HOTLINE. 1980e. Research Libraries Group and Washington Library Network Begin Work on Authority Control System. Information Hotline. 1980 September; 12(8): 5. ISSN: 0360-5817.
INTERNATIONAL FEDERATION OF LIBRARY ASSOCIATIONS AND INSTITUTIONS. 1980. UNIMARC: Universal MARC Format. Recommended by the IFLA Working Group on Content Designators Set up by the IFLA Section on Cataloging and the IFLA Section on Mechanization. 2nd edition revised. London, England: IFLA International Office for UBC; 1980. 131p. ISBN: 0-903043-11-4.
IOWA STATE LIBRARY. OFFICE OF LIBRARY DEVELOPMENT. 1980. A Networking Primer. Des Moines, IA: State Library of Iowa; [1980]. 5p. (Pamphlet). Available from: State Library Commission of Iowa, Historical Building, Des Moines, IA 50319.
JAMES, RICHARD; COPPINGER, REBECCA. 1980. Communication with an OCLC Model 100 Terminal. Journal of Library Automation. 1980 December; 13(4): 282–286. ISSN: 0022-2240.

JONES, C. LEE. 1980. Linking Bibliographic Data Bases: A Discussion of the Battelle Technical Report. Washington, DC: Council on Library Resources, Inc.; 1980 October 15. 28p. Available from: Council on Library Resources, Inc., One Dupont Circle, N.W., Suite 620, Washington, DC 20036.

JONES, RICHARD. 1980. The Tri-Regional Catalogue: A Report on Progress & Costs. Ontario Library Review (Canada). 1980 June; 64(2): 102-105. ISSN: 0030-2996.

JOURNAL OF LIBRARY AUTOMATION. 1980. OCLC Discontinues Talks with Geac. Journal of Library Automation. 1980 June; 13(2); 142-143. ISSN: 0022-2240.

JOURNAL OF THE AMERICAN SOCIETY FOR INFORMATION SCIENCE. 1980. Perspectives On. . . .Library Networks and Resource Sharing. Journal of the American Society for Information Science. 1980 November; 31(6): 404-444. ISSN: 0002-8231.

KANG, JONG H.; ROUSE, WILLIAM B. 1980. Approaches to Forecasting Demands for Library Network Services. Journal of the American Society for Information Science. 1980 July; 31(4): 256-263. ISSN: 0002-8231.

KASKE, NEAL K.; SANDERS, NANCY P. 1980. On-Line Subject Access: The Human Side of the Problem. RQ: Reference Quarterly. 1980 Fall; 20(1): 52-58. ISSN: 0033-7072.

KILGOUR, FREDERICK G. 1980. New Information Systems. Bulletin of the American Society for Information Science. 1980 March; 6(3): 13. ISSN: 0095-4403.

KILTON, TOM D. 1979. OCLC and the Pre-Order Verification of New Serials. The Serials Librarian. 1979 Fall; 4(1): 61-64. ISSN: 0361-526X.

KING, JAMES; DEVRIES, GORDON; THOMPSON, RICHARD. 1979. The Feasibility of Establishing an Interlibrary Telecommunication Network in Northern New York. Plattsburgh, NY: State University College of Arts and Science, Economic Development and Technical Assistance Center; 1979 December. 151p. (Project Director: Stanley A. Ransom). Available from: the publisher, Plattsburgh, NY 12901.

LC INFORMATION BULLETIN. 1980a. Appendix: An Integrated Consistent Authority File Service for Nationwide Use. LC (Library of Congress) Information Bulletin. 1980 July 11: 244-248. ISSN: 0041-7904.

LC INFORMATION BULLETIN. 1980b. Appendix II: A Report on the Third Meeting of the Ad Hoc Group on the Establishment of a Common Communication Format, Ottawa, Canada, May 21-23, 1980. LC (Library of Congress) Information Bulletin. 1980 July 25: 263-264. ISSN: 0041-7904.

LEONARD, W. PATRICK. 1980. The Card Catalog Mentality or We Have Always Done It This Way. Journal of Academic Librarianship. 1980 March; 6(1): 38, 64. ISSN: 0099-1333.

LIBRARY JOURNAL. 1980. Discount Database Rates Offered by OCLC. Library Journal. 1980 November 15; 105(20): 2366. ISSN: 0363-0277.

LIBRARY JOURNAL. 1981. OHIONET Sees New Role, Pegs OCLC Pitfalls. Library Journal. 1981 February 1; 106(3): 292-294. ISSN: 0363-0027.

LJ/SLJ HOTLINE. 1980a. NCLIS/SLA Task Force on Special Libraries Meets Today. LJ/SLJ (Library Journal/School Library Journal) Hotline.

1980 October 27; 9(35): 1. Available from: R. R. Bowker Co., 1180 Avenue of the Americas, New York, NY 10036. ISSN: 0000-0078.
LJ/SLJ HOTLINE. 1980b. Statewide ILL Delivery Service Booms. LJ/ SLJ Hotline. 1980 November 10; 9(37): 2. ISSN: 0000-0078.
LJ/SLJ HOTLINE. 1981. DOBIS to Replace CLSI at Austin Public Library. LJ/SLJ Hotline. 1981 January 5; X(1): 1. ISSN: 0000-0078.
LONG, PHILIP L. 1979. Study of Message Text Formats: Bibliographic Search Queries. Washington, DC: Library of Congress. Network Planning Office; 1979. 28p. (Network Planning Paper no. 5. Edited and revised by David C. Hartmann). Available from: Customer Services Section, Cataloging Distribution Service, Library of Congress, Navy Yard Annex, Bldg. 159, Washington, DC 20541.
LOUISIANA STATE LIBRARY. 1979. Overview of the Statewide Union List Project. [Baton Rouge, LA: Louisiana State Library; 1979]. 46p. Available from: State Librarian, Louisiana State Library, P. O. Box 131, Baton Rouge, LA 70821.
MALINCONICO, S. MICHAEL. 1979. Bibliographic Data Base Organization and Authority Control. Wilson Library Bulletin. 1979 September; 54(1): 36-45. ISSN: 0043-5651.
MALINCONICO, S. MICHAEL. 1980a. Governance Structures for a National Bibliographic Network. Bulletin of the American Society for Information Science. 1980 June; 6(5): 12-13. ISSN: 0095-4403.
MALINCONICO, S. MICHAEL. 1980b. Mass Storage Technology and File Organization. Journal of Library Automation. 1980 June; 13(2): 77-87. ISSN: 0022-2240.
MALINCONICO, S. MICHAEL. 1980c. The National Bibliographic Network: A Patrician Pursuit. Library Journal. 1980 September 15; 105 (16): 1791-1792. ISSN: 0363-0277.
MARKUSON, BARBARA EVANS; WOOLLS, BLANCHE, eds. 1979. Critical Issues in Cooperative Library Development Networks. [s.l.]: Indiana Department of Public Instruction, Division of Instructional Media; [1979?] 16p. (Brochure. Summarizes for delegates to the White House Conference on Library and Information Services the proceedings of a conference on networks for networkers). OCLC: 5873608.
MARKUSON, BARBARA EVANS; WOOLLS, BLANCHE, eds. 1980. Networks for Networkers: Critical Issues in Cooperative Library Development: Proceedings of the Conference on Networks for Networkers. 1979; Indianapolis, IN. New York, NY: Neal-Schuman. 1980. 444p. ISBN: 0-918212-22-7.
MARTIN, SUSAN K. 1980a. Book Review of The Structure and Governance of Library Networks, Edited by Allen Kent and Thomas J. Galvin. New York, NY: Marcel Dekker; 1979. Journal of Academic Librarianship. 1980 July; 6(3): 165. ISSN: 0099-1333.
MARTIN, SUSAN K. 1980b. Treating LC's Schizophrenia. American Libraries. 1980 November; 11(10): 621. ISSN: 0002-9769.
MARTINELLI, JAMES A. 1980. Descriptive Cataloging of Serials: The National Library of Medicine versus the Library of Congress. Bulletin of the Medical Library Association. 1980 January; 68(1): 40-46. ISSN: 0025-7338.
MATTHEWS, JOSEPH R. 1980. Turnkey Automated Circulation Systems: Comparative Information. Cypress, CA, 1980 May. 52p. Available from: the author, 11543 Savaii Street, Cypress, CA 90630.

MAUTINO, PATRICIA H. 1980. School Libraries in New York State: A Networking Potential. The Bookmark. 1980 Spring; 38(7): 398–403. ISSN: 0006-7407.

MCALLISTER, CARYL; MCALLISTER, A. STRATTON. 1979. DOBIS/ LIBRIS: An Integrated, On-Line Library Management System. Journal of Library Automation. 1979 December; 12(4): 300–313. ISSN: 0022-2240.

MCGILL, MICHAEL J. 1980. History of the Future of User Interaction in Information Systems. Special Interest Group on User On-Line Interaction (SIG/UOI) Newsletter. 1980 March; no. UOI-12: 3–4. Available from: American Society for Information Science, 1010 Sixteenth Street, N.W., Washington, DC 20036.

MELIN, NANCY JEAN. 1980. Professional Without Portfolio: The Network Librarian. Wilson Library Bulletin. 1980 January; 54(5): 308–310. ISSN: 0043-5651.

METZ, PAUL; ESPLEY, JOHN. 1980. The Availability of Cataloging Copy in the OCLC Data Base. College and Research Libraries. 1980 September; 41(5): 430–436. ISSN: 0010-0870.

MIDLNET NEWSLETTER. 1980. Can the Midwest be United?—Smith Speaks at MALC. MIDLNET (Midwest Region Library Network) Newsletter. 1980 May; (15): 1. Available from: the editor, c/o University of Wisconsin at Green Bay, Green Bay, WI 54302.

MILLER, SUSAN L. 1980. The Changing Role of a Circulation System: The OSU Experience. RQ: Reference Quarterly. 1980 Fall; 20(1): 47–52. ISSN: 0033-7072.

MINITEX MESSENGER. 1979. OCLC and Library Automation. MINITEX Messenger. 1979 September; 5(2): 4–5. Available from: MINITEX, 30 Wilson Library, University of Minnesota, 309 19th Avenue South, Minneapolis, MN 55455.

NATIONAL LIBRARY NEWS. 1980. Automation of the Canadian Union Catalogue. National Library News (Canada). 1980 March; 12(3): 1–2. Available from: National Library of Canada, Ottawa, Ontario. ISSN: 0027-9633.

NEUMANN, JOAN. 1980. INTERSHARE: A View from the Hole, or Building the Foundation for a Regional Library Network for Intersystem Cooperation. The Bookmark. 1980 Spring; 38(7): 394–397. ISSN: 0006-7407.

NEW YORK. STATE EDUCATION DEPARTMENT. 1980. New Directions: A Report of the Commissioner of Education Gordon M. Ambach to the New York State Legislature on Library Pilot Projects Organized Under Chapter 787, Laws of 1978, Covering the Period July 1, 1979– June 30, 1980. Albany, NY: State Education Department, The University of the State of New York; 1980. 85p.

NEWMAN, DONALD. 1980. Special Report: The Total Library System. Wilson Library Bulletin. 1980 November; 55(3): 201–204. ISSN: 0043-5651.

NEWMAN, WILLIAM L.; BRODIE, NANCY; CLYDE, ERIC; DIMSDALE, JAMES J.; DUNN, MARY JOAN; MOULAND, PAUL. 1979. DOBIS: The Canadian Government Version. Canadian Library Journal. 1979 August; 36(4): 181–194. ISSN: 0008-4352.

NEWMAN, WILLIAM L.; CLYDE, ERIC. 1979. Sharing and DOBIS. In: Proceedings of the 7th Annual Canadian Conference on Information

240 GLYN T. EVANS

Science: Sharing Resources-Sharing Costs; 1979 May 12-15; Banff, Alberta. Ottawa, Ontario: Canadian Association for Information Science (CAIS); 1979. Available from: CAIS, Box 158, Terminal A, Ottawa, Ont. K1N 8V2. ISSN: 0703-3249; ISBN: 0-920-420-02-8.

NEWS FROM THE LIBRARY OF CONGRESS. 1980. Forum on Nation-wide Network and Bibliographic Data to be Held. Washington, DC: Library of Congress; 1980 December 31. 2p. (Press release).

NIETMANN, MELANIE; HIRST, DONNA. 1980. Computerized Cataloging in Law Libraries: OCLC and RLIN Compared. Law Library Journal. 1980; 73(1): 107-128. ISSN: 0023-9283.

OCLC INCORPORATED. 1979. Annual Report 1978/79. Columbus, OH: OCLC, Inc.; 1979. 23p. Available from: OCLC Inc., 1125 Kinnear Road, Columbus, OH 43212.

OCLC INCORPORATED. 1980a. Annual Report 1979/80. Columbus, OH: OCLC, Inc.; 1980. 21p. Available from: OCLC, Inc., 1125 Kinnear Road, Columbus, OH 43212.

OCLC INCORPORATED. 1980b. [Untitled]. Columbus, OH: OCLC, Inc.; 1980 December 10. 2p. (Press release on interlibrary loan). Available from: OCLC, Inc., 1125 Kinnear Road, Columbus, OH 43212.

OCLC INCORPORATED. RESEARCH DEPARTMENT. 1980. Channel 2000 User Manual. Columbus, OH: OCLC, Inc.; 1980. 55p. Available from: OCLC, Inc., 1125 Kinnear Road, Columbus, OH 43212.

OCLC NEWSLETTER. 1981a. OCLC Converts Data Base to AACR2 Form. OCLC Newsletter. 1981 January 16; (134): 4. Available from: OCLC, Inc., 1125 Kinnear Road, Columbus, OH 43212.

OCLC NEWSLETTER. 1981b. OCLC Issues Statement on Battelle Study on Linking Bibliographic Utilities. OCLC Newsletter. 1981 January 16; (134): 2. Available from: OCLC, Inc., 1125 Kinnear Road, Columbus, OH 43212.

OCLC NEWSLETTER. 1981c. The Year in Review-1980. OCLC Newsletter. 1981 January 16; (134): 5-8. Available from: OCLC, Inc., 1125 Kinnear Road, Columbus, OH 43212.

OHIO STATE LIBRARY. OHIO MULTITYPE INTERLIBRARY COOPERATION COMMITTEE. 1979. Ohio Regional Library and Information Systems as Proposed by the Ohio Multitype Interlibrary Cooperation Committee. Columbus, OH: State Library of Ohio; 1979 June. 21p. (Pamphlet). Available from: the author, 65 South Front Street, Columbus, OH 43215.

OHIONETWORK. 1980. Preliminary Discussions About a Circulation System for OHIONET Members. OHIONETWORK: Newsletter of OHIO-NET. 1980 September; 2(9): 35. ISSN: 0163-7819.

OKLAHOMA DEPARTMENT OF LIBRARIES. NETWORK ADVISORY COUNCIL. 1980. The Oklahoma Library Network: A Proposal for Library Cooperation in Oklahoma. Oklahoma City, OK: Oklahoma Department of Libraries; 1980. 37p. Available from: the author, 200 Northeast 18th Street, Oklahoma City, OK 73105.

O'NEILL, EDWARD T.; ALURI, RAO. 1980. Research Report on a Method for Correcting Typographical Errors in Subject Headings in OCLC Records. Columbus, OH: OCLC, Inc., Office of Planning & Research; 1980 October 15. 24p. (Report no. OCLC/OPR/RR-80/3). Available from: OCLC, Inc., User Services Division, Installation Services Section, 1125 Kinnear Road, Columbus, OH 43212.

PALINET NEWS. 1980. PALINET Welcomes 15 New Members, 9 in Maryland. PALINET News. 1980 July; (19): 1. Available from: PALINET, 3420 Walnut Street, Philadelphia, PA 19104.
PALMOUR, VERNON E.; DEWATH, NANCY V. 1980. Missouri Statewide Bibliographic Data Base Survey. Rockville, MD: King Research, Inc.; 1980 August. 93p. (Prepared for: Statewide Bibliographic Data Base Committee, Missouri Libraries Network Board). Available from: the publisher, 6000 Executive Blvd., Rockville, MD 20852.
PENNIMAN, W. DAVID; DOMINICK, WAYNE D. 1980. Monitoring and Evaluation of On-Line Information System Usage. Information Processing & Management. 1980; 16(1): 17-35. ISSN: 0306-4573.
PLOTNIK, ARTHUR. 1979. The Editor's Page One. American Libraries. 1979 October; 10(9): 506. ISSN: 0002-9769.
PLOTNIK, ARTHUR. 1981. CLSI: the Hatvany Hot Touch. American Libraries. 1981 January; 12(1): 16-17. ISSN: 0002-9769.
PRLC NEWSLETTER. 1980. Proceedings of the Delphi Planning Conference. PRLC (Pittsburgh Regional Library Center) Newsletter. 1980 August; (65): 1-2. ISSN: 0196-6709.
PUBLIC SERVICE SATELLITE CONSORTIUM NEWSLETTER. 1981. Library Survey Results Available. Public Service Satellite Consortium Newsletter. 1981 January; 5(1): 3. Available from: the editor, Suite 907, 1660 L Street, N.W., Washington, DC 20036.
PURNELL, KATHLEEN M. 1979. Interfacing a Local System with OCLC: The Documentation Process. Library Resources & Technical Services. 1979 Spring; 23(2): 129-138. ISSN: 0024-2527.
RASTOGI, KUNJ B. 1980. Retrieval Behavior of Derived Truncated Search Keys for a Large On-Line Bibliographic File. Journal of the American Society for Information Science. 1980 March; 31(2): 84-88. ISSN: 0002-8231.
RAYMAN, RONALD. 1980. Automated Interlibrary Lending: An Undiagnosed Problem. Scholarly Publishing (Canada). 1980 October; 12(1): 3-11. ISSN: 0036-634X.
RESEARCH LIBRARIES GROUP, INCORPORATED. 1980. [Research Libraries Group, Inc. and the Washington Library Network announce grant of $318,317.] Stanford, CA: Research Libraries Group; 1980 April 11. 2p. (News release).
RESEARCH LIBRARIES GROUP NEWS. 1980a. East Asian Characters: Ending the Silence. Research Libraries Group News. 1980 September; (2): 2-8. ISSN: 0196-173X.
RESEARCH LIBRARIES GROUP NEWS. 1980b. RLG to Receive total of $2.2 million in Loans from Ford, Carnegie Foundations. Research Libraries Group News. 1980 September; (2): 8p. ISSN: 0196-173X.
REYNOLDS, DENNIS J. 1980. Regional Alternatives for Interlibrary Loan: Access to Unreported Holdings. College and Research Libraries. 1980 January; 41(1): 33-42. ISSN: 0010-0870.
RHODE ISLAND. DEPARTMENT OF STATE LIBRARY SERVICES. 1980. Rhode Island Interrelated Library Network Automation Study: Bid Document. Providence, RI: Rhode Island Department of State Library Services; 1980. 1 volume (discontinuous paging). Available from: the author, 95 Davis Street, Providence, RI 02908.
ROBINSON, BARBARA M. 1980. Cooperation and Competition among Library Networks. Journal of the American Society for Information Science. 1980 November; 31(6): 413-424. ISSN: 0002-8231.

ROCKMAN, ILENE F. 1980. The Potential of On-Line Circulation Systems as Public Catalogs: An Introduction. RQ: Reference Quarterly. 1980 Fall; 20(1): 39-40. ISSN: 0033-7072.

ROUGHTON, MICHAEL. 1980. OCLC Serials Records: Errors, Omissions, and Dependability. Journal of Academic Librarianship. 1980 January; 5(6): 316-321. ISSN: 0099-1333.

ROUSE, SANDRA H., ROUSE, WILLIAM B. 1979a. Analysis of Monographic Obsolescence at Two Levels of an Interlibrary Loan Network. Information Processing & Management. 1979; 15(5): 219-225. ISSN: 0306-4573.

ROUSE, SANDRA H., ROUSE, WILLIAM B. 1979b. Design of a Model-Based Online Management Information System for Interlibrary Loan Networks. Information Processing & Management. 1979; 15(2): 109-122. ISSN: 0306-4573.

ROUSE, WILLIAM B. 1979. Tutorial: Mathematical Modeling of Library Systems. Journal of the American Society for Information Science. 1979 July; 30(4): 181-192. ISSN: 0002-8231.

ROUSE, WILLIAM B.; ROUSE, SANDRA H. 1979. Analysis of Library Networks. Collection Management. 1979 Summer/Fall; 3(2/3): 139-149. ISSN: 0146-2679.

RUSH, JAMES E. 1980. Development and Operation of a Database Machine for Online Access and Update of a Large Database. Online Review. 1980; 4(3): 237-261. ISSN: 0309-314X.

SALTON, GERARD. 1979. Suggestions for Library Network Design. Journal of Library Automation. 1979 March; 12(1): 39-52. ISSN: 0022-2240.

SAVAGE, NOEL. 1980. SOLINET Brings Co-Op Spirit to Annual Meeting. Library Journal. 1980 September 15; 105(16): 1771-1776. ISSN: 0363-0277.

SCHIEBER, PHILIP. 1980. OCLC, Inc. In: Simora, Filomena, ed. The Bowker Annual of Library & Book Trade Information. 25th edition. New York, NY: R. R. Bowker; 1980. 162-167. ISSN: 0068-0540; ISBN: 0-8352-1273-4; LC: 55-12434.

SCHRIEFER, KENT; CHRISTIANI, LINNEA. 1979. Ballots at Boalt. Law Library Journal. 1979; 72: 497-512. ISSN: 0023-9283.

SCOTT, RANDALL W. 1981. Dead End Searches. Technicalities. 1981 January; 1(2): 8-9. ISSN: 0272-0884.

SHINEBOURNE, J. 1980. User Needs, the New Technology and Traditional Approaches to Library Service. Journal of Information Science (U.K.). 1980 October; 2(3/4): 135-140. ISSN: 0165-5515.

SIMPSON, DONALD B. 1980. Achieving Multitype Library Cooperation through a Multi-State Brokerage Organization. Serials Librarian. 1980 Spring; 4(3): 285-289. ISSN: 0361-526X.

SMALLEY, DONALD A.; GRIFFITH, WILLIAM G.; WALKER, ANN W.; WESSELLS, MICHAEL B. 1980. Technical Report on Linking the Bibliographic Utilities; Benefits and Costs. September 15, 1980. 1 Volume (Various foliations). Battelle Columbus Laboratories Report submitted to and available from: Council on Library Resources, Inc., One Dupont Circle, N.W. Suite 620, Washington, DC 20036.

SMITH, LINDA C. 1980a. Public Access to Library Automation. Bulletin of the American Society for Information Science. 1980 August; 6(6): 28-30. ISSN: 0095-4403.

SMITH, LINDA C. 1980b. User Displays in Critical Information Systems. Special Interest Group on User On-line Interaction (SIG/UOI) Newsletter. 1980 July; No. UOI-13: 6-7. Available from: American Society for Information Science, 1010 Sixteenth Street, N.W., Washington, DC 20036.

SOLINEWS. 1980a. Burroughs and SOLINET Join Hands to Build Regional Support System. SOLINEWS: The SOLINET Newsletter. 1980 March/April; 8(2): 3p. ISSN: 0193-273X.

SOLINEWS. 1980b. SOLINET Buys License to WLN System. SOLINEWS: The SOLINET Newsletter. 1980 March/April; 8(2): 2p. ISSN: 0193-273X.

SPECHT, JERRY. 1980. Patron Use of an Online Circulation System in Known-Item Searching. Journal of the American Society for Information Science. 1980 September; 31(5): 335-346. ISSN: 0002-8231.

START OF MESSAGE. 1980. Fifth Annual Meeting Concluded in Richmond. Start of Message: Newsletter of the Health Science OCLC Users Group. 1980 July; (20): 12p. (Minutes of business meeting and summary reports). ISSN: 0361-0241.

STEVENS, NORMAN D. 1980a. The Catalogs of the Future: A Speculative Essay. Journal of Library Automation. 1980 June; 13(2): 88-95. ISSN: 0022-2240.

STEVENS, NORMAN D. 1980b. Library Networks and Resource Sharing in the United States: An Historical and Philosophical Overview. Journal of the American Society for Information Science. 1980 November; 31(6): 405-412. ISSN: 0002-8231.

STIERWALT, RALPH E. 1980. Dissolution of the UNICAT/TELECAT Consortium. Ontario Library Review (Canada). 1980 September; 64(3): 196-209. ISSN: 0030-2996.

STRABLE, EDWARD G. 1980. The Way It Was. In: Gibson, Robert W., ed. The Special Library Role in Networks: Conference Held at the General Motors Research Laboratories: [Proceedings]; 1980 May 5-6; Warren, MI. New York, NY: Special Libraries Association; 1980. 1-16 ISBN: 0-8711-279-5.

SWANSON, DON R. 1980a. Evolution, Libraries, and National Information Policy. Library Quarterly. 1980; 50(1): 76-93. ISSN: 0024-2519.

SWANSON, DON R. 1980b. Libraries and the Growth of Knowledge. Library Quarterly. 1980; 50(1): 112-134. ISSN: 0024-2519.

TENOPIR, CAROL; JOHNSON, MARGARET. 1980. OCLC Card Receipts. Journal of Library Automation. 1980 June; 13(2): 136-138. ISSN: 0022-2240.

THOMSON, MOLLIE. 1979. Authority Files. LASIE: Information Bulletin of the Library Automated Systems Information Exchange (Australia). 1979 January/February; 9(4): 5-21. ISSN: 0047-3774.

THORSON, A. ROBERT; DAVIS, PHYLLIS B. 1980. Borrowing Made Easy: Automated Resource Sharing in Ohio. Wilson Library Bulletin. 1980 April; 54(8). ISSN: 0043-5651.

U. S. FEDERAL LIBRARY COMMITTEE (FLC). 1980. The Federal Library and Information Network: FEDLINK OVERVIEW. 1980 May. 66p. Available from: FLC, Room 405, Navy Yard Annex, Washington, DC 20540.

U. S. LIBRARY OF CONGRESS. 1981. A Nationwide Network: Development, Governance, Support: Discussion Paper Resulting from a Meeting

Held by the Library of Congress Network Advisory Committee, October 1-2, 1980. Washington, DC: Library of Congress; 1981 January. 15p. (Draft document). Available from: Network Development Office, Library of Congress, Washington, DC 20540.

U. S. LIBRARY OF CONGRESS. 1980. Summary of MARC Format Specifications for Technical Reports. Preliminary edition. Washington, DC: Library of Congress; 1980 October. 41p. Available from: Network Development Office, Library of Congress, Washington, DC 20540.

U. S. LIBRARY OF CONGRESS. NETWORK DEVELOPMENT OFFICE. 1980. Machine-Readable Data Files: A MARC Format: Draft, revised October 1980. Washington, DC: Library of Congress, Network Development Office; 1980 October. 1 volume (unpaged). Available from: Network Development Office, Library of Congress, Washington, DC 20540.

U. S. NATIONAL COMMISSION ON LIBRARIES AND INFORMATION SCIENCE (NCLIS). TASK FORCE ON THE ROLE OF THE SCHOOL LIBRARY MEDIA PROGRAM IN THE NATIONAL PROGRAM. 1978. The Role of the School Library Media Program in Networking. Washington, DC: Government Printing Office; 1978. 91p. Also available from: NCLIS, 1717 K Street, N.W., Suite 601, Washington, DC 20036.

UTLAS NEWSLETTER. 1979. Current Awareness Product Announced. UTLAS Newsletter. 1979 October; 4(10): [1]. ISSN: 0225-1760.

UTLAS NEWSLETTER. 1980. Initial Phases of Acquisitions and Serials Control System (ASC) Now Underway. UTLAS Newsletter. 1980 August; 5(8): 1-4. ISSN: 0225-1760.

VENEZIANO, VELMA. 1980. Library Automation: Data for Processing and Processing for Data. In: Williams, Martha E., ed. Annual Review of Information Science and Technology: Volume 15. White Plains, NY: Knowledge Industry Publications; 1980. 109-145. ISSN: 0066-4200; ISBN: 0-914236-65-2; LC: 66-25096.

VONDRAN, RAYMOND F. 1980. National Union Catalog Experience: Implications for Network Planning. Washington, DC: Library of Congress Network Planning Office; 1980. 51p. (Network Planning Paper, 6). Available from: Customer Services Section, Cataloging Distribution Service, Library of Congress, Navy Yard Annex, Bldg. 159, Washington, DC 20541.

WASHINGTON LIBRARY NETWORK. 1980. A Selected Bibliography. Olympia, WA: Washington Library Network; 1980 August. 2p. Available from: Washington Library Network, Washington State Library, AJ-11, Olympia, WA 98504.

WEBSTER, DUANE E.; MARUYAMA, LENORE S. 1980. Working Document: Ownership and Distribution of Bibliographic Data: Highlights of a Meeting Held by the Library of Congress Network Advisory Committee; 1980 March 4-5. Washington, DC: Library of Congress; 1980. 17p. Available from: Library of Congress Network Development Office, Washington, DC 20580.

WEDGEWORTH, ROBERT. 1980. Coordinating National Library Programs. In: Markuson, Barbara Evans; Woolls, Blanche, eds. Networks for Networkers: Critical Issues in Cooperative Library Development: Proceedings of the Conference on Networks for Networkers; 1979; Indianapolis, IN. New York, NY: Neal-Schuman; 1980. 100-108. ISBN: 0-918212-22-7; LC: 79-24054.

WEINTRAUB, D. KATHRYN. 1979. The Essentials of Desiderata of the

Bibliographic Record as Discovered by Research. Library Resources & Technical Services. 1979 Fall; 23(4): 391-405. ISSN: 0024-2527.

WELLISCH, HANS H. 1980. The Exchange of Bibliographic Data in Non-Roman Scripts. Unesco Journal of Information Science, Librarianship and Archives Administration. 1980 January-March; 2(1): 13-21. ISSN: 0379-122X.

WHITE, HERBERT S. 1980. Factors in the Decision by Individuals and Libraries to Place or Cancel Subscriptions to Scholarly and Research Journals. Library Quarterly. 1980 July; 50(3): 287-309. ISSN: 0024-2519.

WHITE HOUSE CONFERENCE ON LIBRARY AND INFORMATION SERVICES. 1980. Resolutions. In: White House Conference on Library and Information Services. Information for the 1980's: Final Report. Washington, DC: Government Printing Office; [1980]. 37-84.

WILSON LIBRARY BULLETIN. 1980. OCLC and the Source to Test-Market Services. Wilson Library Bulletin. 1980 May; 54(9): 554-555. ISSN: 0043-5651.

ZAMORA, ANTONIO. 1980. Automatic Detection and Correction of Spelling Errors in a Large Data Base. Journal of the American Society for Information Science. 1980 January; 31(1): 51-57. ISSN: 0002-8231.

8 Information Systems and Services in the Arts and Humanities

JOSEPH RABEN
Queens College, CUNY

SARAH K. BURTON
North Carolina State University

INTRODUCTION

The difficulty of accumulating hard information on the relation between information science and humanities research is compounded by certain characteristics of both disciplines. Information science, if not yet "hard," at least deals with commodities of that nature; the humanities, on the other hand, are distinctly "soft." When the two interact, we end up seeking hard data on a soft subject. There may be much data to be found, but few mechanisms exist to find them. Little seems to be in the online databases that is not readily available in printed sources. The recently established *Current Contents: Arts and Humanities*, published by the Institute for Scientific Information (ISI), indexes only by keywords in the titles; unless such words as *computer* or *data* or *quantified* appear, a relevant item will not be retrieved.

The diffuseness of the field and the lack of solidarity felt by a spectrum of scholars, stretching from art historians to literary critics, are reflected in the many journals that are publishing articles based on computer research. However, these scholars, seeking advancement and recognition among their peers, frequently neglect to publish also in the specialized journals that cover the interface between computers and the humanities. The databases they create to support their studies—the core topic of this review—are frequently not even mentioned, much less described in any detail. A state-of-the-art report, therefore, must rely largely on secondary materials.

After perusing this material our general conclusion is that the past eight or nine years have witnessed a lateral development—i.e., skills and interests have spread but without major advances in techniques or theory. The recent spate of concordances is an example of this trend. Only a few of the literary concordances published since 1972 enjoy the dignity of a typeset text; photo-offset from printout is a poor economy that is widely practiced. With the initial keyboarding completed, the addition of type codes would be a small effort (and expense) compared with the increased legibility (especially over matrix print), saleability, and smaller format of a typeset book.

Concordances that are slapped together simply because a machine-readable text and a concordance program were available pose two dangers: scholars who are suspicious of computer applications find their fears confirmed, and the possibility of good concordances being published is precluded by the publication of bad ones, for the market will not absorb both. Apparently, however, publishers see a constant market for such conventionally made concordances, and thus resist any embellishments. Further, the belief that computer-oriented research is bogus, since the machine does everything, finds increasing support.

"Hybrid" Scholars

The most significant trend for computer-assisted humanities or social science research in the past few years has been the increase in the number of "hybrid scholars," those who combine training in traditional academic fields with computer technology, and vice-versa. Some, indeed, hold joint appointments in departments of computer science and departments of humanities or social science. Some have degrees in mathematics as well as in music or English. Some alternate their employment as humanities professors with service as computer programmers.

Such scholars are sometimes viewed by their colleagues with suspicion and apprehension. The narrowness of academic disciplines, however, has constantly lost out to multidisciplinary orientations; in the recent past biophysics, biochemistry, biosociology, psychiatry, and anthropology were all responses to a need to expand beyond established borders. Likewise, computer-oriented humanities research, which until recently was colored largely by the novelty and massive impact of the computer, has already become almost ordinary in some universities. Even those bastions of academic tradition, language departments, are occasionally including computer terminals and printers in their requests for standard equipment, and most such departments are more than willing to provide computer time for interested faculty members. Although programming assistance, another matter entirely, is more difficult to come by, younger scholars with growing frequency have had computer training in undergraduate courses or even in high school.

Already no one thinks of making a handmade concordance. Dictionaries and encyclopedias depend more and more on computer techniques. We can expect online bibliographic services to win over many who now avoid or condemn the "new" technology. Those same humanists who once urged their colleagues to move to the computer science department "where they belonged" are now searching for "the computer person in the department."

When whole-text retrieval finally establishes the real and true value of the computer, these requests will increase.

The number of "suitable areas" of research also continues to grow and now embraces language and literature, history, musicology, art history, and archaeology. Past studies in these areas often relied on relatively impressionistic methods. Occasional manual efforts to count the words most frequently appearing in the literature of different centuries, for example, were eccentric and not entirely successful. In general, scholars chose to operate on the level of greatest likelihood of success. Hence, analyses on the microlevel of the basic element, usually the word, were ignored. The most sweeping generalizations were (and often still are) based on a small, unrepresentative sampling of an artist's work. All too often the opinions of earlier published work were uncritically repeated. The computer, however, now allows a scholar, looking with relatively unprejudiced eyes on the fundamental data, to sort, count, search for patterns, analyze statistically, and, in every imaginable way, seek fresh insights.

New Concept: Microunits

What these hybrid scholars quantify, analyze, and generalize about with the aid of computing machines are microunits—i.e., the bits of information that are observed, encoded, and manipulated. For example, in examining a Seurat painting, a researcher might view as microunits such elements as the color, physical location of dots of color on the canoes, chemical composition of the paint, date of creation, and shape of each dot; in examining a novel, one might view as microunits such elements as letter frequency, sentence structure and length, as well as type and frequency of figurative language. Obviously, the choice of microunits determines what may be discovered.

Three key differences distinguish this type of scholarship from traditional methods:

- The scholar is compelled to examine the object under study with great care and in great detail and to justify all conclusions with evidence that is generally more objective than that in traditional study.
- The work of art (and perhaps the process of its creation) comes to be understood as consisting of discrete parts (in physics, quanta) that produce their effects by a logical process.
- The methodology of the scholar—i.e., the scholar's assumptions and rules of procedure—is made utterly explicit, both to the scholar and to his or her audience. The methodology, so clear that the research results are reproducible, thus draws humanistic research closer to the accuracy so admired by scientists. Interpretation of these results, however, remains the purview of inspired humanistic genius.

The use of these microunits, therefore, now makes it possible to study novels in the detail once reserved for sonnets or to look for true or slant rhyme or alliteration patterns in *War and Peace*.

Recognition for Humanistic Research

In the 15 years since serious efforts were made to apply these computer research methods to humanistic problems, the activity has also gained in respectability. The National Endowment for the Humanities (NEH), for example, has promulgated formal criteria covering the computer sections of grant proposals, and has urged editors of historical documents collections to adopt computer methods. Institutions such as the University of Wisconsin (CASSIDY) are sponsoring dictionary projects that depend largely on computers. The *Times Literary Supplement* (London) and a growing list of scholarly journals publish reports on humanistic uses of computers; occasional special issues are devoted totally to the subject. International communication links are being forged, and the prestige of journal publication is being conferred. Computer-assisted humanities research has, in fact, achieved a large measure of respectability.

Conferences

The most visible symptom of this new respectability and growing sense of national and international solidarity among computer researchers is the increasing number of organizations and international conferences dedicated solely to such activities. Starting in 1970, Roy A. Wisbey established a group at Cambridge University that linked itself with other British and European universities to create the Association for Literary and Linguistic Computing (ALLC). The proceedings of their conferences constitute a cumulative record of much that has been important in language-oriented research, chiefly in Europe, but also in other parts of the world (AITKEN ET AL.; JONES & CHURCHHOUSE; WISBEY). Also in 1970, Antonio ZAMPOLLI organized at Pisa a summer school for instruction in computer techniques for language analysis. Gathering an international faculty and student body, he established a biennial training series that is still operating.

Shortly afterward, in 1973, Donald Ross, Jr., Jay Leavitt, and J. Lawrence Mitchell organized the First International Conference on Computers in the Humanities (ICCH) in Minneapolis (MITCHELL). This too is a biennial series. Conferences have been held in Los Angeles, Waterloo, Ontario, Hanover, NH, and Ann Arbor, MI; the 1983 conference will be held in Raleigh, NC. The conferences at Dartmouth and Ann Arbor were held jointly with the new series of Conferences on Data Bases in the Humanities and Social Sciences (CDBHSS). These joint conferences emphasize the interdisciplinarity of problems and their solutions and are now held annually. One was held in Madrid, and a fourth is planned for Pisa in 1982. Thus, as the ALLC and ICCH meetings have alternated between Europe and North America, so the CDBHSS (RABEN & MARKS) also links scholars on both sides of the Atlantic.

Partly to maintain the continuity of the ICCH, the Association for Computers and the Humanities (ACH), was established in 1978. In addition to sponsoring the ICCH biennially, ACH also organizes sessions of related discipline-oriented meetings, such as that of the Modern Language Association (MLA), and publishes a quarterly newsletter. Membership applications and newsletter subscriptions from many parts of the world attest to the worldwide commitment to computer-assisted research in the humanities and social sciences.

APPLICATIONS IN LITERATURE AND LANGUAGE

The most widespread research continues to be in literature and language, and since 1972 two substantial surveys have appeared. Inevitably duplicating some material, the two books complement each other in representing the divergent American and British viewpoints. *Computer Methods for Literary Research* (OAKMAN) makes a commendable effort to represent British activity, but the author seems to have researched European work only through English-language publications. *A Guide to Computer Applications in the Humanities* (HOCKEY) seems to have maintained somewhat closer links with German, French, Swedish, and Italian activity, chiefly on the basis of standard publications. Despite the broad term *humanities* in its title, this book also confines itself essentially to literary and linguistic research.

Both are excellent summaries of the recent efforts to use the computer for producing basic research tools (e.g., concordances and dictionaries), for retrieving special types of information relevant to literary and linguistic research, for editing texts, and for analyzing style. Both books contain adequate but quite different bibliographies. Either could serve as a text for an introductory course, perhaps on the master's level.

These surveys and their bibliographies indicate that the production of concordances and verbal indexes continues to account for the bulk of work done in literature and language. By means of both off-the-shelf programs and others specially written, hundreds of these works have now been prepared, and many have been published. These publications range from a single work, such as Samuel Beckett's *Waiting for Godot*, to the complete works of Corneille or Shakespeare. They represent a vast array of languages, from English and Spanish to local tongues such as Coptic and Navajo. Preeminent in time and size is the multivolume *Index Thomisticus*, the complex analysis of the complete works of Saint Thomas Aquinas, initiated before World War II by BUSA, and now in its final stages of publication (BUSA, 1974). A major benefit of most of these concordance and index projects is the potential for reusing the textual input for other types of research.

The preservation of these input materials depends, however, on the existence of an archive that has not been established yet in the United States. Although the National Historical Publications and Records Commission (NHPRC) has created a Machine-Readable Records Division, it is responsible only for the preservation of records generated by the federal government. No U. S. foundation—government or private—is yet willing to commit itself to the creation and continued support of so speculative a project as a general machine-readable library of literary works. Thus, scholars have relied on ad-hoc efforts to collect, store, and distribute tapes from centers at Dartmouth College and Oxford University.

NEH has supported, however, an ambitious project at Bar-Ilan University in Israel to generate full-text files for a vast corpus of *responsa*, the rabbinical pronouncements on questions of reconciling the edicts of Hebrew scripture with everyday reality. Because these records cover several centuries in the numerous countries of the Diaspora, they contain information of value to linguists, sociologists, and historians. Their conversion to database format should result in great use of the materials and should also establish a model for future comparable projects (CHOUEKA).

Database of Greek

The other major database for humanities research is equally specialized, the Thesaurus Linguae Graecae (Treasure of the Greek Language), established at the University of California, Irvine, by Brunner[1]. The scope of the project is classical Greek, the learned language of the entire Mediterranean basin for about two millennia. Almost all literature as well as scientific, technical, and medical information was written in that language. Making all this material available in a uniform machine code with consistent and complete punctuation, even if it is readable only on IBM machines, was a major undertaking, holistically conceived. It may well serve as a model for databases of similar content and scope.

Dictionaries and Other Natural Language Databases

Several language databases are being derived from projects that were planned as monumental dictionaries. These include the *Trésor de la langue française*, an effort of the French government initiated during the De Gaulle period to restore the grandeur of the nation. Conceived as a computer-based operation, the *Trésor* not only is appearing in serial volumes as a printed dictionary of impressive thoroughness but is also reportedly being converted to a database for searching by contemporary technical means. Other dictionaries similarly suitable for (and presumably in some stage of) such conversion include that of the Accademia della Crusca in Florence (with collaboration of the Laboratorio di Linguistica Computazionale in Pisa), the *Dictionary of Old English* at the University of Toronto, the *Dictionary of the Older Scottish Tongue* at the University of Edinburgh (AITKEN), and the *Dictionary of American Regional English* (DARE) at the University of Wisconsin (CASSIDY).

Certain historical linguistic projects should also yield valuable databases. Maniet's (Universite Laval, Quebec) program, which translates Proto-Italic verses to classical Latin, includes lexicon and etymology for the verses of Hesiod; Lehmann (University of Texas, Austin) has recently received NEH funding for a computer-generated Gothic dictionary; and Burton (North Carolina State University, Raleigh) is establishing the basis for a massive Proto-Indoeuropean dictionary of cognate forms and sound change patterns.

---

[1] Personal interview with Theodore F. Brunner, Irvine, CA, 11 October 1974.

Other natural language database operations are those created by ALLÉN of the University of Gothenburg, Sweden, and the so-called Brown University Corpus by FRANCIS and KUČERA. These represent contrasting approaches to the same problem—i.e., establishing norms of actual usage. Allén is collecting the tapes used to typeset Swedish newspapers and is processing them to establish the everyday frequency of individual words. Francis and Kučera have selected samples from a broader spectrum of popular writing (e.g., detective, fiction, sports, journalism, scientific writing). Word frequency counts are proportional to actual occurrence in published popular literature. Input from any literary source can be compared with the standard frequencies in the corpus.

ARCHIVAL APPLICATIONS

Theater History

A major project, in terms of scope and originality, is the computerized index to *The London Stage, 1660-1800*, prepared by SCHNEIDER. *The London Stage* is a multivolume record of all theatrical activity in London from the reopening of the theaters during the Restoration to the repeal of licensing laws that had limited their number to only four. Throughout this period of censorship, the stage was a popular and powerful medium of communication, presenting drama that either reinforced or (by allusion and metaphor) undermined official government policies.

The editors of *The London Stage* collected all playbills, financial records, and other surviving documents and reprinted them in conventional format. Originally asked to produce only an index to the collection, Schneider was inspired to create an online database, searchable over telephone lines. His aim was to permit access to all the information implicit in the database, such as careers of individual actors, their association with certain types of parts, their financial successes, and audience size at each performance. His account of his struggle to create this database is as remarkable for its literary quality as for its candor and completeness.

Musicology

Humanists who wish to use computers in their research must deal with various media, a complex task. Although most studies in literature, language studies, history, musicology, archaeology, and art history have been encoded in words (i.e., alphabetically), many exist as musical notation, and the rest have no standard notation or at least none that has been widely adopted. Of the various systems advanced for music DARMS seems to be the most frequently mentioned (R. F. ERICKSON). Still to be realized, however, is a large corpus of machine-readable music to provide a basis for studies of the magnitude of those that now exist in language projects, in which million-word corpora are not now uncommon, and in history, where databases containing hundreds of items of data on thousands of individuals are becoming the norm. A step toward such databases in music is an index to a collection of sacred and secular Florentine music of the sixteenth century (LINCOLN, 1970; 1974). Based on *incipits*, the initial phrases by which each piece is recognized, this index is now being prepared for book publication on the laser graphics equipment of the University of Nottingham, England.

Another herald of such databases is the just-announced National Tune Index, developed by RABSON & RABSON in Potsdam, NY [home of the electronic library of the future at Clarkson College (KLEIMAN)]. Information on 40,000 songs, tunes, and dances from eighteenth century America and England is being stored, and full texts are available on microfiche, together with a computerized index to facilitate location even if one knows only the notes of a particular melody. According to the developers of the National Tune Index, the text-sorting problems peculiar to this type of data storage have been resolved, and a significant new research tool has been made available for humanistic research. [Since this database covers much of the same period as the index to *The London Stage*, and since music was an essential ingredient in the theater then, the time is ripe for integrating these complementary databases (discussed later in this chapter).] Other means of accessing stored music information have been reported by NERHEIM and by WENKER.

Visual Art

In music, a universally accepted code representing almost all its denotative aspects has evolved, but in visual art, essentially no agreement on anything beyond the basic elements has evolved. (A simple reason for this distinction is, perhaps, that musical composers must leave instructions for performers who may be remote from them in space and time. Painters and sculptors, on the other hand, are their own "performers" and do not need to develop instructions for others to follow.) Thus, once we have stated that a painting is known to have been produced by a certain artist at a certain time with certain materials on a certain medium, we have presumably exhausted our ability to describe it. After that we can deal only in irrelevancies (at least from the artistic viewpoint): size, price, provenance, title. From musical notation, we can reproduce a composition and from a script we can reproduce a play, but there is no notation from which we can reproduce a painting or sculpture.

The technology for such reproduction is at hand, however. One dramatic advantage of computerization, still being used tentatively and by few humanists, is graphic rather than alphanumeric output, actual pictures "drawn" in all kinds of shading and coloring by a mechanical plotter. Leaving aside for the moment the question of whether "computer art" is art at all (an esthetic question that also embraces Mondrian, Pollock, and other artists who have not used computers), the plotter can generate Egyptian or Mayan hieroglyphs or those of the Indus Valley culture, can draw maps and pinpoint regional vocabulary and pronunciation, can draw vases and other art objects, can sketch a stage setting—in a word, it can create almost any visual counterpart to any humanistic material. These graphic images can be indexed by whatever scheme is finally developed by the iconographers and accessed in all the ways that other materials will be.

Since the means to index the essence of visual art is not available, however, computer analysis of visual art is not yet a reality, for here the humanist faces a major challenge—i.e., determining what information is relevant. The lack of standards for describing visual art is "the major problem facing archivists, curators, and art and slide librarians today" (OHLGREN). Even in representational art, there is a conflict between what is shown and how it is presented. For example, in a Breughel painting, does one catalog every person, every item of clothing, every action, every relation between persons in the painting, every tree, window, etc.? If not, on what basis does one decide what to catalog? Further, assuming that such a basis can be agreed on by all researchers, can the cataloged information be translated into an algorithm and developed in computer programs? To explore this possibility, OHLGREN has indexed the 30,000 "illuminations" of medieval manuscripts in the Bodleian Library at Oxford. He has sought to go beyond the sketchy labels that characterize the older manual systems but at the same time not to burden his system with the detail advocated by BISOGNI, who has recognized and attempted to overcome the almost infinite extension of data produced by efforts at close analysis. In a joint venture of the Information Systems Division of the Smithsonian Institution and the National Museum of Natural History for the National Collection of Fine Arts, FINK has adapted a system called SELGEM (self-generating master) to the special needs of the collection's users. Her three-tiered system permits representational art to be identified to the degree that, for example, an individual's occupation can be labeled.

A standard vocabulary for indexing and retrieving information on visual art and artifacts is the aim of at least four major projects: 1) the Detroit Art Registration Information System (DARIS), sponsored by the Founders Society, Detroit Institute of Art; 2) the Art and Architecture Thesaurus (AAT), a joint venture of Crouch (National Gallery of Art), Molholt (Rensselaer Polytechnic Institute), and Petersen (Bennington College); 3) the Picture Division Thesaurus of Iconographic Terms of the Public Archives of Canada; and 4) the photography index developed at the Yale Center for British Art (SOBINSKI-SMITH).

Problems in standardization of terms are bound to continue for a while. Canada's Picture Division Thesaurus relies on the *Nomenclature for Museum Cataloging: A System for Classifying Man-Made Objects* (CHENHALL); Sobinski-Smith uses standards defined by the Museum Computer Network, headquartered at the State University of New York (SUNY), Stony Brook; others use still different "standards." The solution is international accord on terminology. Toward that end several conferences have been held— e.g., the Conference on Computerized Inventory Standards for Works of Art (November 1979 in Ottawa) and the Conference on Intellectual Access to Visual Resources (August 1980 at the Smithsonian Institution). In addition, the Image Access Society and the Working Group on Canadian Iconography are meeting in conjunction with the database and ALLC conferences and to set standards and exchange information (OHLGREN).

BLURRING OF LINES BETWEEN THE HUMANITIES AND THE SOCIAL SCIENCES

A result of computer-assisted research in the humanities and social sciences is the blurring of traditional boundaries between disciplines. Some may decry this loss of distinction, but many will be gratified to see barriers, which were never completely justified, broken down. Shakespeare's plays, dealing with historical events, psychological complexities, and philosophical considerations, cannot be "pure art." Painting and music also serve social functions. Historians must constantly debate whether they are humanists or social scientists, arbitrary classifications imposed more by the bureaucratic necessities of academic institutions and funding agencies than by the inherent realities of their discipline. Similarly, philosophy and architecture share characteristics of both divisions as well as characteristics of art, history, sociology, etc.

One of the benefits of computer approaches in these areas of research is the freedom, sometimes the necessity, to borrow methods from other disciplines. It seems natural, for example, to approach language-related problems with statistical techniques. Thus, BRAINERD (1980) has sought to determine the chronology of Shakespeare's plays by examining relationships clustered within them. Similar and related methods are used by ZARRI (1979) in his attempt to establish the similarities among various manuscript and printed versions of a single text. In these and similar approaches, the many discrete elements that can be run through the packaged and original programs provide the broad foundation necessary for statistical reliability.

ZARRI (1977) in another project extending the techniques and principles of one computer-based methodology to another, is applying the procedures of artificial intelligence (AI) to a database of historical information. As conceived at the Laboratoire pour l'informatique dans les sciences humaines, this system will permit the searcher to infer many unrecorded events and links between historical personages on the basis of surviving historical information. One of several methods being attempted primarily for research, this project also holds a large potential for education as well. If systems of this sort are realized, education will take a long stride from teaching rote memorization of dry fact (an approach that current computer-based methods can only encourage) to a genuine endeavor to present the past as an organic system that comprises the foundation of the present and the future.

In archaeology, where millions of bits of pottery must be sorted out, statistics may show clear lines of affiliation through what otherwise would remain mere jumbles of data. For George L. Cowgill of Brandeis University, who is analyzing the artifacts discovered at the ancient Mexican city of Teotihuacán (MILLON), the many bits of data to be considered complicate even relatively simple problems. In analyzing an archaeological artifact, one must consider materials, methods of processing, types of decoration, specific locations of finds, and locations relative to other artifacts in the same excavation. The complexity of dealing with such multifaceted data has not yet begun to be resolved.

Historical studies in general are undergoing a significant expansion into what is often called "social science history." Enabled now for the first time to investigate large arrays of discrete data, historians are exploring demographic shifts, voting patterns, and correlations between price fluctuations in basic commodities and social change. There are also occasional efforts to use the methods of language-oriented research for historical purposes, as in the production of concordances to the writings of historical figures like Max Weber.

BIBLIOGRAPHIC AND RELATED SERVICES

In this area, efforts beyond the creation of dictionaries, concordances, and the alphabetization of vocabularies are reported. Studies in dialectology, morphology, stylistics, sound patterns, and textual criticism are predicated on the belief that an algorithmic approach can be developed for problems that historically have required the intelligence and sensitivity of highly trained human beings. However, those qualified for such tasks frequently refuse to accept the detailed work that is required. Thus, there is a continuing search for machine assistance to develop specialized dictionaries dealing with exotic or extinct languages or with regional or dialectal subsets. From parallel efforts, online databases of *technical* definitions for translators are now emerging. These are increasingly essential tools as growing economic communities conduct their affairs in all the languages of their constituent countries.

Such practical applications require scholars to produce working systems that operate within realistic limits of cost, time, and machine capability. Many of these applications have begun to provide services to large numbers of humanists—e.g., the annual bibliography of MLA, the historical bibliography of the ABC-Clio Press, and a variety of specialized databases. Among the last, RILM (Répertoire international de la littérature musicale) holds a prominent place. It is a computer-generated journal of abstracts submitted by national committees around the world that covers all aspects of musicology. With substantial aid from NEH, this project of the City University of New York (CUNY) has verified the use of the computer for storing and indexing such materials, and the ultimate goal of an online database is being partially reached through Lockheed's DIALOG system.

A primary problem in adapting humanities research to computer technology is to identify the available resources. For historians, these consist of thousands, perhaps tens of thousands, of individual archives, scattered in as many locations and maintained with widely varying degrees of professional care. Some have been partially indexed, while others are simply boxes of papers stored away awaiting professional attention. To identify these collections and to establish links among them to aid historians, NHPRC has developed an indexing system called SPINDEX and has established a users' network called SUN (Spindex Users' Network) (SAHL). Hampered by inadequate funding and the vagaries of public support, this organization faces many years of labor in its attempt to catalog the information on which new kinds of historical interpretation may be based.

Within a single archive, a system being developed at Oxford University may serve as a model for parallel efforts elsewhere. Using CODASYL database management techniques, BURNARD has established a method for linking all the elements of a complex set of seventeenth-century court records, by which he has identified, for example, individuals who served on different juries in different years. At Cambridge University, a similar approach is being used by DAWSON & DAWSON to index the archives of the university itself. Many similar individual efforts are reported elsewhere. What is needed is a coordinating mechanism to ensure that all these new records are compatible. It will be disastrous if these materials are encoded in ways that prevent their ultimate retrieval from a universal system.

The Future Outlook

Need for institutional encouragement. The suspicions and occasional hostility of some humanists who do not use computers and who discount computer-assisted research find expression most often in negative peer reviews and denials of tenure and/or promotion. Unfortunately, little organized effort has been made by either government or major private foundations to eradicate the ignorance on which such prejudices are based or to encourage cooperation in the sharing of resources and techniques among groups with common interests, such as archivists and historians. A great need exists to enhance the exchange of information from goal-oriented groups focusing on library automation and artificial intelligence. No medium of transmitting such information has been fostered by the federal government. However, the Centre Nationale de la Recherche Scientifique in France, the Centro Nazionale della Ricerce in Italy, and analogous bodies in other countries have promoted both basic humanities research and the means of publicizing it. The uncoordinated support of individual research projects in the United States, almost always aimed at specific and very limited targets, has deprived our community as a whole of the opportunity to establish priorities, to encourage standardization, and to accumulate data and programs that will support future projects.

Applications in Education

The participation of government or a major foundation in encouraging computer-oriented humanities research can lead to major consequences beyond the pure research that now occupies most scholars in the field—e.g., the development of more successful computer-assisted instruction (CAI). In the past decade, when mainframe computers and time sharing represented the state of the art, efforts at using technology in the educational process seem to have been limited chiefly to unimaginative drills with unacceptably crude representations on a cathode ray tube (CRT). Within the past few years, two technological breakthroughs—the microcomputer and the videodisk—have been combined to create a genuine teaching instrument of clarity, vast storage (the equivalent of more than 100,000 print pages on a single disk), and almost instant access (MERRILL). With imaginative programming, this combination can substantially help the student to learn foreign languages, music, art history, and other subjects in which technique and content must both be mastered. Humanists, who have been teaching such subjects, can better transfer their skills to computers if they have a close acquaintance with the machines through their research activities. The potential for individualized, responsive teaching for all students of all subjects is too great to leave in the hands of only hardware or software merchandisers. All concerned parties, especially including humanists as a prominent group, must help to shape this major new force.

Merging of Classroom and Library

CAI will also topple another artificial barrier—i.e., the one between the classroom and library. If the videodisk becomes a reliable adjunct to or replacement of classroom instruction, instruction will not be confined to the classroom. The resources of the information center (once called "the bookery") can readily include other storage media. The traditions of individual service, of responsiveness to individual needs, and of accessibility for many hours per week combine to provide substantial advantages to such a learning environment. Additionally, students who come to accept the library as a source of satisfactory instruction may more easily learn to exploit its other facilities.

Related Communications Technology

Cable TV is a major adjunct of computer-based services in the humanities. One scenario, already technically possible, is a library of videodisks stored in a "jukebox" at a central location and called up by users from their terminals. Multiple-read heads will permit many users to access the same disk simultaneously, although the size of the library collection should keep overlapping requests at a minimum. From this infinite encyclopedia (the only one that can accurately be called "the whole wheel of knowledge"), each user can request as much or as little as is wanted, in a variety of languages, on a level that is suitable to the user's age and education, and illustrated with holograms that effectively reproduce visual art in full color and in three dimensions. To the accompaniment of stereophonic sound (words or music) the user can follow individual interests or can request the computer (at home or at the central location) to trace any motif that can be conceptualized. For example, one could trace greed from Aristophanes, through Shakespeare and Molière, to von Stroheim; or one could trace the journey into the inner depths of the soul, as symbolized by the descent into hell, from Homer and Virgil, through Dante and Milton, to Coleridge and Joyce. At such a point, the distinction between "teaching" and "learning" is lost. A student, taught basic reading and arithmetic, could "teach" himself most of what he needed to know, without personality conflicts with teachers or fellow students, without fixed schedules, without prescribed semesters, and without prerequisite courses. Such a system assumes, of course, that students want to and will choose to learn, but having failed for several centuries to coerce them into learning, we have nothing to lose by experimenting with the medium of choice. In our information-rich society, exalting a human being who stands before a class may no longer be justifiable; compared with any television talk-show host, he must seem an ignoramus. If audiovisual presentations are appropriate augmentations for classroom instruction, we must not limit ourselves to slides or films but adopt every technology, particularly videodisk and cable TV, all coordinated and expanded by the computer.

Another long-range incentive for encouraging the greater involvement of humanists in computer-aided research is the increasing concern for the ethical use of technology. Since the study and teaching of humanities represent the individual search for and clarification of moral values, humanists are a logical group to construct the new courses in computer ethics. These are needed to provide a foundation for policies on privacy, ethical use of data, technological unemployment, and the whole spectrum of social and moral issues that increasingly confront us. If instructors in language, history, philosophy, and related subjects can add to their qualifications a hands-on knowledge of computers, they will be among those who are preeminently equipped to lead students to a deeper comprehension of their responsibilities in this regard. Coming to the new problems of a technological age with a perspective that goes back thousands of years, humanists may make a substantial contribution to a discipline that not only measures its history in mere decades but also expects in each of those decades dramatic increment over the preceding one in terms of accomplishment.

The Interactive Terminal

One development that seems to be slow in establishing itself is the interactive terminal. The advantages of conducting a research project on a computer are obvious; programs which can be altered to correspond to newly discovered aspects of the data facilitate the spontaneity that is a prime component of research, and the data (or copies of it) can be manipulated as the researcher wishes. The apparent absence of interactive methods from the current repertoire must be attributed to factors other than lack of interest by scholars. Presumably high cost as well as the few available databases are prominent factors. However, in business the failure to take human factors into account is being increasingly identified as the prime reason for rejection of interactive programs. We must assume that when these problems are solved, when terminals and their links cost less, and when the number of databases begins to approximate the volumes in at least a small library, the same paraphernalia available to airline booking clerks will enhance the research of humanistic scholars.

Cable TV

A major contribution to that advance will presumably be the universal installation of cable TV. With dozens of channels available on the new system, room should exist (even amid the "intellectual junk food") for unconventional programming as well as for textual material from central storage. At first, this will probably be "published" material, an electronic journal of articles, perhaps even books. However, humanists who will have learned to search bibliographies online and then to consult the items themselves on a CRT will not see any substantial difference in accessing both research tools (such as concordances) and the basic text. If the pattern of the past holds, the scientists and then the social scientists will have been there before. Then the installations built in response to their needs may serve the humanists as well and may also become models for equipment dedicated to their activities.

CONCLUSION

As reported in a recent national survey (COMMISSION ON THE HUMANITIES), the present situation and the outlook for the future confirm the status of humanities research in this country—i.e., it does not rank high in our national priorities, especially in a time of economic decline. Humanistic research, which provides no power but only knowledge, seems little valued in a culture that is dominated by international confrontation, environmental pollution, drastic shifts in population, and the evanescense of material progress. Added to these impediments is a widespread indifference to and even suspicion of computer-oriented humanities research in both articulating camps; computer scientists and general humanists alike wonder what really can be done with computers to enhance our understanding of and our esthetic response to our experience of art—verbal, musical, and visual.

Nevertheless, some progress is visible. Centers for this type of research abroad continue to receive government support and remain models for parallel institutions in this country. A major function of such centers would be the orderly production of machine-readable texts; these now must often be prepared by scholars themselves, at a great loss of time and therefore money, because they have no funds to hire lower-salaried keyboarders. An electronic library using an optical character recognition (OCR) device (perhaps the recently announced Kurzweil reader) to encode systematically the works of greatest interest to researchers could make them available over the new networks or even by mail on tapes. These centers could also disseminate to, and exchange materials with, the European centers, which are now already a decade or more ahead of us. Special programs, designed for easy use by nonprogrammers, could be developed and distributed. At central sites, summer courses and symposia could be held; fellowship leaves could profitably be spent working with data files, program packages, and the trained personnel assembled there.

For such centers to come into existence requires a national attitude not yet evident, a belief in the value of humanities research in general, a recognition of the many ways in which machines can facilitate that research, and a conviction that this field will grow to provide new, practical ways of teaching the useful subjects—speaking and reading languages (including English)—and the impractical ones—art and music—without which all else is sterile.

As always, humanists are fighting battles that are impossible to win in absolute terms. As always, they seek at least partial success. As always, they seem determined to achieve that certain, if small, degree of success that gives meaning to the promise of technology.

BIBLIOGRAPHY

AITKEN, A. J. 1972. The Literary Use of Computers. In: London Times Literary Supplement. 1972 April 21.

AITKEN, A. J.; BAILEY, R. W.; HAMILTON-SMITH, N., eds. 1973. The Computer and Literary Studies. [Proceedings of the Association for Literary and Linguistic Computing (ALLC) Conference]. Edinburgh, Scotland: University Press; 1973. ISBN: 85224-232-8.

ALLEN, STURE. 1980. The Language Bank Concept. See reference: RABEN, JOSEPH; MARKS, GREGORY A., eds. 171–176.

ARNOLD, KLAUS. 1974. Geschichtswissenschaft und elektronische Datenverarbeitung: Methoden, Ergebnisse und Mölichkeiten. In: Scheider, Theodor, ed. Methodenprobleme der Geschichtswissenschaft. Munich, Germany: Oldenbourg; 1974. 148p. ISBN: 3-486-44101-9.

BISOGNI, FABIO. 1978. The Catalogue of Italian Art with Iconographical Analysis Realized with the Use of the Computer. Florence, Italy; 1978.

BOURRELLY, LOUIS; CHOURAQUI, EUGÈNE. 1975. Le Système documentaire, SATIN 1. Paris, France: Centre National de la Recherche Scientifique (CNRS); 1975. 2 volumes. (Text in French). CNRS 5661012 and CNRS 5314141. ISBN: 2222017 386 (volume 1).

BRAINERD, BARRON. 1974. Weighing Evidence in Language and Literature: A Statistical Approach. Toronto, Canada: University of Toronto Press; 1974. 288p. ISBN: 0-8020-1874-2.

BRAINERD, BARRON. 1980. The Chronology of Shakespeare's Plays: A Study in Statistical Method. Computers and the Humanities. 1980 January-March; 13(1): 3–16. ISSN: 0010-4817.

BULLOCK, ALAN LOUIS CHARLES. 1977. Is History Becoming a Social Science? Cambridge, England: Cambridge University Press; 1977. 22p. ISBN: 0-521-29222-0.

BURNARD, LOU D. 1980. An Application of CODASYL Techniques to Research in the Humanities. See reference: RABEN, JOSEPH; MARKS, GREGORY A., eds. 89–93.

BURTON, MICHAEL L. 1973. Recent Computer Application in Cultural Anthropology. Computers and the Humanities. 1973 September-November; 7(6):337–341. ISSN: 0010-4817.

BUSA, ROBERTO. 1974-. Index Thomisticus. Stuttgart-Bad-Cannstatt, Germany: Frommann-Holzboog; 1974-. ISBN: 3-7728-0532-9.

BUSA, ROBERTO. 1980. The Annals of Humanities Computing: The Index Thomisticus. Computers and the Humanities. 1980 October; 14(2): 83–90. ISSN: 0010-4817.

INFORMATION SYSTEMS—ARTS AND HUMANITIES

CASSIDY, FREDERIC G. 1980. Some Uses of Computers in Lexicography—
The *DARE* Experience. See reference: RABEN, JOSEPH; MARKS,
GREGORY A., eds. 185-189.
CHENHALL, ROBERT G. 1975. Museum Cataloguing in the Computer
Age. Nashville, TN: American Association for State and Local History;
1975. 261p. ISBN: 0-910050-12-0.
CHOUEKA, YACOV. 1980. Computerized Full-Text Retrieval Systems
and Research in the Humanities: The Responsa Project. Computers
and the Humanities. 1980 November; 14(3):153-170. ISSN: 0010-
4817.
CHISHOLM, DAVID. 1977. A Survey of Computer-Assisted Research in
Modern German. Computers and the Humanities. 1977 September-
October; 11(5):279-287. ISSN: 0010-4817.
CLUBB, JEROME M. 1975. The "New" History as Applied Social Science:
A Review Essay. Computers and the Humanities. 1975 September;
9(5):247-251. ISSN: 0010-4817.
COMMISSION ON THE HUMANITIES. 1980. Humanities in American
Life. Berkeley, CA: University of California Press; 1980. ISBN: 0-520-
04208-5.
COUTURIER, MARCEL. 1974. Informatique et Histoire. Informatique
et Sciences Humaines (France). 1974 March; 20:21-29.
DAWSON, JOHN L.; DAWSON, FRAN R. 1980. The Archives of St.
John's College; Cambridge: A Data-Based Catalogue as a Research Tool.
See reference: RABEN, JOSEPH; MARKS, GREGORY A., eds. 41-46.
ERICKSON, CHARLOTTE. 1975. Quantitative History. The American
Historical Review. 1975 April; 80(2):351-365. ISSN: 0002-8762.
ERICKSON, RAYMOND F. 1975. The DARMS Project: A Status Report.
Computers and the Humanities. 1975 November; 9(6):291-298. ISSN:
0010-4817.
FALK, JOYCE DUNCAN. 1980. Controlled and Free Vocabulary Indexing
of the ABC Clio Databases in History. See reference: RABEN, JOSEPH;
MARKS, GREGORY A., eds. 309-313.
FINK, ELEANOR. 1980. Subject Access to Photographic Reproductions
of American Paintings at the National Collection of Fine Arts. See refer-
ence: RABEN, JOSEPH; MARKS, GREGORY A., eds. 229-232.
FLOUD, RODERICK. 1973. An Introduction to Quantitative Methods for
Historians. Princeton, NJ: Princeton University Press; 1973. ISBN:
0-416-71660-9.
FOGEL, ROBERT WILLIAM. 1975. The Limits of Quantitative Methods
in History. The American Historical Review. 1975 April; 80(2):329-
350. ISSN: 0002-8762.
FOSSIER, LUCIE. 1973. Ordinateur et Histoire médiévale. In: Zampolli,
Antonio, ed. Linguistica Matematica e Calcolatori. Florence, Italy:
Leo S. Olschki; 1973. 183-195. LC: 74-302658.
FOSSIER, LUCIE; VAUCHEZ, A.; VIOLANTE, C., eds. 1977. Informa-
tique et Histoire Médiévale. Rome, Italy: École Française de Rome;
1977. 436p. LC: 78-400905.
FRANCIS, W. NELSON. 1980. A Tagged Corpus: Problems and Prospects.
See reference: RABEN, JOSEPH; MARKS, GREGORY A., eds. 183-
184.
FRAUTSCHI, RICHARD L. 1973. Recent Quantitative Research in French
Studies. Computers and the Humanities. 1973 September-November;
7(6):361-372. ISSN: 0010-4817.

GARCÍA CAMARERO, ERNESTO, ed. 1980. Segunda Conferencia Internacional sobre Bases de Datos en Humanidades y Ciencias Sociales; 1980 June 16–19; Madrid, Spain. Madrid, Spain: Facultad de Informatica; 1980. (Abstracts of conference papers). ISBN: 84-85643-08-7.

HIRSCHMANN, RUDOLF. 1974. A Survey of Computer-Aided Research in Early German. Computers and the Humanities. 1974 September-November; 8(5–6): 279–283. ISSN: 0010-4817.

HOCKEY, SUSAN. 1980. A Guide to Computer Applications in the Humanities. Baltimore, MD: The Johns Hopkins University Press; 1980. 248p. ISBN: 0-8018-2346-3.

INGRAM, WILLIAM. 1974. Concordances in the Seventies. Computers and the Humanities. 1974 September-November; 8(5–6): 273–277. ISSN: 0010-4817.

JENSEN, RICHARD. 1974. Quantitative American Studies: The State of the Art. American Quarterly. 1974 August: 225–240. ISSN: 0003-0678.

JONES, ALAN; CHURCHHOUSE, ROBERT F., eds. 1976. The Computer in Literary and Linguistic Studies: [Proceedings of the Association for Literary and Linguistic Computing (ALLC) Conference]. Cardiff, Wales: The University of Wales Press; 1976. 362p. ISBN: 7083-0590-3.

KLEIMAN, DENA. 1980. Futuristic Library Does Away with Books. New York Times. 1981 October 21; C1: C6.

KOSTKA, STEFAN M., comp. 1974. A Bibliography of Music Applications. Hackensack, NJ: Joseph Roonin; 1974. ISBN: 0-91374-07-4.

KUČERA, HENRY. 1980. Some Grammatical Properties of a Large English Data Base. See reference: RABEN, JOSEPH; MARKS, GREGORY A., eds. 177–181.

LINCOLN, HARRY B. 1970. The Computer and Music. Ithaca, NY: Cornell University Press; 1970. 354p. ISBN: 0-8014-0550-5.

LINCOLN, HARRY B. 1974. Use of Computers in Music Research: A Short Report on Accomplishments, Limitations, and Future Needs. Computers and the Humanities. 1974 September-November; 8(5-6): 285–289. ISSN: 0010-4817.

MACKESY, EILEEN M. 1980. The MLA International Bibliography: Enumerative Classification in an On-Line Data Base. See reference: RABEN, JOSEPH; MARKS, GREGORY A., eds. 285–289.

MERRILL, PAUL F. 1980. Education and Training Applications of Video Disc Technology. In: Sigel, Efrem; Schubin, Mark; Merrill, Paul F., et al. Video Discs: The Technology, the Applications and the Future. White Plains, NY: Knowledge Industry Publications, Inc.; 1980. ISBN: 0-814236-56-3.

MILLON, RENÉ. 1973. Urbanization at Teotihucàn, Mexico. Austin, TX: University of Texas Press; 1973. ISBN: 0-292-78501-1. (volume 1).

MITCHELL, J. LAWRENCE, ed. 1974. Computers in the Humanities: [Proceedings of the 1st International Conference on Computers and the Humanities (ICCH); 1973; Minneapolis, MN]. Edinburgh, Scotland: Edinburgh University Press; 1974. ISBN: 0-8166-07311.

NERHEIM, ROSALEE. 1980. A New Tool for Music Theorists. See reference: RABEN, JOSEPH; MARKS, GREGORY A., eds. 263–267.

OAKMAN, ROBERT L. 1980. Computer Methods for Literary Research. Columbia, SC: University of South Carolina Press; 1980. 235p. ISBN: 0-87249-381-4.

OHLGREN, THOMAS H. 1980. Subject Access to Iconographic Data Bases: Theory and Practice. See reference: RABEN, JOSEPH; MARKS, GREGORY A., eds. 245–250.

RABEN, JOSEPH, comp. 1977. Computer-Assisted Research in the Humanities: A Directory of Scholars Active. Elmsford, NY: Pergamon Press; 1977. 251p. ISBN: 0-08-019870-8.

RABEN, JOSEPH; MARKS, GREGORY A., eds. 1980. Data Bases in the Humanities and Social Sciences; Proceedings of the International Federation for Information Processing Society Working Conference on Data Bases in the Humanities and Social Sciences; 1979 August 23–24; Dartmouth College, Hanover, NH. Amsterdam, The Netherlands: North-Holland Publishing Co.; 1980. 329p. ISBN: 0-444-85499-1.

RABSON, GUSTAVE; RABSON, CAROLYN. 1981. The National Tune Index: A System Overview. Computers and the Humanities. 1981 January; 15(1). ISSN: 0010-4817.

SÁEZ-GODOY, LEOPOLDO. 1975. Situation and Prospects of Computer-Aided Literary Research in Spanish. Computers and the Humanities. 1975 September; 9(5): 245–246. ISSN: 0010-4817.

SAHLI, NANCY. 1980. The NHPRC Data Base on Historical Source Materials in the United States. See reference: RABEN, JOSEPH; MARKS, GREGORY A., eds. 1–4.

SCHNEIDER, BEN ROSS, JR. 1974. Travels in Computerland: or, Incompatibilities and Interfaces. Reading, MA: Addison-Wesley; 1974. 180p. ISBN: 0-201-06737-4.

SCHNORE, LEO FRANCIS, ed. 1974. The New Urban History: Quantitative Explorations by American Historians. Princeton, NJ: Princeton University Press; 1974. ISBN: 0-691-04624-7; 0-691-10026-8.

SOBINSKI-SMITH, MARY JANE. 1980. Standards for Subject Cataloging and Retrieval at the Yale Center for British Art. See reference: RABEN, JOSEPH; MARKS, GREGORY A., eds. 233–237.

STOUT, HARRY S. 1975. Culture, Structure, and the "New" History: A Critique and an Agenda. Computers and the Humanities. 1975 September; 9(5):213–230. ISSN: 0010-4817.

SWIERENGA, ROBERT P. 1974a. Computers and American History: The Impact of the "New" Generation. Journal of American History. 1974 March: 1045–1070. ISSN: 0021-8723.

SWIERENGA, ROBERT P. 1974b. Computers and Comparative History. Journal of Interdisciplinary History. 1974 Autumn; 5(2): 267–286. ISSN: 0022-1953.

THIBODEAU, KENNETH. 1976. Machine Readable Archives and Future History. Computers and the Humanities. 1976 March-April; 10(2): 89–92. ISSN: 0010-4817.

VANCE, DAVID. n.d. [Brochure on Museum Computer Network]. Available from: Center for Contemporary Arts and Letters, Library E-2340, State University of New York, Stony Brook, NY 11794.

VANDERMEER, PHILIP R. 1977. The New Political History: Progress and Prospects. Computers and the Humanities. 1977 September-October; 11(5): 265–278. ISSN: 0010-4817.

WENKER, JEROME. 1980. Creating and Maintaining Music Data Bases. See reference: RABEN, JOSEPH; MARKS, GREGORY A., eds. 269–273.

WIDMANN, R. L. 1975. Trends in Computer Applications to Literature. Computers and the Humanities. 1975 September; 9(5): 231–235. ISSN: 0010-4817.
WILSON, DAVID. 1975. The New Archaeology. New York, NY: Alfred A. Knopf; 1975. 349p. ISBN: 0-394-47936-X.
WISBEY, ROY A. 1971. The Computer in Literary and Linguistic Research: [Proceedings of the Association for Literary and Linguistic Computing (ALLC) Conference]. Cambridge, England: Cambridge University Press; 1971. 309p. ISBN: 0-521-08146-7.
ZAMPOLLI, ANTONIO, ed. 1973. Linguistica Matematica e Calcolatori. Florence, Italy: Leo S. Olschki; 1973. LC: 74-302658.
ZARRI, GIAN PERO. 1977. Sur le traitement automatique de données biographiques médiévales: Le projet RESDA. In: Lusignan, Serge; North, John S., eds. Computing in the Humanities: Proceedings of the 3rd International Conference on Computing in the Humanities. Waterloo, Ontario, Canada: University of Waterloo Press; 1977. 151–161. (Text in French). ISBN: 0-88898-104-0.
ZARRI, GIAN PERO. 1979. La Pratique des Ordinateurs dans la Critique des Textes. Paris, France: Editions du Centre Nationale de la Recherche Scientifique; 1979.
ZETTERSTEN, ARNE. 1976. Current Scandinavian Computer-Aided Language and Literature Research. Computers and the Humanities. 1976 September-October; 10(5):275–280. ISSN: 0010-4817.

9   Information Systems and Services in the Life Sciences

NANCY G. VAUPEL
BIOSIS

A. W. ELIAS
BIOSIS

INTRODUCTION

Today more scientists are at work than the total of all those who have lived in the past, and more than 95% of all modern scientists work in countries which together contain only 25% of the world's population. The discoveries of modern science have created an information explosion, which has led to the rapid growth of scientific information systems and services, especially in the western world where most scientists have lived.

In the life sciences, information systems and services first appeared as abstracting journals, indexes, libraries, and specialized reference services. The early major life science abstracting journals were published in Germany during the nineteenth and early twentieth centuries—e.g., *Botanisches Zentralblatt, Zoologischer Bericht,* and *Zentralblatt für Bakteriologie.* The *Zoological Record,* first published by zoologists affiliated with the Zoological Society of London, is the oldest continuing index in the life sciences. It appeared first in 1864 and exists today as a joint publication of the Zoological Society of London and BioSciences Information Service (BIOSIS) of the United States.

Most life science information resources appeared in the twentieth century in response to the information explosion. In fact, most of the major systems and services have appeared in operational form during the past 10-20 years (KRUZAS & SCHMITTROTH) although there are exceptions. *Biological Abstracts,* a large bibliographic life science information system, was founded in Philadelphia in 1926 after World War I made German information resources inaccessible (STEERE). The Commonwealth Agricultural Bureaux (CAB) also originated in the late 1920s, providing abstracting journals to British life scientists. A major French scientific information resource, the

National Center for Scientific Research, publisher of *Bulletin Signaletique* and the PASCAL database, was founded in 1940.

A brief history of life science information resources shows how far this area has progressed. Traditional services existed side by side with the new indexing and abstracting tools of the early 1900s. Reference services, card catalogs, journal collections, and subject specialists were available to the information seeker, but computerized online information retrieval, personalized computers, data banks, and information networks were far in the future. Life science information services have now changed dramatically through computerization, networking, information education, cooperative arrangements and, finally, through greater recognition of the value of both information and the life sciences.

Our purpose is to review the literature on current developments in life science information, concentrating on the past five years, 1975-1980. The literature of the years 1965-1975 was analyzed in a large-scale bibliographic essay by FOOTE & ZIDAR. Their discussion is considered here as relevant recent history. Foote and Zidar suggest that life scientists during 1965-1975 were beginning to realize that as individuals they could no longer handle all the data needed for or resulting from their research. They began to think about how they could use laboratory computers for information systems or how they could use existing systems and services to solve their information problems.

What was being contemplated in 1965-1975 was being implemented in 1975-1980. The literature of the past five years gives examples of fully operational information systems on laboratory computers as well as on those of the commercial search services. It includes papers concerned with the quality and value of existing information sources as well as with their weaknesses. This literature is aimed at both the scientist end user and the life science information professional and was written by both groups.

The literature emphasizes various life science areas. Because articles about medical and hospital information systems and services dominate the literature, they hinder any attempt to study all aspects of life science information in a balanced fashion. Therefore, our emphasis is on information systems in all other major life science disciplines: botany, microbiology, zoology (including veterinary science), and biochemistry. Papers on information systems and services that provide data on living organisms, on life processes, and on the interaction of life with its environment are reviewed. Those that consider systems and services designed for health care are omitted. However, systems and services used to further research in areas related to medicine, such as pharmacology and toxicology, are included.

Several hundred documents were identified as being relevant. Those that focus on the major themes reviewed here numbered just over 250. Approximately 100 of those are important works that best express the present and future concerns of life scientists and information professionals with regard to systems and services. These are included in the bibliography.

The papers reviewed concentrate on: 1) comparisons of the information resources available; 2) the creation of highly specialized information systems and services (including networks); 3) descriptions of particular databases; and 4) the development of database indexing structures. Topics that are not discussed here but were found include: 1) the costs of information systems and services; 2) the work of information analysis centers (IACs) in the life sciences; and 3) information education in the use of life science systems and services.

Documents on the costs of using or producing information systems and services were excluded because most of them focused on the comparative costs of searching databases online through various vendors.

IACs were excluded because they were analyzed in detail in *ARIST* Volume 15 (CARROLL & MASKEWITZ) and because many IACs in the life sciences work closely with the medical profession.

Education was excluded for three reasons. First, many education papers cover the role of the library or other service organization in overall information education and not just life science education. Second, although educational packages exist for life science information education, few papers discuss the use of these packages. Third, end-user education as well as information specialist education is a topic that might be handled better from an education point of view, especially since only a few documents relate specifically to life science information instruction.

Of the four major themes in this chapter—information resource comparisons, specialized systems and services, database descriptions, and database indexing—only one relates to services. The literature emphasizes systems, and so does our discussion. For this chapter, this concept has a specific meaning. An information system, whether on cards, in print, on computer tape or disk, or in some other physical state, is characterized by the organization and storage of information (data, facts, documents, etc.) in a retrievable form to satisfy some future need. In a system, data have usually been organized to achieve the objectives of an expected end user group. In contrast, an information service is characterized by the use of a system or systems for retrieving the needed data, facts, documents, etc., for a customer or for one's own use. Service and system are often used interchangeably in the literature. Also sometimes an author describes an information system in terms of the information services it incorporates. That is not done here.

Unfortunately, the service concept as defined above is nearly lost in the literature. Paper after paper focuses on systems that provide data or references. They analyze what information is stored, how it is stored, and how well the retrieved information answers the questions at hand. Only a few authors are concerned with the services provided by libraries, information centers, brokers, or distributors. Nevertheless, we review the service literature. Life scientists and information professionals may find that discussion of effective service and new ways to give service should be given higher priority in the future.

BACKGROUND LITERATURE

The annotated bibliography of more than 300 references on information-handling activities in biology, published by FOOTE & ZIDAR, analyzed ten years' of literature. One conclusion of this study, already mentioned, was that biologists were beginning to look for information systems to handle the growing amount of data being generated in the life sciences. The authors also noted that information systems devoted to bibliographic control of the life science literature had made significant progress during the ten-year span. In other areas of data control progress was less evident.

In comparing the hundreds of references that have appeared in the past five years with those of Foote and Zidar, we can say that life scientists, particularly those in the applied biological sciences, are showing more awareness and understanding of the capabilities of information systems. This is true mainly because of scientists becoming more familiar with the computer. At the same time they are showing only slightly greater awareness of the significant traditional databases in their fields, such as *The Zoological Record* and *Biological Abstracts*. These large secondary information databases, designed to handle life science bibliographic information, are rarely mentioned or analyzed in scientific publications by scientists, whereas systems that are developed by the scientists for their own special needs, such as the mosquito control information system (RUSSO & MCCAIN), are mentioned.

A comparison of references shows that numerous information professionals are becoming actively involved with research on the effective use of information resources. The journal and meeting literature in library science and information science is increasingly devoted to studies of databases and reference tools in which they are compared and evaluated.

The information science community as a whole is benefiting greatly from these activities. It gains expertise from these studies, which can be used in various professional capacities. Its information specialists become aware of the strengths and weaknesses of databases that they may have had no opportunity to evaluate. They become aware of new resources or unique ways to use traditional resources. Database suppliers not only learn what users need but also what information to index and how to make it retrievable. Database comparisons can also show suppliers new subject areas to index or important database characteristics to emphasize (such as timeliness, etc.). The information professionals, although becoming more expert in the use of information resources, do not seem to be sharing their findings with the life science community or vice versa. It is still uncommon to find members of the information community and end users addressing each other at conferences or in each other's publications.

KISSMAN, who is the Director of NLM's Toxicology Information Program and an information professional, is one author who departs from this pattern. His review on information retrieval in toxicology is aimed at the practitioners in toxicology, pharmacology, and the allied sciences. Citing over 100 recent bibliographic references in the field, Kissman writes about the major printed and computerized information resources in a review written mostly for and by research scientists. Such information transfer from information professional to end user as well as from scientist to information professional is necessary to ensure viable information systems in the future. Unfortunately, most of the communication lines still need to be developed.

INFORMATION SYSTEM COMPARISONS

Papers that compare information systems have become more frequent since the advent of large online bibliographic retrieval systems. These systems have made it feasible to compare many of the databases because large amounts of data can be searched in minutes and printouts of results are easily available and comparable. In some cases particular data elements or database attributes worth comparing are only available online. Finally, although the costs of online searching may hinder comparison done via computer, information professionals may not have access to important databases through any other means. Nearly all the authors are information professionals. Nearly all the papers appeared in journals or conferences aimed at the information professional. Of the numerous studies we read, several were done in-depth and are highly evaluative works. A major work in agricultural information studies is the study by HARVEY. In this project, which took more than a year to complete and involved 100 Dutch and British end user scientists, Harvey compared the U. S. Department of Agriculture (USDA) AGRICOLA (Agricultural Online Access) database with the Commonwealth Agricultural Bureaux (CAB) database. Her final evaluation is based on database content, indexing policies, currency, computerized selective dissemination of information (SDI) performance, cost, and end user attitudes. Probably her most significant finding is that the scientific community has a definite preference for SDI output containing abstracts.

No other comparative study was as extensive as the one by Harvey, but several others are important. KRABBE also compared CAB and AGRICOLA. He found that while end users appreciated abstracts, they needed complete results and were willing to pay for searches of both databases. Krabbe's conclusion that multi-database searching is optimal when several databases are relevant is supported by: BURTON, CITTADINO ET AL., and VAN DER VEER & KOOGER (agriculture and food science); BRODAUF ET AL. (veterinary science); BAC (toxicology); SIMKINS (pharmacology); GAWORKSKA (biochemistry); EPSTEIN & ANGIER (the behavioral sciences); and CORTH (marine biology).

The remarks of BRODAUF ET AL., scientist-end users, are especially significant because of the size of their study. Ninety test questions from veterinarians in various European countries were searched via computer against ten databases. More than 70,000 retrieved references were analyzed. The authors found that: 1) each of the ten databases consulted contained many of the same references as well as unique relevant references; 2) none of the databases gave a complete answer to any of the questions posed; 3) not all of the databases included records with abstracts (which were judged to be the best document surrogate); 4) differences in indexing, titling, and author vocabulary made retrieval difficult; and 5) information professionals who hold credentials in veterinary science best served the information needs of veterinarians. As one solution to the problems of database searching BRODAUF ET AL. recommend cooperation among database producers so that each could focus on certain subject areas and reduce overlap. They also recommend that authors title their articles with thesaurus-controlled concepts and write informative abstracts for inclusion into databases.

A similar conclusion is reached by BAC. He advocates a central indexing point for all toxicological papers accepted for publication so that keywords can be standardized. He envisions this indexing and vocabulary control as happening on an international scale before publication.

There are many database comparison studies in the literature. Interested readers should check not only the references cited here but also the bibliographies in the articles by KISSMAN and by FOOTE & ZIDAR.

Guidelines are needed for comparisons of life science databases. The criteria used to compare the different databases are never exactly the same. The criteria need to be evaluated and ranked in terms of their importance in promoting information flow. What is the best method or what are the best criteria to use to judge the overall quality of life science information resources? We are not sure. To date, database evaluations have been based on some combination of the following factors:

- Relevancy of information retrieved
- End user judgments and/or attitudes (obtained through questionnaires and interviews) on numerous database attributes
- Language(s) used in database records
- Amount of unique information in the database
- Cost
- Online availability
- Ease of searching (related to database data elements, access points, spelling consistency, etc.)
- Timeliness of database content
- Amount of relevant information missing from the database
- Database access points
- Database emphasis on information originating in particular geographical areas
- Number of nonunique references
- Quality of information retrieved
- False drops or "noise" in the database
- Type of documents covered—i.e., conference proceedings, journals, books
- Continuity of source coverage
- Choice of journals (or other documents) covered
- Data elements in the citations
- Accessibility of documents
- Database size
- Recall ratio
- Quality and/or reliability of indexing
- Internal duplication of database citations
- Availability of abstracts (and other data elements)

The results of comparative studies even differ in regard to the same databases, depending on which criteria are used. In the study by HARVEY, CAB received a higher overall evaluation than AGRICOLA. In the study by KRABBE, AGRICOLA and CAB were evaluated as near equals. The science or art of evaluation needs closer study.

SPECIALIZED SYSTEMS AND SERVICES

The literature on specialized systems, services, and networks that have been created or are proposed in the life sciences is one that includes numerous papers written by life scientists. Most papers describe the use of computers in the creation of specialized information systems. These computerized systems, in general, are data- or fact-oriented and are mainly in areas that are relevant to the applied life sciences. Specialized agricultural databases include a genealogical database for fruit propagation records (CLARKE & CASIERO), a barley cultivar database (THOMPSON & BAUM), a plant gene database (SEIDEWITZ), a poisonous plants database (GARROW), and animal feed databases (HAENDLER). In the veterinary sciences, databases have been designed or proposed for the management of turkeys (WILEY), for cattle breeding (VERHEIJEN), for the surveillance of farm animal disease (BURRIDGE & MCCARTHY; COMBS; DAVIES), and for laboratory animals (GLUCKSTEIN ET AL.). Other specialized databases exist in pharmacology (PAGE ET AL.), toxicology (JOHNSTONE; SCHECHTER ET AL.; SCHOLTEN), and ecology (DITTBERNER & BRYANT; KNIGHT & POWELL; PATTON; WHITSON & MASSEY).

Many more specialized databases have been developed, but how many more is unknown. We can assume that many other systems exist for which there is no documentation. The substantial efforts made to document the databases and data banks in the agricultural and veterinary sciences are impressive and should encourage a similar effort in the other life science areas.

To date documentation on databases and information activity in the nonagricultural disciplines is either widely scattered or unavailable. Thus, one should expect duplication of effort in creating systems for specialized needs. For example, although the data may be different, several specialized toxicology systems store and manipulate insecticide and pesticide data (JOHNSTONE; SCHECHTER ET AL.).

Specialized databases have been developed in nearly identical fields to meet similar needs. Several ecology systems attempt to computerize information concerning habitats (DITTBERNER & BRYANT; PATTON). Even some of the systems in the agricultural sciences, set up before a conference on data banks was organized, were developed to meet the same need to control the spread of animal diseases (BURRIDGE & MCCARTHY; DAVIES). Most of the scientists probably did not exchange plans and ideas before they developed their systems, but this is an important consideration in eliminating duplication of effort and in promoting progress in database development.

The fact that this exchange is not happening on a regular basis in all the life science disciplines is one problem that needs to be solved. There is a second, even more serious, problem. It concerns the development of effective methods to inform inquiring scientists about all the information systems or resources available to answer their questions. The literature on specialized services indicates a possible solution.

Library networks have been growing over the past several years to link all end users with the appropriate information tools. The network idea in the life science literature comes from librarians who are serving agricultural scientists. WU describes the large Agricultural Canada Libraries Information Network, in which the libraries cooperate to provide public access to *all* information systems and to coordinate library resources and acquisitions. The use of telecommunications and computers has made the coordination possible and effective.

The network idea in the United States has developed along similar lines. An article in *AGRICULTURAL LIBRARIES INFORMATION NOTES* reports the progress on and the rationale for the long-planned U.S. agricultural information network. Instead of trying to become a complete storehouse of all agricultural knowledge, the National Agricultural Library is linking resources with public and private agricultural information centers. It is hoped the ultimate nationwide agricultural information resource will be created through extensive idea exchange, meetings, and planning, and with the backing of Congress.

In forestry, a field related to agriculture, YERKE writes about the Pacific Coast Foresters Network (PACFORNET), the first information network service developed for foresters. PACFORNET's services are oriented to the needs of the network users and not to traditional library archival goals. Three services are emphasized: 1) current awareness, 2) document delivery, and 3) hotline reference help (for literature searches, facts, names of specialists, and special information). Yerke indicates that the ten-year-old network is already used heavily. To increase use even more, plans are being formulated for training users. The PACFORNET success seems impressive in terms of bringing the forestry community closer to its information resources, whether these are databases, books, journals, other foresters, or facts. Further linkage of specialized information center and facilities is planned.

Another information service in forestry deserves discussion. FINLAYSON ET AL. detail the services offered jointly by the Commonwealth Forestry Bureaux and the Commonwealth Forestry Institute Library, both in Oxford, England. The two organizations collaborate to give the end users access to an extensive collection of periodicals that can be photocopied as needed, access to card versions of *Forestry Abstracts* and *Forest Products Abstracts* before the journal form is published, access to the forestry specialists of both organizations, and access to most of the traditional library services. These services are not unique or new to information centers, but when offered together, they go a long way toward meeting the information needs of a specific discipline. These two information organizations show what can be accomplished when an information center and a database producer cooperate.

Life science information services not only benefit from linkage with information systems but also benefit when information systems link with each other. The producers of the *Chemical Abstracts* (*CA*) database (CA Search) and the BIOSIS Previews database (which includes *Biological Abstracts* and *Biological Abstracts/RRM*) have undertaken a cooperative venture to produce biweekly subject bibliographies derived by interfiling hits obtained from searches of both databases. Thus, these database producers can meet user needs for more complete information retrieval as well as for bibliographies where duplicate citations are eliminated.

Although database producers have made vast amounts of information accessible and although cooperative opportunities exist with them on various levels, information services have sometimes found it necessary to set up their own systems for special user needs. The Primate Information Center, described by TERRY, is such a service as is the National Poisons Information Service, described by WISEMAN. Wiseman indicates that the telephone inquiries handled at the Poisons Information Service actually become an important information source for their system, Poisons Index. Like few other indexes, Poisons Index can be described as a living, highly up-to-date information system, upon which a very vital service is based. The idea that information from queries can be used to augment an established database is a service idea worthy of note.

One characteristic of many specialized information services is the willingness of their personnel to consult all available resources to serve the end users. Whether these services function basically as libraries or referral centers or whether they also run a specialized database, their staff seem highly aware of the resources available in the field.

The same is not necessarily true of the producers of specialized information systems (except when they are linked to an information service). Very few authors who describe operational or proposed specialized information systems, refer to using information already in any of the existing databases. Some papers describe systems that are so specialized that only little use could have been made of existing systems, so use was not expected. Other papers, such as that by PARKA on weed biology information, discuss subjects that are treated by several major existing life science databases, yet Parka never mentions any of them. Only a few authors made extensive mention of existing bases (KAMINUMA & KURIHARA; WILEY). This may be a symptom of the communication problem facing the life science information community. The established database producers still need to find effective avenues for reaching life scientists and making both the existence and value of their databases known. The producers of small, specialized database systems who want national or international recognition have an even greater task.

DESCRIPTIONS OF DATABASES

One way that databases attain recognition is through descriptive essays in the literature. Databases that are interdisciplinary, large, or online through a major system (and therefore visible and easily accessible) have the advantage of being compared, contrasted, or noted in many articles on information science. Numerous papers that compare databases have been discussed. Many of the authors who describe information systems in detail are associated with database producers and write about their database as experts. They usually do not compare their database with others or critically examine its strengths or weaknesses, except historically. They do, however, give valuable insight into the database producer's objectives, policies, and future plans as well as information about the database's construction, scope, content, and coverage.

Among the database producers, BioSciences Information Service (BIOSIS) has frequently been the subject of papers written by its staff or affiliates. The book by STEERE, published in 1976, is devoted entirely to the history of BIOSIS. More recently ELIAS, MARCHISOTTO, and KELLY ET AL. have written about the BIOSIS database, looking at its subject coverage, its indexing structure, and its place in promoting biological communication.

WOOD ET AL. and METCALFE deal with the information system of the Commonwealth Agricultural Bureaux (CAB). Both include details on history and subject coverage as well as information about the organizational structure of CAB. Wood et al. depart from the usual pattern by comparing CAB with other agricultural databases.

Numerous papers and reports describe various databases. GILREATH reviews the interdisciplinary nature of AGRICOLA. SMITH has written a comprehensive essay on the history, indexing and production systems, coverage, scope, and future goals of Zoological Record. PELISSIER gives extensive information on the PASCAL file structure, data elements, and content, with emphasis on online searching. GAILLARDIN ET AL., not affiliated with the producer, have also analyzed PASCAL. Their paper aims to promote better information retrieval by examining PASCAL's indexing rules. The paper by FREEMAN involves policy more than any other aspect with regard to Aquatic Sciences and Fisheries Abstracts, an international database; GLUCKSTEIN ET AL. report on the Laboratory Animal Data Bank now available online. COLLINS examines two databases for aquatic animal literature.

An analysis of these works leads to several conclusions. First, agricultural databases are the most frequently discussed. In addition to the studies on CAB and AGRICOLA (GILREATH; METCALFE; WOOD ET AL.), studies of other agricultural bibliographic files, such as AGRIS (International Information System for the Agricultural Sciences and Technology) are widespread (ALLEN & DUBOIS; BADRAN; LANCASTER & MARTYN). Agricultural research project files, such as CARIS (Current Agricultural Research Information System), CRIS (Current Research Information System) of the U. S. Department of Agriculture, ARCIS (Agricultural Research Current Information System), and AGREP (Agricultural Research Projects) are also mentioned often (ARNOULD; DOPKOWSKI; FELL; MOLSTER ET AL.).

Second, although database descriptions are numerous, publicly available descriptions do not exist for every system, not even as in-house reports. Several database suppliers who were contacted indicated that they knew of no documents that describe their database. Third, most descriptive studies examine bibliographic databases, and fourth, only a few of these studies have been written for the end user life scientist. To a great extent the descriptions are written by information professionals for other informational professionals. The information systems not yet described need to be documented, with emphasis on factual databases in the life sciences, and more descriptions need to be written for the scientific end user. More emphasis is also needed on analyses of database indexing structures. Indexing is important to end users and information professionals alike. More use will be made of a database with an indexing structure that is easy to understand and use as well as being effective in terms of recall and relevance.

DATABASE INDEXING

Papers have already been mentioned that analyze, in part, database indexing structures. The database producers almost always explain their general indexing policies and rules in their descriptive essays (MARCHISOTTO; PELISSIER; SMITH). It is also not uncommon for papers that compare databases to compare their indexes. At least one comparison (FUJIMOTO) concentrates solely on indexing while most others look at indexing structure as one feature of a database (BRODAUF ET AL.; HARVEY).

The paper by Fujimoto, an analysis of Excerpta Medica's Drugdoc and Derwent's Ringdoc (Pharmaceutical Literature Documentation) databases details a method that can be used to compare indexing. Fujimoto selects nine citations from each database and classifies them according to their emphasis on particular drugs. Three of the citations look at the pharmacological aspects of the drugs, three look at therapeutic aspects, and three look at toxicological aspects. Each of the nine entries appears in both databases, each pair was found to have the same basic bibliographic details but different indexing features. Fujimoto considers: 1) the correlation between the added indexing terms and article content, 2) the hierarchical character of the indexing structures, 3) the use of synonyms, and 4) the distribution of the indexing terms according to their pharmaceutical or biomedical content. He concludes that both databases have strengths that reflect their historical backgrounds. Drugdoc makes superior use of medical terminology and does an excellent job in indexing all major points of the articles; Ringdoc is superior in providing indexing terms that are relevant to pharmaceutical aspects and focuses more on the main theme of the articles. In terms of its hierarchical structure of codes and indexing terms, Ringdoc is extremely useful for retrieving drugs that have the same principal action or for retrieving all the drug derivatives of a parent chemical structure. The two databases, developed from different perspectives, meet the needs of two different groups—medical researchers and pharmacologists.

AVIDON ET AL. look at the problems of indexing drug and chemical information for a factual database. The indexing of specific information on the effects of biologically active compounds is discussed in the light of experiences with an inadequate manual information system. The new computerized system described is based heavily on a controlled, three-faceted indexing structure. One facet is used to index the effect of the chemical or drug, another to index the mechanism of action, and the third to index the locus of activity. The ideas in each facet have code equivalents and can be searched as such. Words can also be searched. The words entered in the thesaurus as well as in the database are analyzed on several levels. If the words have more than one meaning, polysemy is removed by assigning strictly defined meanings to all words. If significant words are locked into multiword phrases, the phrases are broken down. Their significant components become entry points for the thesaurus. If phraseology sometimes helps to define precise meaning better, phrases became entry points for the thesaurus. Other factors were considered in the indexing structure and thesaurus design, such as the user and advantages of arranging ideas hierarchically.

Avidon et al. emphasize controlled vocabulary and code use in indexing. While the indexing system they described is more complex than usual in most small specialized systems, it reflects the general concern of the life science community with both high information recall and relevance. The indexing systems developed by end-user scientists are usually well structured and easy to use.

RUSSO & MCCAIN describe an operational mosquito control information system, where each record contains 11 fields. The five indexing fields are: habitat description (field 5), life stage of mosquito present or condition of site (field 7), insecticide applied (field 8), species code (field 10), and comments (field 11). Only 16 descriptors are possible for field 5, five are possible for field 7, and just under 50 are possible for field 10, presenting the organism name in terms of its genus and species. Fields 8 and 11 are uncontrolled. The controlled indexing fields are always present in the record while the uncontrolled fields, which are not highly important access points in this system, are not. The database, which was compiled to enable the user to determine the complete mosquito breeding history for a particular site, is simple. Nevertheless, it is said to have significantly improved the productivity of a program that produces more than 15,000 records on mosquito breeding sites every year (RUSSO & MCCAIN).

This success story has been repeated numerous times on both the national and international levels. HAENDLER reviews the impressive work of the International Network of Feed Information Centres in his report on animal feed data banks. The members of this group cooperate to produce a highly specialized information system. Data units, which Haendler calls "informemes," are extracted from relevant documents and put into special, controlled formats indicating feed nutritional value, energy value, toxic components, active ingredients, and more. Although much of the information is in numeric form, controlled word descriptors are also used. The controlled indexing structure enables each node of the network to perform basically equivalent indexing operations on documents in many different languages and with varying content. It also enables the user to search the database and receive output in any language that the network makes available. The system currently handles queries and produces output in German, English, French, and Spanish.

Whenever the information system can focus on several controlled data elements, it can often be simple yet effective. THOMPSON & BAUM, discussing how they developed and built a more comprehensive information system out of a barley cultivar register, describe the addition of a bibliographic file to the original barley register. In their system the controlled barley cultivar genusspecies names are used as the only access point to the documents that discuss the cultivars. The index to the bibliographic information file, the newest module added to the system, is therefore straightforward and effective. Only as the number of papers on barley cultivars increases or as the questions asked of the system become more complex will the indexing structure become inadequate.

The larger database systems in the life sciences as a rule show greater indexing complexity as well as greater retrieval flexibility. These systems developed indexing structures to meet the requirements of their large audiences. Since they handle numerous documents that reflect the ideas of all or many life science disciplines, they rarely concentrate on indexing the special quantitative information contained in only some of the documents. As noted by HARVEY, MARCHISOTTO, and PELISSIER, each writing about different, large multidisciplinary bibliographic databases, controlled vocabulary and subject code access is usually provided along with free-text indexing and other uncontrolled term retrieval points. In no case is vocabulary control as tight as that described by the producers of specialized databases.

One of the conclusions of FOOTE & ZIDAR from their study of the literature in 1975 was that biologists were becoming aware that they needed ways to handle biological information. We can conclude from our study that the life science community is actively beginning to come to terms with its information needs. Specialized systems are being discussed in the literature with respect to indexing structure, data element retrieval, and file expansion possibilities. The major interdisciplinary database producers are also analyzing these aspects. In any of these discussions the needs of the end user for structured, yet flexible, highly reliable indexing systems must be given top priority. No database producer should underestimate the importance of developing indexing structures suitable to both the variety of life science information and the needs of the end user. In the future, end users will want to search for their own information as well as rely on information services. If indexing structures suitable to their needs are not developed by the database producers, end users will develop them. End-user friendly, easily searched, and easily understood indexing structures are essential to the survival of the information professional as the provider of information systems and services.

SUMMARY

The accomplishments of life scientists with respect to information are concentrated in one area—namely, the development of specialized databases. Much of the work on these systems has occurred outside the information community. Nevertheless, the projects are extremely important in telling the information community that life scientists are now actively concerned with handling the data of their discipline. These specialized (mostly computerized) systems show that the life science community is ready for much more communication with information professionals, especially with regard to computerized information systems and services.

This communication for the most part has not taken place and needs emphasis in the future. Only in the agricultural sciences have conferences successfully brought together information professionals and end users on a large scale. Other disciplines in the life sciences are ready for full-scale discussions of the existing information resources in their field as well as the resources that are lacking or are poor in quality. Discussions in the near future could take place about the information resources in pharmacology and toxicology because many end users as well as information professionals seem to be concentrating their efforts there.

The accomplishments of the information professionals in gaining more expertise through comparative studies about the resources available and in designing services or systems that offer unique solutions to information problems (such as service networks) have had a positive effect on professional status. The ability of information professionals to use the computer for problem solving, however, has probably been the greatest factor in bringing them closer to the scientists they serve. The scientist and the information professional are beginning to speak a common language, that of computer science. Both groups are becoming computer users and are learning the terminology. Information professionals speak now of data elements and retrieval points, for example, rather than of card catalogs and bookshelves. Because some scientists are creating databases on computers, they speak now of indexing systems and searching, whereas in the past these concepts were of little interest to them.

The computer has given life scientists and information professionals a new front on which to communicate. The opportunities are vast and need to be exploited by all concerned parties. The small personalized information system is possible. The large information system is now manageable and searchable. Indexing can be done at greater depth and in more detail. The number of information systems available to services can be nearly doubled in a day's time via computer search services and computer networks. Larger information systems are possible, and cooperative efforts between database suppliers are feasible. The period of transition and experimentation is well under way. It remains for future reviews to document the results.

BIBLIOGRAPHY

AGRICULTURAL LIBRARIES INFORMATION NOTES. 1980. An Agricultural Information Network. Agricultural Libraries Information Notes. 1980 July; 6(7): 11–15. ISSN: 0095-2699.

ALLEN, LIDA L.; DUBOIS, G. 1978. Animal Health Information in the AGRIS System. In: Proceedings of the International Symposium on Animal Health and Disease Data Banks; 1978 December 4–6; Washington, DC. Beltsville, MD: U.S. Department of Agriculture; 1979. 25–32. (USDA Miscellaneous Publication no. 1381).

ARAKAKI, T.; KAWANO, M. 1980. JAPIC Cards and the Japanese Drug Literature Information System. Paper presented at: Asian Congress of Pharmaceutical Sciences; 1980 Summer. 3p. Available from: Japan Pharmaceutical Information Center, 2-12-15 Shibuya, Shibuya-ku, Tokyo, Japan.

ARNOULD, J. P. 1978. The Role Which the CARIS System Could Play in Providing Information on Current Agricultural Research in Relation to Animal Health and Disease. In: Proceedings of the International Symposium on Animal Health and Disease Data Banks; 1978 December 4–6; Washington, DC. Beltsville, MD: U.S. Department of Agriculture; 1979. 175–186. (USDA Miscellaneous Publication no. 1381).

AVIDON, V. V.; MIKHAILOVSKII, E. M.; PIRUZYAN, L. A. 1977. Specialized Three-Faceted Information Retrieval Thesaurus as a Means of Indexing and Retrieving Biologically Active Compounds According to Their Biological Effects. Pharmaceutical Chemistry Journal. 1977 June; 11(6): 757–764. CODEN: PCJOAU.

BAC, ROBERT. 1980. A Comparative Study by the Pharma Documentation Ring of Toxicology Information Retrieval from Online Literature Databases. Online. 1980 April; 4(2): 29–33. ISSN: 0340-1545; CODEN: ONLNAZ.

BADRAN, OSMAN A. 1977. Report on the Independent Appraisal of Agris. Paris, France: UNESCO; 1977. 118p.

BAWDEN, D.; DEVON, T. K. 1980. RINGDOC—The Database of Pharmaceutical Literature. Database. 1980 September; 3(3): 29–39. ISSN: 0162-4105.

BAWDEN, D.; JACKSON, F. T. 1978. On-line Searching for the Toxicology of Chemical Substances. In: Proceedings of the 2nd International Online Information Meeting; 1978 December 5–7; London, England. Oxford, England: Learned Information (Europe) Ltd.; 1978. 195–204. ISBN: 0-904933-15-6.

BLUMENBACH, D. 1979. Information Services in the Field of Plant Pathology of the Federal Biological Research Centre. International Association of Agricultural Librarians and Documentalists Quarterly Bulletin. 1979 Spring-Summer; 24(2): 35–38. ISSN: 0020-5966; CODEN: QBALAE.

BRODAUF, H.; HOFFMAN, W. D.; KLAWITER-POMMER, J. H. T.; GRAY, D. E. 1977. Searching the Literature of Veterinary Science: A Comparative Study of the Use of 10 Information Systems for Retrospective Searches from January 1972 to December 1974. Veterinary Record. 1977 December; 101(23): 461–463. CODEN: VETRAX.

BROOKS, KRISTINA. 1980. A Comparison of the Coverage of Agricultural and Forestry Literature on AGRICOLA, BIOSIS, CAB, and SCISEARCH. Database. 1980 March; 3(1): 38–49. ISSN: 0162-4105.

BURGESS, R. L. 1979. National Biological Monitoring Inventory. Oak Ridge, TN: Oak Ridge National Laboratory, 1979. 29p. (Oak Ridge National Laboratory Report no. CONF-780376-1).

BURRIDGE, M. J.; MCCARTHY, S. M. 1978. The Florida Veterinary Clinical Data Retrieval System. In: Proceedings of the International Symposium On Animal Health and Disease Data Banks; 1978 December

4-6; Washington, DC. Beltsville, MD: U.S. Department of Agriculture; 1979. 155-162. (USDA Miscellaneous Publication no. 1381).

BURTON, HILARY D. 1978a. Computerized Bibliographic Services for USDA Research. Journal of Forestry. 1978 February; 76(2): 93-96. CODEN: JFUSAI.

BURTON, HILARY D. 1978b. Multi-Data Base Searching in Agriculture: A Cooperative, Computerized Service. Special Libraries. 1978 July; 69(7): 244-249. ISSN: 0038-6723.

CARROLL, BONNIE (TALMI); MASKEWITZ, BETTY F. 1980. Information Analysis Centers. In: Williams, Martha E., ed. Annual Review of Information Science and Technology: Volume 15. White Plains, NY: Knowledge Industry Publications, Inc.; 1980. 147-189. ISSN: 0066-4200; ISBN: 0-914236-65-2; LC: 66-25096.

CITTADINO, MARY L.; GIESE, RONALD L.; CASWELL, JERRY V. 1977. Three Computer-Based Bibliographic Retrieval Systems for Scientific Literature. BioScience. 1977 November; 27(11): 739-742. ISSN: 0006-3568; CODEN: BISNAS.

CLARKE, P. A.; CASIERO, B. 1979. A Genealogical Database for Plant Propagation Records. Euphytica. 1979; 28: 785-792. CODEN: EUPHAA.

COBLENTZ, A. M. 1976. A Human Biometry Data Bank. Paris, France: Universite Rene Descartes U.E.R. Biomedicale; 1976. 7p. Available from: Ergodata, Laboratoire d'Anthropologie et d'Ecologie Humaine Universite Rene Descartes, 45 rue des Saints-Peres - 75270 - Paris Cedex 06, France.

COLLINS, ELAINE V. 1978. Two Sources of Bibliographic Information on Aquatic Animals. In: Proceedings of the International Symposium on Animal Health and Disease Data Banks; 1978 December 4-6; Washington, DC. Beltsville, MD: U.S. Department of Agriculture; 1979. 45-47. (USDA Miscellaneous Publication no. 1381).

COMBS, GARY P. 1978. The Emergency Programs Information Center (EPIC). In: Proceedings of the International Symposium on Animal Health and Disease Data Banks; 1978 December 4-6; Washington, DC. Beltsville, MD: U.S. Department of Agriculture; 1979. 41-44. (USDA Miscellaneous Publication no. 1381).

CORTH, ANNETTE. 1977. Coverage of Marine Biology Citations. Special Libraries. 1977 December; 68(2): 439-446. ISSN: 0038-6723.

DAGNELIE, P. 1977. Some Comments on Agricultural Data Banks: The User's Viewpoint. In: Proceedings of the Commission of the European Communities Symposium on Factual Data Banks in Agriculture; 1977 July 12-13; Kirchberg, Luxemburg. Wageningen, The Netherlands: Centre for Agricultural Publishing and Documentation; 1978. 62-64. ISBN: 90-220-0674-3.

DATTA, V. 1978. Coverage of Specialized Biological Information by On-line Databases and Comparison of this Coverage with an In-House Manual System of a Special Library Information Unit. Program: News of Computers in Libraries (U.K.). 1978 April; 12: 55-63. ISSN: 0033-0337.

DAVIES, GARETH. 1978. Animal Disease Surveillance in Great Britain. In: Proceedings of the International Symposium on Animal Health and Disease Data Banks; 1978 December 4-6; Washington, DC. Beltsville, MD: U.S. Department of Agriculture; 1979. 67-86. (USDA Miscellaneous Publication no. 1381).

DITTBERNER, P. L.; BRYANT, G. 1978. The Use of the Plant Information Network in High Altitude Revegetation. In: Proceedings of the International Congress for Energy and Ecosystems; 1978 June 12-16; Grand Forks, ND. Oxford, England: Pergamon; 1978. 1022-1035.

DOPKOWSKI, PHILIP L. 1978. USDA/CRIS as a Source of Project Information on Animal Health and Disease Research. In: Proceedings of the International Symposium on Animal Health and Disease Data Banks; 1978 December 4-6; Washington, DC. Beltsville, MD: U.S. Department of Agriculture; 1979. 199-208. (USDA Miscellaneous Publication no. 1381).

DWINELL, DAVID L. 1978. Advances in Information Systems and Services for the Forestry Community. Journal of Forestry. 1978 February; 76(2): 80-83. CODEN: JFUSAI.

ELIAS, ARTHUR W. 1980. BioSciences Information Service: Information Resources for Biomedicine. Health Communications and Informatics. 1980; 6(3-4): 170-190. ISSN: 0378-9845.

EPSTEIN, BARBARA A.; ANGIER, JENNIFER J. 1980. Multi-database Searching in the Behavioral Sciences, Part 1: Basic Techniques and Core Databases. Database. 1980 September; 3(3): 9-15. ISSN: 0162-4105.

FELL, ELIZABETH. 1979. ARCIS: An Agricultural Research Current Information System. Aslib Proceedings (U.K.). 1979 March; 31(3): 138-143. ISSN: 0001-253X.

FINLAYSON, W.; HEMMINGS, BRIDGET BIGGS; DAVIS, CHRISTINE; ELBOURN, C. A.; HYDE, A. H. 1978. Forestry Information from Oxford. Journal of Forestry. 1978 February; 76(2): 97-99. CODEN: JFUSAI.

FOOTE, RICHARD H.; ZIDAR, JUDITH. 1975. A Preliminary Annotated Bibliography of Information Handling Activities in Biology. Journal of the Washington Academy of Sciences. 1975 January; 65(1): 19-32. ISSN: 0043-0439; CODEN: JWASA3.

FREEMAN, R. R. 1979. Development of a Policy for Access to an International Database, Aquatic Sciences and Fisheries Abstracts. In: Tally, R. D.; Dueltgen, R. R., eds. Information Choices and Policies: Proceedings of the American Society for Information Science, 42nd Annual Meeting: volume 16; 1979; Minneapolis, MN. White Plains, NY: Knowledge Industry Publications; 1979. ISSN: 0044-7870; CODEN: PAISDQ.

FUJIMOTO, RIHEI. 1976. Investigation of the Index Structure of Drugdoc and Ringdoc. Journal of Chemical Information and Computer Sciences. 1976; 16(4): 227-231. ISSN: 0095-2338; CODEN: JCISD8.

FUSONIE, ALAN; MORAN, LEILA, eds. 1977. Computerized Literature Data Files in Agriculture: Proceedings of the Symposium in Honor of the One Millionth Citation in the Agricola Data Base; 1977, Beltsville, MD. Beltsville, MD: Associates of the National Agricultural Library; 1977. 51p.

GAILLARDIN, R.; GOURD, F.; SANZ, D. 1980. PASCAL Data Base: File Description and Indexing Rules in Chemistry, Biology and Medicine. Stockholm, Sweden: Royal Institute of Technology (RIT) Library; 1980. 22p. (RIT Report no. TRITA-LIB-4066).

GARROW, C. 1978. Development of a Poisonous Plants Data System: A Potential U.S.-Australia Collaboration. In: Proceedings of the International Symposium on Animal Health and Disease Data Banks; 1978 December 4-6; Washington, DC. Beltsville, MD: U.S. Department of

Agriculture; 1979. 121-122. (USDA Miscellaneous Publication no. 1381).

GAWORKSKA, SUSAN JANE. 1977. An Evaluation of Secondary Services for Biochemistry. London, England: City University; 1977. 136p. (M.S. thesis).

GILREATH, CHARLES L. 1978. Agricola: Multipurpose Data Base for Agricultural and Life Science Libraries. Serials Librarian. 1978 Fall; 3(1): 89-95. ISSN: 0361-526X.

GLUCKSTEIN, FRITZ P.; DOSZKOCS, TAMAS E.; HOAG, WARREN G. 1978. The Laboratory Animal Data Bank. In: Proceedings of the International Symposium on Animal Health and Disease Data Banks; 1978 December 4-6; Washington, DC. Beltsville, MD: U.S. Department of Agriculture; 1979. 147-154. (USDA Miscellaneous Publication no. 1381).

HAENDLER, H. 1977. Feed Data Banks and the International Network of Feed Information Centres. In: Proceedings of the Commission of the European Communities Symposium on Factual Data Banks in Agriculture; 1977 July 12-13; Kirchberg, Luxemburg. Wageningen, The Netherlands: Centre for Agricultural Publishing and Documentation; 1978. 18-23. ISBN: 90-220-0674-3.

HARVEY, SUSAN. 1979. CAB/CAIN Evaluation Project. A Comparative Study on the Performance of Two Agricultural Databases in a Computerized Current Awareness Service. Wageningen, The Netherlands: Centre for Agricultural Publishing and Documentation; 1979. 93p. ISBN: 90-220-0704-9.

HAYES, HOWARD M.; WILSON, GEORGE P.; MORAFF, HOWARD. 1978. The Veterinary Medical Data Program; Past, Present, and Future. In: Proceedings of the International Symposium on Animal Health and Disease Data Banks; 1978 December 4-6; Washington, DC. Beltsville, MD: U.S. Department of Agriculture; 1979. 127-132. (USDA Miscellaneous Publication no. 1381).

HILMAS, JOANN; FLUEGEL, WALTER. 1978. Dictyostelium Discoideum's 35-Year Contribution to Growth of Biology: A Bibliometric Analysis: Journal of the Minnesota Academy of Science. 1978; 44(3): 21-24. ISSN: 0026-539X; CODEN: JMNAAC.

JOHNSTONE, A. 1979. A System for the Storage and Retrieval of Field Trials Data. Aslib Proceedings (U.K.). 1979 March; 31(3): 144-145. ISSN: 0001-253X.

KAMINUMA, TSUGUCHIKA; KURIHARA, AKIHIRO. 1979. A Data Base of Data Banks for Toxicological Information. Tokyo, Japan: The Tokyo Metropolitan Institute of Medical Science; 1979. 15p. Available from: Mr. T. Kaminuma, Tokyo Metropolitan Institute of Medical Science, Tokyo, Japan.

KELLY, MAUREEN C.; ELIAS, ARTHUR W.; SMITH, J. R. 1979. Transfer of Biological Information. Encyclopedia of Computer Science and Technology: Volume 13. New York, NY: Marcel Dekker, Inc.; 1979. 470-486. ISBN: 0-8247-2263-9.

KISSMAN, HENRY M. 1980. Information Retrieval in Toxicology. In: George, R.; Okun, R., eds. Annual Review of Pharmacology and Toxicology; Volume 20. Palo Alto, CA: Annual Reviews Inc.; 1980. 285-305. ISBN: 0-8243-0420-9.

KNIGHT, S. J. T.; POWELL, H. T. 1977. The Intertidal Community and Habitat Survey of Great Britain 2: Information Storage and Retrieval Using a Computer. Journal of Phycology Supplement. 1977; 13: 205. (Abstract). CODEN: JPYLAJ. Full text available from: authors at Scottish Marine Biological Association, P.O. Box 3, Oban, Scotland.

KONIGSHOFER, HEINZ O. 1978. International Collection and Compilation of Animal Disease Information. In: Proceedings of the International Symposium on Animal Health and Disease Data Banks; 1978 December 4–6; Washington, DC. Beltsville, MD: U.S. Department of Agriculture; 1979. 56–66. (USDA Miscellaneous Publication no. 1381).

KRABBE, HENNING. 1979. The Agricola and CAB Databases: A Danish Comparison. In: Proceedings of the 3rd International Online Information Meeting; 1979 December 4; London, England. London, England: Learned Information, Ltd.; 1979 December. 245–249. ISBN: 0-904933-21-0.

KRUZAS, ANTHONY T.; SCHMITTROTH, JOHN, JR. 1981. Encyclopedia of Information Systems and Services. Detroit, MI: Gale Research Co.; 1981. 933p. ISBN: 0-8103-0942-4.

KUBO, YASUMASA; TAMAI, TETSUO. 1980. Information Service Activities of Japan Information Center of Science and Technology in the Fields of Biological Science, Medical Science and Agriculture. Health Communications and Informatics. 1980; 6(3–4): 207–211. ISSN: 0378-9845.

KUNZ, LAWRENCE J. 1976. Computerization in Microbiology. Human Pathology. 1976 March: 7(2): 169–175. CODEN: HPCQA4.

LANCASTER, F. W.; MARTYN, JOHN. 1978. Assessing the Benefits and Promise of an International Information Program: AGRIS. Journal of the American Society for Information Science. 1978 November; 29(6): 283–288. ISSN: 0002-8231; CODEN: AISJB6.

LAUX, WOLFRUDOLF. 1979. Present State and Problems in the Information and Documentation of Phytomedical Literature. International Association of Agricultural Librarians and Documentalists Quarterly Bulletin. 1979 Spring-Summer; 24(2): 31–34. ISSN: 0020-5966.

LEGGATE, P.; SMITH, B.; STOW, J.; WILLIAMS, M. I. 1972. The Development and Evaluation of a Mechanised S.D.I. Service for Biologists. Oxford, England: Experimental Information Unit; 1972. 26p. (Synopsis of the final report; DSTI Report no. 5139).

LEINERT, S. 1977. Establishing a Technical Information Center for Forestry. In: Proceedings of the Commission of the European Communities Symposium on Factual Data Banks in Agriculture; 1977 July 12–13; Kirchberg, Luxemburg. Wageningen, The Netherlands: Centre for Agricultural Publishing and Documentation; 1978. 83–85. ISBN: 90-220-0674-3.

LORENT, J. P. 1979. Online Literature Retrieval in Poison Control. Clinical Toxicology. 1979 January; 14(1): 115–122. CODEN: CTOXA0.

MACK, ROY. 1978. Veterinary Literature Documentation at the Commonwealth Bureau of Animal Health. In: Proceedings of the International Symposium on Animal Health and Disease Data Banks; 1978 December 4–6; Washington, DC. Beltsville, MD: U.S. Department of Agriculture; 1979. 33–39. (USDA Miscellaneous Publication no 1381).

MARCHISOTTO, ROBERT. 1978. Animal Health Information in the BIOSIS Data Base. In: Proceedings of the International Symposium on

Animal Health and Disease Data Banks; 1978 December 4-6; Washington, DC. Beltsville, MD: U.S. Department of Agriculture; 1979. 11-24. (USDA Miscellaneous Publication no. 1381).

MARSHALL, K. E. 1979. On-line Retrieval of Information—A Comparison of Different Systems Used to Produce a Bibliography on Ephemeroptera and Pollution 1969-78. Winnipeg; Canada: Fish Marketing Service; 1979. 18p.

MELLO, JAMES F. 1977. Computerization of Synonomy Data from Biological Systematics. Rochester, NY: Margaret Wood Strong Museum, Museum Data Bank Committee; 1977. 21p. ERIC: ED 161-426.

METCALFE, JOHN R. 1979. The CAB World Agricultural Information Service. Aslib Proceedings (U.K.). 1979 March; 31(3): 110-117. ISSN: 0001-253X.

MILNE, A. 1977. A Pilot Study to Examine the Comparative Usefulness of the Iowa Drug Information Service (IDIS) and Medline in Meeting the Demands of Pharmacy-Based Drug Information Service. Journal of Clinical Pharmacology. 1977; 2(4): 227-237. CODEN: JCPHDA.

MOLSTER, H. C.; BOSMA, H.; VOOREN, M. 1979. Are Agricultural Scientists Interested in Current Research Projects in Europe? Experience with the AGREP Data Base. International Association of Agricultural Librarians and Documentalists Quarterly Bulletin. 1979 Spring-Summer; 24(2): 42-46. ISSN: 0020-5966.

NFAIS NEWSLETTER. 1958-. Neufeld, M. Lynne, ed. Philadelphia, PA: National Federation of Abstracting and Indexing Services (NFAIS). (Issued bimonthly; available on subscription from: NFAIS, 3401 Market Street, Philadelphia, PA 19104). ISSN: 0090-0893; CODEN: NFNLA6.

PAGE, J. A.; THEISEN, R.; KUHL, F. 1978. An Integrated Chemical and Biological Data Retrieval System for Drug Development. Washington, DC: Walter Reed Army Institute of Research; 1978. 20p. NTIS: AD-A067-811.

PARKA, S. J. 1976. The Identification and Utilization of Weed Biology Information. Weed Science. 1976 May; 24(3): 282-287. CODEN: WEESA6.

PATTON, DAVID R. 1979. Run Wild 11: Data Files for Wildlife Species and Habitat for Arizona and New Mexico. Washington, DC: Forest Service, 1979. 1582p. NTIS: PB 296-984.

PELISSIER, DENISE. 1980. PASCAL Database File Description and On-line Access on ESA/IRS. Online Review. 1980 March; 4(1): 13-31. ISSN: 0309-314X.

RESEARCH RESOURCES INFORMATION CENTER. 1980. Animal Resources: A Research Resources Directory. Bethesda, MD: U.S. Department of Health and Human Services. National Institutes of Health, 1980. 40p. (NIH Publication no. 80-1431).

RUSSELL, HAMISH M., ed. 1979. Information in Agriculture: Proceedings of the National Workshop on Agricultural Information; 1979; Melbourne, Australia. Melbourne, Australia: Standing Committee on Agriculture and Federation International de Documentation (FID). 1979. 142p. ISBN: 0-7241-7833-3.

RUSSO, R. J.; MCCAIN, T. L. 1979. Use of Computerized Information Retrieval in Mosquito Control. Mosquito News. 1979; Spring; 39(2): 333-338. ISSN: 0027-142X; CODEN: MOSQAU.

SCHECHTER, M. S.; SULLIVAN, W. N.; CAWLEY, B. M.; HAYES, D. K.; BAFFOE, A.; MENZER, R. E.; BURTON, D. H. 1977. Computer Storage and Retrieval of Insecticide Test Data. Journal of Economic Entomology. 1977 December; 70(6): 759-767. CODEN: JEENAI.

SCHOLTEN, K. F. 1979. Data Banks on Pesticides: A Feasibility Study. Bulletin de l'Organisation Europeene et Mediterraneene pour la Protection des Plantes (France). 1979; 9(3): 317-322. CODEN: OEPBAO.

SEIDEWITZ, L. 1977. Establishment of a Data Base for Gene Bank Purposes. In: Proceedings of the Commission of the European Communities Symposium on Factual Data Banks in Agriculture; 1977 July 12-13, Kirchberg, Luxemburg, Wageningen, The Netherlands: Centre for Agricultural Publishing and Documentation; 1978. 39-41. ISBN: 90-220-0674-3.

SIMKINS, M. A. 1977. A Comparison of Data Bases for Retrieving References to the Literature on Drugs. Information Processing & Management. 1977; 13(3-A): 141-153. CODEN: IPMADK.

SINGER, D. D. 1977. The Needs of Data Bank Users and Some Data Banks in Food Science. In: Proceedings of the Commission of the European Communities Symposium on Factual Data Banks in Agriculture; 1977 July 12-13; Kirchberg, Luxemburg. Wageningen, The Netherlands; Centre for Agricultural Publishing and Documentation; 1978. 5-9. ISBN: 90-220-0674.

SMITH, BARRIE D. S. 1978. The Zoological Record—A Review. Boston Spa, England: The Zoological Record; 1978. 15p. Available from: BIOSIS, User Services, Philadelphia, PA 19103.

SPANN, MELVIN L.; HUMMEL, D. J.; SCHULTHEISZ, ROBERT J.; VALLEY, SHARON L.; WALKER, DONALD F., JR. 1978. Chemline: A Chemical Structure Search Key to Biological Information. In: Howe, W. Jeffery; Milne, Margaret M.; Pennel, Ann F., eds. Retrieval of Medicinal Chemical Information: Proceedings of the 175th Meeting of the American Chemical Society; 1978 March 13-17; Anaheim, CA. Washington, DC: American Chemical Society; 1978. 58-72. ISBN: 0-8412-0465-9.

STEERE, WILLIAM CAMPBELL. 1976. Biological Abstracts/BIOSIS—The First Fifty Years. New York, NY: Plenum Press; 1976. 233p. ISBN: 0-306-30915-7.

TERRY, MARYEVA W. 1979. The Primate Information Center (PIC). Journal of Medical Primatology. 1979; 8(1): 66-68. ISSN: 0047-2565; CODEN: JMPMAO.

THOMPSON, B. K.; BAUM, B. R. 1978. Preparation of a Barley Register: An Information Retrieval System for Cultivars. Taxon. 1978 November; 27(5/6): 471-477. CODEN: TAXNAP.

UCHIDA, H. 1979. Information System, Databases, and Online Services of the Japan Information Center of Science and Technology. Journal of Chemical Information and Computer Sciences. 1979; 19(4): 199-201. ISSN: 0095-2338; CODEN: JCISD8.

VAN DER VEER, O.; KOOGER, J. P. 1978. Evaluation of Abstract Journals and Other Sources Consulted for 75 Literature Searches on Food Science and Food Technology. Aslib Proceedings (U.K.). 1978 August; 30(8): 302-311. ISSN: 0001-253X.

VERHEIJEN, J. H. 1977. Automation and the Use of Data Banks in Milk Recording, Artificial Insemination and Registration of Cattle in the

Netherlands. In: Proceedings of the Commission of the European Communities Symposium on Factual Data Banks in Agriculture; 1977 July 12-13; Kirchberg, Luxemburg. Wageningen, the Netherlands: Centre for Agricultural Publishing and Documentation; 1978. 18-23. ISBN: 90-220-0674-3.

WETMORE, CLIFFORD M. 1979. Herbarium Computerization at the University of Minnesota. Systematic Botany. 1979; 4(4): 339-350. CODEN: SYBODA.

WHITE, LINDA M. 1978. Forestry Literature Access through Computer Systems. Journal of Forestry. 1978 February; 76(2): 84-88. CODEN: JFUSAI.

WHITSON, PAUL D.; MASSEY, J. R. 1978. Information Systems for Use in Studying the Biological Status of Threatened and Endangered Plant Populations. Bulletin of the Association of Southeastern Biologists. 1978 April; 25(2): 75-76. CODEN: BABIA8.

WILEY, WILLIAM H. 1977. A Computer-based Information Retrieval System on Turkeys. Poultry Science. 1977 July; 56(4): 1337-1338. CODEN: POSCAL.

WILLMOTT, S. 1978. Report of the Meeting on Information Services in Parasitology—Are They Meeting Users' Needs? In: Slusarski, W., ed. Review of Advances in Parasitology: Proceedings of the 4th International Congress of Parasitology; 1978 August; Warsaw, Poland. Warsaw, Poland: Polish Academy of Sciences; 1981 (In Press). 10p.

WISEMAN, HEATHER M. 1980. The National Poisons Information Service. Aslib Proceedings (U.K.). 1980 May; 32(5): 228-231. ISSN: 0001-253X.

WOOD, D. E.; JOHNSON, B. K.; BURTON, J.; NEWTON J. 1978. CAB Abstracts on Dialog. Database. 1978 December; 1(4): 68-79. ISSN: 0162-4105.

WU, JANE M. 1979. The Agricultural Canada Libraries Information Network. Canadian Journal of Information Science. 1979 May; 4: 68-73. CODEN: CJISDE.

YERKE, THEODOR B. 1978. PACFORNET: Technical Information Services for Pacific Coast Foresters. Journal of Forestry. 1978 February; 76(2): 89-92. CODEN: JFUSAI.

YSKA, GERDA; MARTYN, JOHN. 1976. Final Report on Databases Suitable for Users of Environmental Information. London, England: Aslib Research and Development Department; 1976. 21p. ISBN: 0-85142-113-X.

IV

The Profession

This section includes chapters by Elaine Svenonius and Rutherford (Rudy) Witthus of the University of Denver, and by Elaine Caruso of the University of Pittsburgh.

Svenonius and Witthus see the information age as characterized by an information-centered economy that has given rise to the view of information as a commodity of value, which if properly managed can improve industrial productivity. They see management of information as encompassing effective utilization of technology, reduction of paperwork and rationalization of the flow of information. Nearly half the U.S. work force is employed in information-related jobs, most of them in industry. The locales for education and training for information work are as diverse as the jobs themselves. There is little literature about this education except as it takes place in library schools, computer science departments, and business and management schools. Given the diversity and number of information workers it is not possible to identify a single information profession. Svenonius and Witthus point out distinctions in the attitudes of certain subgroups (e.g., records managers, librarians, and computer scientists) toward professional concerns such as education, certification, and the encroachment of paraprofessionals. A matter of general debate, which is interesting as it relates to information professionals, is whether the information age will be characterized by increasing or decreasing professionalization.

In her chapter on "Computer Aids to Learning [CAL] Online Retrieval" Elaine Caruso distinguishes CALs that are tutorial (used prior to the search) from those that are online assistants, providing guidance while the user is making the search. The five tutorial systems, *MEDLEARN*, SCORPIO, TRAINER, DIALOG with PET, and ONTAP are reviewed as are three programs that assist the searcher, CONIT, IIDA, and CCL. The economic base for CAL is examined for initial development and for maintenance and updating. Problems of distribution, identifying the user population, and assessing CAL are surveyed. CAL can meet many of the needs for online search training, but potential users need to be made aware of it and it must be made available to them. CAL provides a real advantage for continuing professional education because it can be used at the work place and can be used when needed. CAL "publishers" and "facilitating" networks are seen as the mechanisms to bring CAL to the level of use required to make meaningful evaluations and to establish CAL as an economically viable and professionally rewarding field for creative authorship.

10 Information Science as a Profession

ELAINE SVENONIUS
University of Denver

RUTHERFORD WITTHUS
Denver Public Library

INTRODUCTION

This chapter reviews literature on who information workers are, how they are educated, and the degree to which they are professionalized. Most of the citations are to the literature of 1978, 1979, and 1980 although appropriate references from 1977 and 1976 are also cited. Also, most of the literature cited is of U.S. origin. This is regrettable for the parochial view it gives. On the other hand, the "information profession" is characterized by parochialism, particularly on the national level. A global view would have required more bibliography and explanation than this chapter could accommodate and would have made generalization even more difficult than it has been.

Previous *ARIST* writers on the profession are HARMON (1976) and SHERA & CLEVELAND. Shera and Cleveland discuss the rise of documentation and identify key events in its transformation into information science. They argue that "if information science is to be accepted as an academic discipline, then it must find a strong theoretical foundation and, clearly, such a foundation must be structured around some consistent notions of information" (p264). Harmon examines traditional and emerging information manpower markets, and argues that curricula for professional education must be designed to produce graduates who can seize new opportunities and assume nontraditional roles. Thus, in different ways, previous writers have issued challenges to the academic institutions that are educating information workers.

The Information Age

Several writers have speculated on the place of information in future society (BELL, 1976; MACHLUP; PORAT). Still one of the best depictions is the post-industrial society of Bell, which is characterized by the preeminence of theoretical knowledge, the professionalization of everyone, and an economy in which the emphasis has shifted from providing goods to providing information services. Bell observes that technology in pre-industrial society was based on raw materials, and in industrial society it was based on energy; in post-industrial society it will be based on information. Society is becoming post-industrial to the extent that robots can perform the work of white and blue collar workers. The number of blue collar workers continues to decrease, and they now comprise 33% of the U.S. work force, while white collar workers comprise 50% (CRENNER). It is expected that with the advent of the automated office and the substitution of electronic methods for paper record keeping, the proportion of white collar clerical workers will also decrease, perhaps by as much as 20–30% (BELL, 1977). Displaced blue and white collar workers will be forced to find more intellectual occupations; they may become knowledge or information workers in the information industry. The degree to which U.S. society is already post-industrial can be measured by the size of its information industry. According to a recent report of the U.S. CONGRESS, the increase in productivity in the information industry accounts for a quarter of the total increase in U.S. productivity; in U.S. exports, information equipment and services are second only to agricultural products; more than half of the U.S. labor force is occupied in information-related jobs.

Information Science and Information Management

During the 1960s and, to a lesser extent, during the 1970s attempts were made to define information. According to MACHLUP: "Information science, at the present stage of its development, is a not fully integrated assemblage of systematic studies of the processes regarded as information, particularly of the systems, operations and devices, technology, and organization by which men—which of course stands for men and women—transmit and receive, and therefore transfer, knowledge among one another" (p111). Because a definition is only as good as its impact on theory or action, early definitions are wanting. Thus, it is noteworthy that the 1970s saw an increasing perception of information as a resource or a commodity. Indeed, in its seeming ability to provide direction and purpose the view of information as a commodity of value could be regarded as paradigmatic.

Associated with the concept of information as a resource is the belief that information can be managed and therefore that productivity can be increased. Managing information in an organization means harnessing information technologies, reducing paperwork, and rationalizing the flow of information. The formalization of functions and activities, characteristic of post-industrial society, applies to the management of information. DUMAS observes that a few decades ago no one ever spoke of a vice-president of marketing, but companies still sold their products. Marketing was done informally by "natural devices." The same is true of information management; once done informally, it is now being formalized.

Some doubt that information can really be managed (CARLSON), but many proclaim that it can and see economic benefits as a result of relating its value to productivity (e.g., HORTON, 1979a; LANDAU; U. S. COMMISSION ON FEDERAL PAPERWORK). Some dislike a view of information that is concerned chiefly with informed decisions and actions (MACHLUP), but there is room for many views of information. While the view of information as a commodity is attractive to business and industry, it also may be useful in generating valid operational definitions of "information" that can function as variables in theories that describe the production, processing, distribution, and use of information (e.g., BARRETT; BRANSCOMB; PORAT; TAYLOR, 1980).

Future Information Systems

A romantic quality characterizes the writing of many who depict the potential of the new technology for future information systems. NANUS sees the marriage of telecommunications and computers as the fifth in a series of information revolutions; it will result in the establishment of community information utilities, in the development of multinational computer systems, and in the emergence of new roles for libraries. LANDAU enumerates forces for change that will determine the design of future information systems: 1) the continuing miniaturization and increasing power of computers; 2) the decreasing costs of electronic transmission; and 3) the eventual integration of voice systems, micrographic systems, and computer systems. The theme of integrated systems is sounded repeatedly, and the integration is not only of different technologies but of different kinds of information (numeric, bibliographic, and factual). Another recurring theme is that of paperless information systems, whose most eloquent visionary is LANCASTER. He epitomizes the paperless society in terms of an intelligent terminal located in one's home through which one can access, in interactive mode, books and periodicals, factual information such as airline schedules and football scores, and the information in one's personal files. Through the same terminal one can also shop, bank, receive and send mail, and participate in conferences. More attention is being focused on the human dimension in the design of information systems. WERSIG & SEEGER see new kinds of information systems developing in response to qualitatively different information needs—e.g., information systems that are problem or project oriented and systems that produce synoptic, synthesized, or consolidated information. MEADOW sees the results of artificial intelligence (AI) research paying off in the form of more intelligent information systems.

Although the potential of the new technology continues to dominate the information science literature, there is a counter theme gaining momentum, one that questions whether computers and satellites are the deus ex machina that can remedy the ills of the information explosion. The new technology may be powerless to combat information overload. ARTANDI reminds us that the computer cannot extend man's information-processing capabilities because these are limited biologically. A thought-provoking volume, edited by

CHARTRAND & MORENTZ, reports on a conference that addressed the problems of the federal government in coping with information overload. It is reported that from 1970 to 1976 the amount of information produced by Congress went from 400,000 to 800,000 printed pages. The view of information as an anticommodity is depressingly evident in the private sector as well. A report of the U. S. COMMISSION ON FEDERAL PAPERWORK estimates that the cost of federal paperwork to the business community runs between $25 and $32 billion a year. Goodyear Tire and Rubber Co. had to produce 3,200 pounds of paper in just one week in 1980 to meet one new governmental regulation (WINTER). It is not surprising that economists cite excessive federal demands for information as a factor in sluggish productivity. The need for managing information is urgent.

INFORMATION MANPOWER

Occupational Surveys

Who are information workers? Good operational definitions seem to be lacking. APPLEYARD rejects broad definitions that include all activities related to the production, distribution, and consumption of knowledge. Similarly, PORAT observes that all human endeavor involves some component of information processing, but to define information activity (and information workers) in such terms would be operationally useless. Thus, a difficult problem that surveys of information workers must address is to define the population to be studied.

DEBONS & KING conducted an extensive occupational survey of information workers. It delineated information professionals according to three characteristics: 1) work performed, 2) work sector (e.g., industrial, governmental), and 3) work field (e.g., computer science, librarianship). The categories within these three areas are not mutually exclusive, and some are ambiguously labeled, making it difficult to analyze the results. Nevertheless, this ambitious and large survey is of great interest. It found 1.64 million information workers in the United States, approximately 70% of whom are working in the industrial sector. According to work performed, it found the largest concentration (22%) in information systems analysis and/or design. Close to 17% manage information operations, programs, services, or databases, and the same number perform operational functions. By field, it found the largest number in computers (42%), with management support, library, and nonlibrary services accounting for about 10% each.

A similar survey, but limited to information professionals within the American Society for Information Science (ASIS), was conducted by KING ET AL. (1980b). Data were gathered on demographic characteristics, such as field of highest degree obtained, years of experience, job title, and primary work function. The fields of degrees numbered more than 100, and the most frequently mentioned were library and information science. One of the interesting differences between the two surveys is that many more ASIS members are involved in management (nearly 29%) than information professionals at large (17%). In an editorial on the two surveys, KING says that the work of information professionals falls into four areas: "1) *information science and technology*, including research and development, systems analysis, and systems design; 2) *management* of information operations, programs, services or databases; 3) *education or training* of information professionals or workers; and 4) *operational information functions*, including searching, preparation, and analysis of information or data on behalf of others" (p3). He believes that as a matter of policy ASIS should emphasize the first area because it would focus on the unity rather than the diversity of information professionals.

Several writers have looked at the manpower market in the computer field. From a National Research Council (NRC) report of employment characteristics of Ph.D.'s FAIRLEY extracted those portions pertaining to computer science Ph.D.'s and other Ph.D. scientists and engineers working in the computer field. This group consists of about 5,500 persons, 1,500 of whom have Ph.D.'s in computer science. Of the latter, nearly 80% are employed in the computer field and over half are employed in business and industry. TAULBEE & CONTE, reporting the results of several annual surveys on the production and employment of computer science Ph.D.'s, found that from 1975 to 1976 the number of graduates who took positions in industry increased from 26% to 38%. There was a significant decline in the number of U.S. citizens enrolled in Ph.D. computer science programs. CHERLIN fears that those involved in computer science teaching and research may be a dying breed. The problem is largely economic—the starting salary in academia is about half of that in industry. A governmental task force found the shortage of computer science Ph.D.'s so severe that the country's defense program may be endangered (CHERLIN).

On behalf of the Committee on the Status of Women in Librarianship (COSWL), ESTABROOK & HEIM conducted a survey of 1,583 members of the American Library Association (ALA) and found the following distribution by type of employment: school libraries 13.6%, public libraries 28%, academic libraries 31.8%, special and other libraries 23.3%, and nonlibrary other 2.5%. The COSWL study was done to compare data for men and women, and, not surprisingly, it found women concentrated in lower-paying, lower-status positions. The discrepancy between men's and women's salaries has widened from 1970 to 1979. Correlations of salary with other variables showed most of the variance to be due to personal characteristics such as age, sex, race, mobility, and date of M.L.S.

Occupational surveys of information workers describe their present activities, and the literature speculates on their future activities. The following sections survey this literature under two rubrics: 1) information managers, and 2) library/information specialists; the latter covers literature that does not focus explicitly on management.

Information Managers

An information manager, or an information resource manager, is viewed as a generalist who has management training and an understanding of information technologies. Different writers construe the activities of information managers differently, depending on the aspects they wish to emphasize. BECKER and HORTON (1979b), for instance, emphasize management. Becker sees an information manager's duties as "a) coordinating relevant information activities; b) providing policy oversight and guidance; c) planning programs and budgets; d) managing personnel; e) planning, developing, and operating automated and non-automated information systems; and f) providing information technology support services." GREENWOOD and LANDAU emphasize the new technologies. Greenwood reserves the designation of "information resource manager" for those who are on what he calls a "new fast track." He warns systems personnel who limit their concerns to processing data on large mainframe computers that they are in danger of becoming obsolete and losing their jobs. The modern information-processing manager must be sensitive to the new technologies of word processing, image processing, reprographics, and telecommunication and must be responsible for harnessing these new technologies to increase office productivity. BRATTON, CALDWELL, and MARCHAND emphasize the generalist perspective required of information managers. A generalist is more than a technician; he is one who can envision and oversee many systems applications. Caldwell sees the emerging information manager as a new breed of top management personnel responsible for various office functions, such as the copy service, computer services, mail services, printing services, and records management (interestingly, he does not include library services).

The information management paradigm is a framework within which systems personnel, records managers, and special librarians conceptualize role change. Role change implies a movement forward and, often, a broadening of horizons. LANDAU epitomizes the forward movement for systems personnel as going "from MIS to IRM" (from management information systems to information resources management); "the principles behind IRM encompass the idea that all media and technologies can be combined in a way that will optimize the productivity of the individuals in the organization, thereby optimizing the total information handling activities. In essence, the principles of IRM look beyond MIS, which is primarily computer-based, but still employ the systems approach to the larger information problems of an organization" (p24). Systems personnel who wish to broaden their horizons must not only master new technologies but also assume managerial functions. FERREIRA & COLLINS predict that as the emphasis in business changes from technology and systems to managing information, systems personnel will have to develop administrative skills. PULLEN & SIMKO predict that the data-processing systems business will be replaced by information systems business as firms begin to combine their administrative, communication, and data-processing departments. While HOLMES predicts that information managers and top information executives will come from the systems and data-processing field, an opposing opinion is advanced by MCCRIRICK & GOLDSTEIN. In a survey of 257 organizations they found the view of a data administrator as a technician repeatedly confirmed.

Records managers are eyeing the job of information managers. They see the automated office offering them greater responsibilities. LANGEMO defines records management as "the application of systematic analysis and scientific management of records and information from their creation through processing, maintenance, protection and to final disposition or archival retention" (p14). He goes on to argue that "records management should, can and must become organization wide 'information management' during the 1980s." PORTER also urges records managers to develop the expertise to understand information, not just the records embodying it: "a true dedication to IRM requires a total overview of all services, equipment, and people in all aspects of creating, using and processing information" (p13). Views such as these are expressed repeatedly in the literature of the records managers.

Special librarians also aspire to the title of "information manager." They see themselves assuming more active roles, enlarging the scope of their existing jobs, and becoming involved in all the information activities of a business firm (GARDNER; THURSTON). Gardner warns librarians that they will become dated if they remain process oriented rather than market oriented. She argues that "it is the integration of skilled librarianship with other disciplines, such as marketing, data processing, word processing, strategic planning, and records management that extends the horizons of information management" (p376). Predicting that a market for information managers could be in the thousands by 1985, the Syracuse University School of Information Studies recently established a semi-autonomous school to educate them (SYRACUSE UNIVERSITY). The school defines information management as being concerned with "the design, management and evaluation of cost-effective systems (i.e., the appropriate combinations of people, information, and technologies) to fulfill the objectives of a particular corporate body (or group of clients) by providing an efficient flow of information to those who need it when they need it."

Library/Information Specialists

The perception of changing roles and self-images of information workers also occurs outside the information management paradigm. This is particularly true for library/information specialists. Some writers address the continuity of traditional libraries and information centers in near-apocalyptic terms. P. W. BERGER, for instance, expects "the relationships between libraries will be so changed that the terms we now use to describe [them] . . . terms like public, academic, research, or special, may no longer fit, because they no longer convey the structure, governance, or even the resource bases of aggregated libraries functioning through networks" (p391–392). KALBA likens the public libraries of today to "the small 'Ma and Pa' farms, trying to make a living side by side with agribusiness, only that the 'infobusiness' is already several times the size of agribusiness" (p316).

While many believe that the traditional job market for library/information specialists in the United States is depressed, there have been few statistically based manpower studies confirming it. One such study was done by COOPER, who used regression analyses to predict future employment levels in public, school, community college, and university libraries in California.

Some writers see the breakdown in the traditional job market being compensated for by a breakthrough into a new market. NEILL predicts that by the year 2010 close to 75% of library school graduates will find jobs in information brokerage. Others also predict a need for and a growth in the number of organizations and self-employed individuals who can supply information to those who need it for a fee (BOSS; LANCASTER ET AL.; MEADOW). Lancaster et al. see the future librarian/information specialist as an indispensable guide to electronic information resources and predict a boom in employment opportunities for librarians once they are liberated from their traditional settings. CRICKMAN also is optimistic about the new markets for library school graduates, but M. S. WHITE cautions that these new markets must be cultivated and urges national library associations to educate business and industry to the importance of information and to the services of information brokers.

Emphasis on the user of information can be detected in the way new roles for library/information specialists are defined. LIPETZ distinguishes between an information scientist and an information professional; the former studies records and their use, and the latter facilitates the use of records by those who need them. Several writers believe that the essential function of library/ information specialists is to facilitate the use or "transfer" of information (GALVIN, 1978; GREER ET AL.; WERSIG & SEEGER) and speculate on the skills needed for this function. Galvin lists the skills of abstracting, analyzing, evaluating, and repackaging the intellectual content of documents. SEWELL gives an exhaustive specification of knowledges and skills that may be required of future library/information specialists. She looks in particular at the present standards for job categories GS1410 (Librarian) and GS1412 (Technical Information Services) and concludes that these are outdated since the work of librarians and information specialists is changing rapidly. This change is from the collection and organization of information to the assimilation (consolidation) of information, i.e., the "sifting, interpreting, educating, evaluating and promoting" of information. To her, subject knowledge is needed for the assimilation function. The library/information specialist also must be able to identify information needs and to design systems to meet them. Sewell's report is notable for an 11-page table that delineates the major functions performed in library and information centers and the knowledges and skills needed to perform them, now and in the future.

This section has reviewed the activities of information workers as reported in occupational surveys and as speculated on in the information science literature. The surveys show the diversity of information work performed; the speculation shows the need felt by several groups of information workers to broaden their occupational outlooks, beyond computer technology and beyond technology generally to managing information and understanding information needs.

EDUCATION AND TRAINING FOR INFORMATION WORK

Diversity of Educational Background

DEBONS & KING report that about half of the academic education of information professionals occurs in disciplines other than computer science, information science, and library science. KING ET AL. (1980b) found more than 100 fields of degrees represented by ASIS members. Degrees in library and information science were the most frequent (34%), followed by degrees in social science (27%), science and engineering (22%), the arts and humanities (11%), and surprisingly, in that it is last, business (5%). Perhaps specialized education for information work is either not available or not required.

SARACEVIC (1979b) is concerned over the variety of locales for information science education. He fears that the scatter of information science education programs, together with their poor quality, will militate against the field's ever unifying as an academic discipline. HARMON (1980), however, sees some value in the variety of locales in that information professionals should not be tied to a "singular cultural outlook."

Interestingly, Debons and King found that the number of people involved in educating and training information workers in academia (5,400) is small compared with the number similarly engaged in industry (22,200) and government (15,200). P. W. BERGER speculates that the transfer of certain aspects of professional education to locales outside academia may be a natural concomitant of the technological revolution—e.g., many networks provide comprehensive training on online systems. Education outside academia tends to be pragmatic and skill oriented. SWANSON laments that information science does not yet have two of the hallmarks of professionalism: "an extended period of study and training [at a level] appropriate for inclusion in the offerings of a university" (p149-150).

In the following review, educational programs in information science are considered in three categories: 1) computer science programs, 2) library school programs, and 3) business and management school programs. Training programs outside academia are not included. There is little substantive literature on such programs, and one can argue that nonacademic training is not truly professional education. Other educational programs are also not included because there is little in the literature about them. Noteworthy exceptions are the independent program at the Georgia Institute of Technology (SLAMECKA & GEHL) and the subject-specialized program at the University of California, San Francisco (UNIVERSITY OF CALIFORNIA).

Computer Science Programs

Graduate curricula in computer science seem to be well-defined, well established, and relatively static. An important recent paper, "Curriculum

'78" (ASSOCIATION FOR COMPUTING MACHINERY), summarizes developments in computer science education over the past decade and recommends an undergraduate degree curriculum in computer science. It attempts to isolate those areas, primarily computer programming, that should be common to all such curricula. RALSTON & SHAW criticize "Curriculum '78" for not taking proper cognizance of the mathematics needed by computer scientists and for supporting the popular view that "computer science = programming." They maintain that this view is false, citing advances during the 1970s in the development of the principles and theoretical underpinnings that characterize a mature science. Despite this observation, information science as it is taught in many computer science departments may be narrowly defined. At least the literature shows some concern over the inadequacy of formal education for such groups as systems analysts. TOWNSEND, for instance, sees systems analysis as the key to the future and worries that the education of systems personnel is for the most part on-the-job and hit-or-miss. Computer science departments may not be altogether to blame; they seem to be having difficulty in finding qualified faculty.

Library School Programs

HAYES observes that how a library school defines its commitment to information science depends on its institutional context, its orientation, and its objectives. He categorizes three approaches: 1) some schools attempt to integrate library and information science; 2) some attempt to update traditional courses by introducing information components into them; and 3) some establish independent departments to handle the new material.

There is some debate over what is meant by integration. GARRISON stresses the need for altering the traditional core curriculum to make it "truly central" to a diversifying profession. It should reveal a common base underlying all information activity. It should deal with information in the broadest sense; it should be built around concepts, not details. SVENONIUS believes that it is possible to teach general principles of information organization that apply no matter how the information is embodied—in books, in a machine, or in a person's head. Moreover, teaching at the level of principle is teaching for the future since principles tend to endure, while specific techniques and practices change. In a similar vein GREER ET AL. believe that management courses in library schools should be more general than they normally are— e.g., they should not be linked to specific library types. The authors believe a shift in emphasis from books to those who use information could give the modus operandi for integrating information science components, particularly managerial and quantitative skills, into a traditional curriculum.

Some library schools aggregate information science components into traditional courses. TAGUE identifies four such components: 1) a technology component, 2) an analytical and quantitative component, 3) a component that has as its concern principles and systems for organizing information, and 4) a research-based component that investigates generalizations and laws about information and its use. KENT presents a similar breakdown. Two

Delphi studies forecasting the future of library school education see the incorporation of information science components into library school curricula as an ongoing process, particularly as these relate to changing technology and the design of information systems (BOAZ; VANCE ET AL.). Some good reviews of information science components in library school curricula are available (FOSKETT; JACKSON & WYLLYS; SIMPSON).

Some writers question the degree to which library schools should attempt to integrate information science. TAGUE argues that if information science becomes too integrated, its essential analytical, technological, quantitative, and research-based nature will be diluted and responsibility for information science education will be assumed by computer science departments and business schools. Considerations of this sort may have led some library schools to establish autonomous or semi-autonomous departments for educating information scientists. Boldly conceived among these is the information management program at the Syracuse University School of Information Studies (SYRACUSE UNIVERSITY). While several library schools are showing increasing interest in teaching information management, Syracuse is the first to present a total program blueprint. The program covers three substantive areas: 1) information, 2) systems, and 3) management, including courses from the departments and schools of management, engineering, computer/information science, and citizenship/public affairs.

To the extent that information science is a "science," its concerns extend beyond the technologies of library automation and information retrieval to encompass research and theory—e.g., empirically derived, mathematically formulated laws that describe the search for information and its use. SHERA & CLEVELAND argue that information science must develop such a theoretical foundation if it is to be accepted academically. The degree to which library schools have incorporated a concern for theory might be taken as one index of the degree to which they have assimilated information "science." At the 1980 ASIS annual meeting, the question of whether theory has a place in library school education was raised (AMERICAN SOCIETY FOR INFORMATION SCIENCE). Some participants felt that it was unnecessary to teach theories about the creation, search for, use of, and management of information. Others believed that such teaching would enhance or provide a framework for the traditional aspects of library school education. SHAUGHNESSY finds that a concern for theory in library schools is lagging and urges renewed efforts, noting that post-industrial society will be characterized by the centrality of theoretical knowledge. Two recent monographs touch on the place of theory in library school education (CONANT; HOUSER & SCHRADER) and also find it wanting; neither, however, takes much cognizance of information science components in library school curricula. Theory may be beyond the grasp of many library school educators but they think about it, write about it, and argue that it is desirable. This perhaps is not so true of information science faculties in other academic disciplines. JACKSON & WYLLYS predict that it is from the library schools that future information science teachers will come since it is here the search for theory obtains.

Library schools have had difficulties in assimilating information science. One problem is that students in library education programs do not have technical backgrounds in computers, mathematics, or statistics (GARRISON; HAYES; SARACEVIC, 1979a). Also many faculty members do not have these backgrounds, and this lack of qualified faculty is seen by some as critical (WILSON). Another difficulty is time. For example, in one year how can students be educated for traditional library jobs as well as for all other information-related jobs. Garrison observes that library schools are reluctant to change and readily leap to the excuse, "we already have more to do than we can handle" (p180). BUCKLAND advises that while we may be inspired by a vision of information science as embracing linguistics, philosophy, psychology, neurology, cybernetics, etc., library schools must focus on only a part of the whole. The difficulty is in determining which part, the traditional or the new. Wilson despairs at seeing library schools stagnant and unresponsive to changing markets. She believes that the American Library Association (ALA) actively inhibits change now when library schools are at a turning point and survival depends on the field's enlarging its knowledge base. Similarly, KLEMPNER says that library schools must develop new curricula that are based on potential not existing job markets. TAYLOR (1979) advises library schools to "move from a 'Ptolemaic' universe with the library at the center to a 'Copernican' world view with information at the center and the library but one of the satellites. . . .To educate librarians to think only in terms of a place called a library as we currently know that institution is to do them a disservice and probably doom them to ineffectuality" (p1871-1872).

Business and Management School Programs

To answer the question of what is the best education for a career in information systems, ANDERSON surveyed employers and system practitioners and concluded that a double-barreled education in business and computers is essential. YOUNG feels that the credibility gap between specialists and managers in management information systems might best be bridged through in-company training. However, many writers assume that a more formal educational structure is needed to produce the information manager who is also a technologist. LUCAS describes the M.B.A. program at the Graduate School of Business Administration at New York University; this program seeks to marry management skills with technical proficiency by offering a specialization in Computer Applications and Information Systems. DELUTIS describes the information systems curriculum at the College of Administrative Science at Ohio State University. Here there is close cooperation between the computer science and business administration faculties. SPROWLS describes the Computer and Information Systems program in the Graduate School of Management at the University of California, Los Angeles. How to manage technology effectively is not the only skill needed by information managers. Communication and problem solving—in particular, better writing and better information-gathering skills—are also in demand (REEVES & BUSSOM).

Records managers, keenly aware of the role that education can have in broadening their horizons, have established a range of educational possibilities (*INFORMATION AND RECORDS MANAGEMENT*, 1978). For instance, the Association of Records Managers and Administrators, Inc., (ARMA) has published three course syllabi for three different levels of records management education: 1) the four-year college and university level, 2) the community, vocational-technical and junior college level, and 3) the high school level. MOTZ summarizes records management education in four-year programs and identifies as curricular components the management of information systems, the application of data processing to records management, and the evaluation of the effectiveness of records management programs. ARMA and the Institute of Certified Records Managers recently surveyed U.S. and Canadian schools with courses in records management. The courses fell into five categories: 1) records management principles and program organization; 2) records generation and control; 3) active records retrieval systems and equipment; 4) records retention scheduling, records protection, and records centers; and 5) technology of records management (ASSOCIATION OF RECORDS MANAGERS AND ADMINISTRATORS, INCORPORATED & INSTITUTE OF CERTIFIED RECORDS MANAGERS).

PROFESSIONALISM

Professionalization or Deprofessionalization

The famous paper by WILENSKY, "The Professionalization of Everyone?", was written in 1964, and in 1976 BELL forecast the dominance of professional occupations in post-industrial society, a consequence of more white collar workers. HAUG agrees that post-industrial society will require high levels of technical expertise but questions whether it will continue to be ensconced in the trappings of professionalism. To her professions are in danger of losing control over their exclusive turf. The image of the professional as trustworthy has become tarnished. In addition a better educated public questions the specialized knowledge of the professional that sets him apart. Finally, increased specialization in the work force has relegated clerical and menial tasks to nonprofessionals or paraprofessionals, who can advance to professional positions. BERG also discusses the economic encroachment of paraprofessionals. He questions the motives of professionals who use tactics such as licensing and credentialing. These professionals would argue that they wish to safeguard standards in job performance, but Berg states that there is no demonstrated correlation between educational achievement and job performance. He cites the Supreme Court decision (Griggs v. Duke Power Co.) that ruled that it is illegal for employers to impose educational requirements on job attainment if the requirements cannot be shown to be directly related to job performance.

The term "information professional" is used by some authors to describe those whose occupations are related to information. DEBONS & KING surveyed "information professionals." Career-oriented articles in the *BULLETIN OF THE AMERICAN SOCIETY FOR INFORMATION SCIENCE* use the term "professional" (M. C. BERGER). Some assume tacitly that information workers can be banded into a profession. Others, looking at the disparity of the activities and education of those who call themselves information workers, suggest this may not be realistic (e.g., SARACEVIC, 1979a; SARA-CEVIC, 1979b; SWANSON). For certain subgroups of information workers professionalism is a matter of concern. Insofar as certification is a professional matter, it is an issue for computer scientists. It is very much an issue for records managers and librarians.

Computer Scientists

Computer scientists have a straightforward interest in professionalism. Having established curriculum blueprints for graduate and undergraduate programs, their current efforts are directed toward certification. MCCRACKEN, as president of the Association for Computing Machinery (ACM), urges computer scientists to certify themselves by taking one of the examinations given by the Institute for Certification of Computer Professionals. Examinations are given for certificates in Computer Programming and in Data Processing, and currently in preparation is an examination for the Certificate in Systems Analysis. According to McCracken approximately 40,000 applicants have taken the exam for the Certificate in Computer Programming, but fewer than half have passed it.

Records Managers

The literature of records managers is rife with phrases attesting to their "new professionalism" (e.g., *INFORMATION AND RECORDS MANAGE-MENT*, 1980). BOZAK discusses their 15-year history of certification activity and describes the Certified Records Manager's examination, which is administered by the Institute of Certified Records Managers (ICRM). By June 1979 about 250 persons had been certified as records managers. Even special groups within records management seem to be claiming professional status. WARNER reports the deliberations at a Business Forms Management Association Seminar, in which participants were asked to define "professional" as the term applies to forms management. The line between records management and information management is somewhat blurred. More correctly, perhaps, records managers seek to blur the line as they try to broaden their horizons.

Librarians

Librarians' rights to the jobs they hold and the jobs to which they aspire are being challenged. A professional librarian has a degree from an accredited library/information science school, but increasingly, the need for the degree is being questioned. Could paraprofessionals not do many of the same tasks? Some think so themselves (GRADY), and DOWELL sees many who are aggressively seeking to override the barriers that hold them back. In her Delphi survey of members of the Association of American Library Schools (AALS), BOAZ found that almost 75% of the respondents believed "the substitution of paraprofessional workers in many of the types of professional library positions" to be probable (p319). MACCAMPBELL presents a scenario of an academic library in which only six to eight of 85-100 staff members are professionally educated. He sees "the profession" becoming considerably diminished but more professional. SCHWARTZ reports that one university personnel department no longer requires librarians to hold an M.L.S. degree. A diminished profession may put many library schools out of business. In the survey by BOAZ 60% of the respondents thought it probable that 10% of all library schools would be discontinued or merged.

There has been very little testing to see if the M.L.S. is correlated with successful job performance (DOWELL). Part of the difficulty is in isolating the jobs whose performance is to be measured. Several writers note that the line between professional and nonprofessional activities has always been somewhat hazy. BURR and BORDA both lament that librarians often perform nonprofessional tasks. The former depicts the special librarian as a victim who is forced to be a "Girl Friday." Both urge the isolation of that part of librarianship that is truly professional by distinguishing clerical from professional tasks. Boaz found that 75% of the respondents felt it probable that "new criteria for professional library and information science positions" would be established.

It is difficult to tell how widespread within librarianship is the phenomenon of paraprofessionals' climbing career ladders to positions once assumed to be the exclusive domain of professionals. A career ladder program is defined by BAYLESS as "a series of classes taught by practicing librarians in one public library system which are designed to train paraprofessionals for professional positions in the same system" (p1716). Bayless sees a mushrooming of alternate routes into the library profession. She says that one can achieve professional status by: 1) experience alone, i.e., climbing a career ladder (Cleveland Public Library); 2) graduation from an in-house training program (Orange County Public Library); 3) experience combined with graduation from college classes (Tucson Public Library); and 4) passing an examination (Sacramento City-County Library System).

The last route seems to be on the upswing, a phenomenon that is alternately regarded as a threat to and as a safeguard of professionalism. As contributing to the upswing, VIRGO cites pressures from minorities who feel that they should not be denied jobs simply for want of a formal education. She observes that in moving toward a certification system the United States seems to be following long-time models in the British Commonwealth; the Commonwealth, in turn, is considering rejecting these models in favor of the U.S. model of accrediting degree programs. Virgo's article reviews the new certification code of the Medical Library Association (MLA), which was adopted in 1977. It requires that a competency exam be passed, whereas the old code allowed various routes to certification. The new code also requires recertification. Virgo cautions that valid examinations can be developed only where the competencies to be tested are relatively specific and routine. SCHMIDT also discusses the new MLA certification code. To assess its impact he determined how certification was achieved under the old code. Of those certified from 1974 to 1977, only 5% met the requirement by taking an examination; 69.2% met the requirement by taking one course, 25% by taking two or more courses, and 0.8% by internship. Certification programs for public librarians have been established in at least nine U.S. states and several Canadian provinces. BURR, disturbed by incompetent practices, sees certification as a matter of survival. Other writers doubt the efficacy of certification, either in obtaining jobs or in convincing the world that librarians are truly professional (DOWELL).

How library professionals react to encroachments by paraprofessionals could indicate how aggressively they will defend their turf and whether they will be able to conquer new territory in the information management sector. One reaction is the National Librarians Association (NLA), created in 1975 to protect the professional interests of librarians (DOLLARD). Many of its members endorse examination-based certification. However, NLA lacks funds, and its membership is not much more than 100.

Another reaction is the questioning of what professionalism entails. KLEMENT feels that information brokerage will strengthen the professional base of librarianship, in that self-employment is associated by the public with professionalism (e.g., doctors and lawyers). BIRDSALL argues for abandoning outmoded sociological models of professionalism and concentrating on strengthening the relationship between clients and librarians. He believes that online reference will provide an opportunity for improving professional status. NIELSEN is somewhat skeptical on this point. Examining data that support both sides of the debate as it relates to online reference, he concludes that while online seems now to be a professionalizing force in librarianship, its effect may be short lived as technology moves toward end-user access. RAYWARD believes that the hallmark of professionalism is professional discourse—i.e., discourse that encompasses "theory, research, description, analysis and so on, and practice" (p151).

Another reaction is rhetoric on the value of professional ideals. DAIN decries the "deschooling" of society and cites as an example the "dethroning" of the M.L.S. as a qualification for library positions. She sees librarians as one group that struggles to maintain humanistic ideals in society. A sophisticated voice for idealism is that of ASHEIM. He traces attitudes toward professionalism from the 1950s through the 1970s. For him the professions were triumphant in the 1950s; in the 1960s they were the object of questioning and outright revolt; the 1970s witnessed a return to professional goals, foremost among which are client orientation and a belief in public benefit before private gain. Asheim sharply distinguishes the professional from the businessman; the former is concerned with service and community interest and the latter with profit and self-interest. The 1960s viewpoint, which rejects the sincerity of professional goals, still has its adherents. An outspoken critic of librarians' professional idealism is H. S. WHITE. He asks if librarians do not really wish to remove themselves from the competitive pressures of the commercial world. He calls for stronger library managers, who will think in terms of productivity and cost-effectiveness, who will adopt the value systems not of the profession but of those to whom they report. Libraries are not ends in themselves but are parts of larger systems and are useful only insofar as they contribute to achieving the goals of these larger systems. The information management paradigm, with its focus on the cost-effective management of information to improve business productivity, may be at odds with certain professional ideals.

CONCLUSIONS

The information age is characterized by an information-centered economy. Signifying that we have entered this age is the emergence of the information management paradigm within which the management of information is linked to improved business productivity. It is difficult to characterize the activities of information workers because they are so numerous and diverse. One estimate is that more than half of the U.S. labor force is employed in information-related jobs. General occupational surveys show the diversity of information workers. However, special surveys indicate that some subgroups, such as computer scientists, are fairly homogeneous with respect to work performed. The information management paradigm is useful to several groups—systems analysts, records managers, and, to some extent, librarians—as a framework within which they can refashion their roles. The refashioning is in the direction of broadening occupational outlooks beyond computer technology and beyond technology generally to managing information and understanding information needs.

The diversity of information-related jobs is reflected in the diversity of locales within which education for these jobs occurs. The three locales mentioned most in the literature are computer science schools, library schools, and schools of business and management. Graduate computer science curricula are relatively well established. A blueprint for undergraduate curricula has recently been established and has received at least one challenge for its lack of theoretical perspective. Library schools continue to encounter difficulties in trying to graft information science onto library science—e.g., lack of time and lack of qualified faculty. Business schools, often in cooperation with computer science schools, attempt to educate information managers who possess both technical competency and management skills.

Given the diversity and number of information workers, a single information "profession" is hardly possible. It is possible, however, to identify the attitudes of certain subgroups toward professionalism. Computer scientists consider themselves professionals insofar as professionalism means a specialized education and certification. Records managers use the flag of professionalism in their upward mobility. Librarians continue to question their professionalism, but with a new seriousness as paraprofessionals begin to encroach on their turf. A matter of sociological debate is whether post-industrial society will see an increasing or decreasing professionalization of the U.S. work force. It is interesting to speculate on the possible effects the information management paradigm may have on professionalism.

BIBLIOGRAPHY

APPLEYARD, RAYMOND K. 1979. The Information Industry: What It Contributes, Where It is Going, Its Impact on Information Provision in the Public Sector: A General and Official View from the Standpoint of the Operator and Producer. Aslib Proceedings (U.K.). 1979 February; 31(2): 64–73. ISSN: 0001-253X.

AMERICAN SOCIETY FOR INFORMATION SCIENCE. SPECIAL INTER-
EST GROUP/FOUNDATIONS OF INFORMATION SCIENCE (FIS);
SPECIAL INTEREST GROUP/EDUCATION FOR INFORMATION
SCIENCE (ED). 1980. A New Look at the Theory-Practice Dichot-
omy Issues in Information and Library Science Education: Session 119
at the American Society for Information Science 43rd Annual Meeting;
1980 October 5-10; Anaheim, CA. Tapes available from: Minute-Tape
International, Inc., 14411 Vose Street, Suite 30, Van Nuys, CA 94105.

ANDERSON, LANE K. 1977. Systems Education to Match Employers'
Needs. Journal of Systems Management. 1977 November; 28(11): 6-
9. ISSN: 0022-4839.

ARTANDI, SUSAN. 1979. Man, Information, and Society: New Patterns
of Interaction. Journal of the American Society for Information
Science. 1979 January; 30(1): 15-18. ISSN: 0002-8231; CODEN:
A1SJB6.

ASHEIM, LESTER. 1978. Librarians as Professionals. Library Trends.
1978 Winter; 27(3): 225-257. ISSN: 0024-2594.

ASSOCIATION FOR COMPUTING MACHINERY (ACM). COMMITTEE
ON COMPUTER SCIENCE. 1979. Curriculum '78: Recommendations for the Undergraduate Program in Computer Science. Communications of the ACM. 1979 March; 22(3): 147-153. ISSN: 0001-0782.

ASSOCIATION OF RECORDS MANAGERS AND ADMINISTRATORS,
INC.; INSTITUTE OF CERTIFIED RECORDS MANAGERS. 1981.
Directory of Collegiate Schools Teaching Records Management. Records
Management Quarterly. 1981 January; 15(1): 43-48. ISSN: 0034-
172X.

BARRETT, J. W. 1978. Challenge and Opportunity. The Information
Scientist. 1978 December; 12(4): 132-136. ISSN: 0020-0263.

BAYLESS, SANDY. 1977. Librarianship is a Discipline. Library Journal.
1977 September 1; 102(15): 1715-1717. (Professionalism—An LJ Mini-
Symposium). ISSN: 0000-0027.

BECKER, LOUISE GIOVANE. 1980. Information Resources Management
(IRM): A Revolution in Progress. Bulletin of the American Society for
Information Science. 1980 August; 6(6): 26-27. ISSN: 0095-4403.

BELL, DANIEL. 1976. The Coming of the Post-Industrial Society: A Venture in Social Forecasting. New York, NY: Basic; 1976. 507p. ISBN:
0-46501-281-7; LC: 76-372278; OCLC: 2913208.

BELL, DANIEL. 1977. Teletext and Technology: New Networks of Knowledge and Information in Post-Industrial Society. Encounter. 1977
June; 48(6): 9-29. ISSN: 0013-7073.

BERG, IVAR. 1977. The Licensing of Paraprofessionals. In: Estabrook,
Leigh, ed. Libraries in Post-Industrial Society. Phoenix, AZ: Oryx
Press; 1977. 85-93. ISBN: 0-912700-009; LC: 77-8928.

BERGER, MARY C. 1976. Young Information Professionals. Bulletin of
the American Society for Information Science. 1976 December; 3(2):
11-16. ISSN: 0095-4403.

BERGER, PATRICIA WILSON. 1980. Managing Revolutions: Coping with
Evolving Information Technologies. Special Libraries. 1980 September;
71(9): 386-397. ISSN: 0038-6723.

BIRDSALL, WILLIAM F. 1980. Librarians and Professionalism: Status
Measured by Outmoded Models. Canadian Library Journal. 1980 June;
37(3): 145-148. ISSN: 0008-4352.

BOAZ, MARTHA. 1978. The Future of Library and Information Science Education. Journal of Education for Librarianship. 1978 Spring; 18(4): 315-323. ISSN: 0022-0604.

BORDA, OWEN M. 1977. It Takes More than Credentials. Library Journal. 1977 September 1; 102(15): 1727. (Professionalism—An LJ Mini-Symposium). ISSN: 0000-0027.

BOSS, RICHARD W. 1979. The Library as an Information Broker. College and Research Libraries. 1979 March; 40(2): 136-140. ISSN: 0010-0870.

BOZAK, VINCENT. 1980. Celebrating a New Professionalism. Information and Records Management. 1980 September; 14(9): 58, 64. ISSN: 0019-9966.

BRANSCOMB, LEWIS M. 1979. Information: The Ultimate Frontier. Science. 1979 January 12; 203(4376): 143-147. ISSN: 0036-8075.

BRATTON, GARY L. 1978. Information Management and the Generalist. Information and Records Management. 1978 May; 12(5): 16. ISSN: 0019-9966.

BUCKLAND, MICHAEL. 1980. Communication, Information, and Training the Information Professional. In: Benenfeld, Alan R.; Kazlauskas, Edward John, eds. Communicating Information: Proceedings of the American Society for Information Science 43rd Annual Meeting; 1980 October 5-10; Anaheim, CA. White Plains, NY: Knowledge Industry Publications; 1980. 370-372. ISSN: 0044-7870; ISBN: 0-914236-73-3; LC: 648303; CODEN: PAISDQ.

BULLETIN OF THE AMERICAN SOCIETY FOR INFORMATION SCIENCE. 1976. I Speak as an Information Professional. Bulletin of the American Society for Information Science. 1976 October; 3(1): 30. ISSN: 0095-4403.

BURR, ROBERT L. 1977. Certification and Competence. Library Journal. 1977 September 1; 102(15): 1728-1729. (Professionalism—An LJ Mini-Symposium). ISSN: 0000-0027.

CALDWELL, DON L. 1980. Managing Information Resources. Information and Records Management. 1980 April; 14(4): 14-22. ISSN: 0019-9966.

CARLSON, WALTER M. 1980. Information is not a Manageable Resource. The Information Manager. 1980 Summer; 2(2): 6. ISSN: 0160-6123.

CHAMOT, DENNIS. 1977. Professional Employees Turn to Unions. In: Estabrook, Leigh, ed. Libraries in Post-Industrial Society. Phoenix, AZ: Oryx Press; 1977. 94-106. ISBN: 0-912700-00-9; LC: 77-8928.

CHARTRAND, ROBERT LEE; MORENTZ, JAMES W.; JR., eds. 1979. Information Technology Serving Society. Oxford, England: Pergamon Press; 1979. ISBN: 0-08-021979-9; LC: 79-40352; OCLC: 5008201.

CHERLIN, MERRIL. 1980. Experimentalists: A Dying Breed. Datamation. 1980 November; 26(11): 89-92. ISSN: 0011-6963.

CONANT, RALPH W. 1980. The Conant Report: A Study of the Education of Librarians. Cambridge, MA: The MIT Press; 1980. 210p. ISBN: 0-262-03072-1.

COOPER, MICHAEL D. 1978. California's Demand for Librarians: Projecting Future Requirements. Berkeley, CA: University of California Institute of Governmental Studies; 1978. 128p. ISBN: 0-87772-256-0.

CRENNER, JAMES J. 1980. Productivity—The Information Explosion. The Information Manager. 1980 Summer; 2(2): 15-33. ISSN: 0025-181X.

CRICKMAN, ROBIN D. 1979. The Emerging Information Professional. Library Trends. 1979 Fall: 28(2): 311-327. ISSN: 0024-2594.

DAIN, PHYLLIS. 1980. The Profession and the Professors. Library Journal. 1980 September 1; 105(15): 1701-1707. ISSN: 0000-0027.

DEBONS, ANTHONY; KING, DONALD W. 1980. Final Report on the Manpower Requirements for Scientific and Technical Communication: An Occupational Survey of Information Professionals. Pittsburgh, PA: University of Pittsburgh; 1980. 224p. Available from: Anthony Debons, University of Pittsburgh School of Library and Information Science, Pittsburgh, PA 15260.

DELUTIS, THOMAS G. 1977. Information Systems Curriculum. Journal of Systems Management. 1977 September; 28(9): 14-20. ISSN: 0022-4839.

DOLLARD, PETER. 1977. Lock the Loonies in a Stereotype! Library Journal. 1977 September 1: 102(15): 1725-1726. (Professionalism—An LJ Mini-Symposium). ISSN: 0000-0027.

DOWELL, DAVID R. 1977. Certification: More Study Needed. Library Journal. 1977 September 1; 102(15): 1720-1721. (Professionalism—An LJ Mini-Symposium). ISSN: 0000-0027.

DUMAS, PHILIPPE. 1975. A New Breed of Managers: The Information Manager. Management International Review. 1975; 15(4-5): 49-56. ISSN: 0025-181X.

ELMAN, STANLEY A. 1976. The Humanization of Information Science. Special Libraries. 1976 September; 67(9): 421-427. ISSN: 0038-6723.

ESTABROOK, LEIGH S.; HEIM, KATHLEEN M. 1980. A Profile of ALA Personal Members. American Libraries. 1980 December; 11(11): 654-659. ISSN: 0002-9769.

FAIRLEY, RICHARD E. 1979. Employment Characteristics of Doctoral Level Computer Scientists. Communications of the ACM. 1979 February; 22(2): 77-78. ISSN: 0001-0782.

FERREIRA, JOSEPH; COLLINS, JAMES F., JR. 1979. The Changing Role of the MIS Executive. Datamation. 1979 November; 25(13): 26-32. ISSN: 0011-6963.

FOSKETT, D. J. 1976. NATIS: Preliminary Survey of Education and Training Programs at University Level in Information and Library Science. Paris, France: UNESCO; 1976. 149p. (COM.75/WS/34).

GALVIN, THOMAS J. 1976. Change in Education for Librarianship. Library Journal. 1976 January 1; 101(1): 273-277. ISSN: 0000-0027.

GALVIN, THOMAS J. 1978. The Profession's Response to a Crisis-Based Society. Journal of Education for Librarianship. 1978 Spring; 18(4): 269-277. ISSN: 0022-0604.

GARDNER, ROBERTA J. 1980. Is Tension Inevitable Between SLA and Associated Information Managers? Special Libraries. 1980 September; 71(9): 373-378. ISSN: 0038-6723.

GARRISON, GUY. 1978. Needed: A Core Curriculum for a Diversifying Profession. Journal of Education for Librarianship. 1978 Fall; 19(2): 179-183. (Papers presented at a workshop on the Integrated Core Curriculum; 1977 March 6-8; Chapel Hill, NC). ISSN: 0022-0604.

GRADY, RUTH ELLEN. 1977. Library Work without an M.L.S. Library Journal. 1977 September 1; 102(15): 1726. (Professionalism—An LJ Mini-Symposium). ISSN: 0000-0027.

GREENWOOD, FRANK. 1979. Your New Job in Information Management Resources. Journal of Systems Management. 1979 April; 30(4): 24-27. ISSN: 0022-4839.

GREER, ROGER; BENNION, BRUCE; GROVER, ROBERT; HALE, MARTHA; KAZLAUSKAS, EDWARD JOHN. 1980. Information Transfer: A New Focus for Library Education. In: Benenfeld, Alan R.; Kazlauskas, Edward John, eds. Communicating Information: Proceedings of the American Society for Information Science 43rd Annual Meeting; 1980 October 5-10; Anaheim, CA. White Plains, NY: Knowledge Industry Publications; 1980. 373-375. ISSN: 0044-7870; ISBN: 0-914236-73-3; LC: 64-80303; CODEN: PAISDQ.

HARMON, GLYNN. 1976. Information Science Education and Training. In: Williams, Martha, ed. Annual Review of Information Science and Technology: Volume 11. Washington, DC: American Society for Information Science; 1976. 347-380. ISSN: 0066-4200; ISBN: 0-87715-212-8; CODEN: ARISBc.

HARMON, GLYNN. 1980. Conclusion: Implications of the Occupational Survey. 1980 October 12. 13p. (Unpublished draft). Available from: the author, University of Texas Graduate School of Library and Information Science, Austin, TX 78712.

HARMON, GLYNN; RATHSWOHL, EUGENE. 1978. Education for Information Management: Some Future Dimensions. Paper presented at the American Society for Information Science 7th Midyear Meeting; 1978 May 22-24; Houston, TX. 5p. Available from: the author. University of Texas Graduate School of Library and Information Science, Austin, TX 78712.

HAUG, MARIE R. 1977. The Deprofessionalization of Everyone? In: Estabrook, Leigh, ed. Libraries in Post-Industrial Society. Phoenix, AZ: Oryx Press; 1977. 67-84. ISBN: 0-912700-00-9; LC: 77-8928.

HAVARD-WILLIAMS, P. 1976. The Future of Library and Information Studies. In: Harrison, K. C., ed. Prospects for British Librarianship. London, England: The Library Association; 1976. 29-42. ISBN: 0-85365-009-8.

HAYES, ROBERT M. 1980. The Core Curriculum for Library and Information Science Education. Paper presented at the International Federation of Library Associations (IFLA) Conference; 1980 August 11-15; Manilla, Philippines. 22p. (To be published in the proceedings of the Conference). Available from: the author, Univeristy of California at Los Angeles Graduate School of Library and Information Sciences, Los Angeles, CA 90024.

HOLMES, FENWICKE W. 1977. Information Resource Management. Journal of Systems Management. 1977 September; 28(9): 6-9. ISSN: 0022-4839.

HORTON, FOREST W., JR. 1979a. Information Resources Management: Concept and Cases. Cleveland, OH: Association for Systems Management; 1979. 343p. ISBN: 934356-01-7; LC 79-53322; OCLC: 5575650.

HORTON, FOREST W., JR. 1979b. Occupational Standard for the Information Resources Manager. Journal of Systems Management. 1979 May; 30(5): 35-41. ISSN: 0022-4839.

HOUSER, L.; SCHRADER, ALVIN M. 1978. The Search for a Scientific Profession. Metuchen, NJ: Scarecrow Press; 1978. 180p. ISBN: 0-8108-1062-X.

INFORMATION AND RECORDS MANAGEMENT. 1978. Education: The Mark of Professionalism. Information and Records Management. 1978 November; 12(11): 16-20, 48, 52. ISSN: 0019-9966.

INFORMATION AND RECORDS MANAGEMENT. 1979. ICRM Sets Professional Standards. Information and Records Management. 1979 June; 13(6): 58, 62. ISSN: 0019-9966.
INFORMATION AND RECORDS MANAGEMENT. 1980. Portraits in Professionalism: Profiles of ARMA's Outstanding Records Managers. Information and Records Management. 1980 September; 14(9): 26-27. ISSN: 0019-9966.
JACKSON, EUGENE B.; WYLLYS, RONALD E. 1976. Professional Education in Information Science: Its Recent Past and Probable Future. In: Hammer, D. P., ed. The Information Age: Its Development, Its Impact. Metuchen, NJ: Scarecrow Press, Inc.; 1976. 166-209. ISBN: 0-8108-0945-1; LC: 76-10603.
JOURNAL OF SYSTEMS MANAGEMENT. 1979. The Diebold Report. Journal of Systems Management. Part I: 1979 June; 26(6): 50-92. Part II: 1979 October; 26(10): 41-120. ISSN: 0022-4839.
KALBA, KAS. 1977. Libraries in the Information Marketplace. In: Estabrook, Leigh, ed. Libraries in Post-Industrial Society. Phoenix, AZ: Oryx Press; 1977. 306-320. ISBN: 0-912700-00-9; LC: 77-8928.
KARSH, MICHELLE. 1978. Associations Promote Records Management Education. Information and Records Management. 1978 December; 12(11): 10-11, 44-48. ISSN: 0095-4853.
KENT, ALLEN. 1977. Information Science. Journal of Education for Librarianship. 1977 Winter; 17(3): 131-139. ISSN: 0022-0604.
KING, DONALD W. 1980. Thoughts for ASIS Members. Bulletin of the American Society for Information Science. 1980 August; 6(6): 3-4. ISSN: 0095-4403.
KING, DONALD W.; DEBONS, ANTHONY; MANSFIELD, ÚNA; SHIREY, DONALD L. 1980a. A National Profile of Information Professionals. Bulletin of the American Society for Information Science. 1980 August; 6(6): 18-22. ISSN: 0095-4403.
KING, DONALD W.; KRAUSER, CHERI; SAGUE, VIRGINIA M. 1980b. Profile of ASIS Membership. Bulletin of the American Society for Information Science. 1980 August; 6(6): 9-17. ISSN: 0095-4403.
KLEMENT, SUSAN. 1977. Draft Proposal: A Graduate Course on Alternatives in Librarianship. Canadian Library Journal. 1977 April; 34(2): 131-134. ISSN: 0008-4352.
KLEMPNER, IRVING M. 1976. New Imperatives: Decisions for Library School Curricula. Special Libraries. 1976 September; 67(9): 409-414. ISSN: 0038-6723.
LANCASTER, F. WILFRID. 1978. Toward Paperless Information Systems. New York, NY: Academic Press; 1978. 179p. ISBN: 0-12-436050-5.
LANCASTER, F. WILFRID; DRASGOW, LAURA S.; MARKS, ELLEN B. 1979. The Changing Face of the Library: A Look at Libraries and Librarians in the Year 2000. Collection Management. 1979 Spring; 3(1): 55-77. ISSN: 0146-2679.
LANDAU, ROBERT M. 1980. Information Resources Management. New York, NY: AMACOM; 1980. 37p. (An AMA briefing). ISBN: 0-8144-2250-0; LC: 80-14443.
LANGEMO, MARK. 1980. Records Management in the 1980's. Information and Records Management. 1980 June; 14(6): 14-15. ISSN: 0095-4853.

LIPETZ, BEN-AMI. 1980. Educating the Information Science Professional. Bulletin of the American Society for Information Science. 1980 April; 6(4): 21-22. ISSN: 0095-4403.

LUCAS, HENRY C., JR. 1979. New Directions in MBA Programs: Preparing Executives for Corporate Information Management. Journal of Systems Management. 1979 October; 26(10): 114-119. (The Diebold Report). ISSN: 0022-4839.

MACCAMPBELL, JAMES C. 1977. Better Utilization of Personnel. Library Journal. 1977 September 1; 102(15): 1718-1720. (Professionalism—An LJ Mini-Symposium). ISSN: 0000-0027.

MACHLUP, FRITZ. 1979. Meeting Review: An Economist's Reflections on an Institute for the Advanced Study of Information Science. Journal of the American Society for Information Science. 1979 March; 30(2): 111-113. ISSN: 0002-8231.

MARCHAND, DONALD A. 1978. Information Management in Public Organizations: Defining a New Resource Management Function. The Bureaucrat. 1978 Winter; 7(4): 4-10. (Information Management Series). ISSN: 0045-3544.

MASON, DONALD. 1978. Information Management. Stevenage, England: Peter Peregrinus, Ltd.; 1978. 121p. ISBN: 0-90604-805-2; OCLC: 4969186.

MCCRACKEN, DAN. 1979. The Institute for Certification of Computer Professionals: A Call for ACM Action. Communications of the ACM. 1979 March; 22(3): 145-146. ISSN: 0010-0782.

MCCRIRICK, IAN B.; GOLDSTEIN, ROBERT C. 1980. What Do Data Administrators Really Do? Datamation. 1980 August; 26(8): 131-134. ISSN: 0011-6963.

MCKINLAY, JOHN. 1977. The Professional Regulation of Change. In: Estabrook, Leigh, ed. Libraries in Post-Industrial Society. Phoenix, AZ: Oryx Press; 1977. 47-66. ISBN: 0-912700-00-9; LC: 77-8928.

MEADOW, CHARLES T. 1979. Information Science and Scientists in 2001. Journal of Information Science. 1979; 1(4): 217-222. ISSN: 0165-5515.

MOTZ, ARLENE. 1979. An Analysis of Records Managers, Literature, and Current College Course Offerings with Implications for Four-year Collegiate Records Management Training. Boulder, CO: University of Colorado, 1979. 159p. (Ph.D. dissertation). Available from: University Microfilms, Ann Arbor, MI. UM: 7923268.

NANUS, BURT. 1976. Information Science and the Future. Bulletin of the American Society for Information Science. 1976 March; 2(8): 57-58. ISSN: 0095-4403.

NEILL, SAM D. 1980. Canadian Libraries in 2010. Vancouver, B. C., Canada: Parabola Systems; 1980. 144p.

NELSON, BONNIE R. 1980. The Chimera of Professionalism. Library Journal. 1980 October 1; 105(17): 2029-2033. ISSN: 0000-0027.

NIELSEN, BRIAN. 1980. Online Bibliographic Searching and the Deprofessionalization of Librarianship. Online Review. 1980 September; 4(3): 215-224. ISSN: 0309-314X.

PORAT, MARC URI. 1977. The Information Economy: Definition and Measurement. Washington, DC: U.S. Department of Commerce, Office of Telecommunication; 1977. 249p. (OT Specification Publication no. 77-12(1).

PORTER, JOHN. 1980. The Changing World of Information Management: People in Records Management Have to Decide What Their Role Will Be. Information and Records Management. 1980 May; 14(5): 13-14. ISSN: 0019-9966.
PULLEN, EDWARD W.; SIMKO, ROBERT G. 1977. Our Changing Industry. Datamation. 1977 January; 23(1): 49-55. ISSN: 0011-6963.
RALSTON, ANTHONY; SHAW, MARY. 1980. Curriculum '78—Is Computer Science Really that Unmathematical? Communications of the ACM. 1980 February; 23(2): 67-70. ISSN: 0001-0782.
RAYWARD, W. BOYD. 1980. The Problem of Professional Knowledge in Librarianship. In: White, Peter, ed. Changes and Exchanges: Australian Viewpoints. Lindfield, New South Wales, Australia: Kuring-Gai College of Advanced Education; 1980. 135-154. ISBN: 0-909177-18-X.
REEVES, GARY R.; BUSSOM, ROBERT S. 1979. Information Systems Curriculum. Journal of Systems Management. 1979 March; 30(3): 18-21. ISSN: 0022-4839.
SARACEVIC, TEFKO. 1979a. An Essay on the Past and Future (?) of Information Science Education—I. Historical Overview. Information Processing & Management. 1979; 15: 1-15. ISSN: 0306-4573.
SARACEVIC, TEFKO. 1979b. An Essay on the Past and Future (?) of Information Science Education—II. Unresolved Problems of "Externalities" of Education. Information Processing & Management. 1979; 15: 291-301. ISSN: 0306-4573.
SCHMIDT, DEAN. 1979. Certification of Medical Librarians, 1949-1977: Statistical Analysis. Bulletin of the Medical Libraries Association. 1979 January; 67(1): 31-35. ISSN: 0025-7338.
SCHWARTZ, NARDA L. 1977. The Professional Attitude. Library Journal. 1977 September 1; 102(15): 1729-1731. (Professionalism—An LJ Mini-Symposium). ISSN: 0000-0027.
SEWELL, WINIFRED. 1978. Study of Federal Library/Information Service Staffing as Affected by Classification and Qualification Standards. Springfield, VA: National Technical Information Service; 1978. 81p. (Prepared for the Federal Library Committee). NTIS: PB 291540; OCLC: 6353272.
SHAUGHNESSY, THOMAS W. 1976. Theory Building in Librarianship. Journal of Library History. 1976 April; 11(2): 167-176. ISSN: 0022-2259.
SHERA, JESSE H.; CLEVELAND, DONALD B. 1977. History and Foundations of Information Science. In: Williams, Martha, ed. Annual Review of Information Science and Technology: Volume 12. White Plains, NY: Knowledge Industry Publications, Inc.; 1977. 249-276. ISSN: 0066-4200; ISBN: 0-914236-11-3; CODEN: ARISBc.
SIMPSON, I. S. 1979. Education for Information Science—I. The United Kingdom. Journal of Information Science (U.K.). 1979 April; 1(1): 49-57. ISSN: 0165-5515.
SLAMECKA, VLADIMIR; GEHL, JOHN, eds. 1978. Information Sciences at Georgia Institute of Technology: The Formative Years 1963-78. Information Processing & Management. 1978; 14(5): iii-iv, 319-361. ISSN: 0306-4573.
SLATER, MARGARET. 1979. Manpower Forecasting and Planning. Journal of Information Science. 1979; 1(3): 131-143. ISSN: 0165-5515.

SPROWLS, CLAY. 1978. The Computer and Information Systems Program at the Graduate School of Management, UCLA. In: Brenner, Everett H., ed. The Information Age in Perspective: Proceedings of the American Society for Information Science 41st Annual Meeting; 1978 November 13-17; New York, NY. White Plains, NY: Knowledge Industry Publications; 1978. 318-321. ISSN: 0044-7870; ISBN: 0-914236-22-9; LC: 64-8303; CODEN: PAISDQ.

SVENONIUS, ELAINE. 1977. The Integration of Information Science into the Library School Curriculum at the University of Western Ontario. Paper presented at the Association of American Library Schools Annual Meeting; 1977 January 28-30; Washington, DC. 11p. Available from: the author, University of Denver Graduate School of Librarianship and Information Management, Denver, CO 80208.

SWANSON, ROWENA WEISS. 1978. Education for Information Science as a Profession. Journal of the American Society for Information Science. 1978 May; 29(3): 148-155. ISSN: 0002-8231.

SYRACUSE UNIVERSITY. SCHOOL OF INFORMATION STUDIES. 1980. Program in Information Resources Management. Syracuse, NY: Syracuse University School of Information Studies; 1980. 34p. Available from: Syracuse University School of Information Studies, Syracuse, NY 13215.

TAGUE, JEAN. 1979. Information Science in Graduate Library Programs. Canadian Library Journal. 1979 June; 36(3): 89-99. ISSN: 0008-4352.

TAULBEE, ORRIN E.; CONTE, S. D. 1979. Production and Employment of Ph.D.'s in Computer Science—1977 and 1978. Communications of the ACM. 1979 February; 22(2): 75-76. ISSN: 0001-0782.

TAYLOR, ROBERT S. 1979. Reminiscing about the Future: Professional Education and the Information Environment. Library Journal. 1979 September 15; 104(16): 1871-1875. ISSN: 0000-0027.

TAYLOR, ROBERT S. 1980. Value Added Aspects of the Information Process. In: Benenfeld, Alan R.; Kazlauskas, Edward John, eds. Communicating Information: Proceedings of the American Society for Information Science 43rd Annual Meeting; 1980 October 5-10; Anaheim, CA. White Plains, NY: Knowledge Industry Publications; 1980. 344p. ISSN: 0044-7870; ISBN: 0-914236-73-3; LC: 64-8303; CODEN: PAISDQ.

THOMAS, DIANA M. 1977. Integration of Information Science in UCLA's Two-Year Program. Paper presented at the Association of American Library Schools Annual Meeting; 1977 January 28-30; Washington, DC. 5p. Available from: the author, University of California at Los Angeles Graduate School of Library and Information Science, Los Angeles, CA 90024.

THURSTON, SHIRLEY B. 1980. Leadership or Dependency: A Question for Every Information Manager. The Information Manager. 1980 Summer; 2(2): 8. ISSN: 0160-6123.

TOWNSEND, DWIGHT F. 1980. Systems Analysis: Key to the Future. Datamation. 1980 October; 26(10): 145-148. ISSN: 0011-6963.

U. S. COMMISSION ON FEDERAL PAPERWORK. 1977. Information Resources Management. Washington, DC: Commission on Federal Paperwork; 1977 September 9. 76p. (y 3.P 19:2 In3). Available from the Superintendent of Documents, Government Printing Office, Washington, DC 20402. GPO: 052-003-00464-0.

U. S. CONGRESS. HOUSE. 1981. Remarks of Congressman George Brown speaking on The Information Science and Technology Act of 1981. Congressional Record. 1981 April 8; 127: H1410-H1415.

UNIVERSITY OF CALIFORNIA. LABORATORY OF MEDICAL INFORMATION SCIENCE. 1979. Graduate Program in Medical Information Science. Student Handbook. San Francisco, CA: University of California; September 1979. 3p. Available from: University of California Laboratory of Medical Information Science, San Francisco, CA 94143.

VANCE, KENNETH E.; MAGRILL, ROSE MARY; DOWNEN, THOMAS W. 1977. Future of Library Education: 1975 Delphi Study. Journal of Education for Librarianship. 1977 Summer; 18(1): 3-17. ISSN: 0022-0604.

VIRGO, JULIE A. 1976. Degree or License. Wilson Library Bulletin. 1976 December; 51(4): 341-345. ISSN: 0043-5651.

WARNER, JO. 1978. Profile of a Forms Professional: An Individual with Knowledge and Motivation. Information and Records Management. 1978 August: 12(7): 14. ISSN: 0019-9966.

WERSIG, GERNOT; SEEGER, THOMAS. 1978. Future Main Trends of Information Systems and Their Implications for Specialization of Information Personnel. International Forum on Information and Documentation (The Netherlands). 1978; 3(4): 6-14. ISSN: 0304-9701.

WHITE, HERBERT S. 1978. Management: A Strategy for Change. Canadian Library Journal. 1978 October; 35(5): 329-339. ISSN: 0008-4352.

WHITE, MARTIN S. 1980. Information for Industry: The Role of the Information Broker. Aslib Proceedings (U.K.). 1980 February; 32(2): 82-86. ISSN: 0001-253X.

WILENSKY, HAROLD L. 1964. The Professionalization of Everyone? American Journal of Sociology. 1964 September; 70(2): 137-158. ISSN: 0002-9602.

WILLIAMS, JAMES G. 1978. Information Science Education. In: Brenner, Everett H., ed. The Information Age in Perspective: Proceedings of the American Society for Information Science 41st Annual Meeting; 1978 November 13-17; New York, NY. White Plains, NY: Knowledge Industry Publications; 1978. 353-357. ISSN: 0044-7870; ISBN: 0-914236-22-9; LC: 64-8303; CODEN: PAISDQ.

WILSON, PAULINE. 1978. Impending Change in Library Education: Implications for Planning. Journal of Education for Librarianship. 1978 Winter; 18(3): 159-174. ISSN: 0022-0604.

WINTER, RALPH. 1980. Paper Weight: Many Businesses Blame Governmental Policies for Productivity Lag. The Wall Street Journal. 1980 October 28: 1, 18.

YOUNG, LAWRENCE F. 1978. In-Company User Training. Journal of Systems Management. 1978 May; 29(5): 28-31. ISSN: 0022-4839.

11 Computer Aids to Learning Online Retrieval

ELAINE CARUSO
University of Pittsburgh

Antoine de Saint-Exupéry said, "As for the future, your task is not to forsee, but to enable it."

—Mosteller

INTRODUCTION

This chapter discusses computer-assisted instruction (CAI) and other computer-aided learning (CAL) systems for online bibliographic retrieval systems. Earlier *ARIST* authors who have covered training and education for online searching include MCCARN and WANGER (1979a). Their reviews should be consulted to put this discussion into a larger context. Here we enumerate and describe the computer training or learning aids that have been reported in the literature and distinguish them according to the kinds of training they offer and the populations they serve. The CAL programs are then compared on the basis of their features, usefulness, and availability. Studies of the use of CAL systems are noted, although little real use in actual training is reported. The maturing of CAI technology, the advent of usable and economical telecommunication networks that permit many users to share CAL programs, and the growing demand for online search training are factors that have contributed to the present level of CAL use and development.

EIGHT POTENTIALLY VIABLE CAL SYSTEMS

Three Levels of Learning Assistance

The computer can help the user of machine readable databases in many ways. The approaches range from those in which the total initiative and control are taken by the user to those in which the entire learning program is guided, directed, measured, and certified by the computer. The CAL programs surveyed fall into three categories: 1) tutorials, 2) search aids, and 3) explanations and error diagnostics that are available within specific online retrieval systems. The five tutorials listed below and described more fully in the next section are computerized attempts to aid the user of bibliographic retrieval systems without limiting or controlling his learning. It is expensive for the user to learn how to use retrieval services by actually using them, but many users do just this. The CAL systems discussed here attempt to make such learning more efficient and less expensive. In addition CAL provides the learning experience within the computing environment in which it will be used and within the educational or professional environment of the user, as classes and workshops do not.

The three systems that provide assistance during the search are designed to eliminate or minimize the need for training by simplifying the online search dialog. The last category of aids—online *HELPs* and diagnostic messages—is not considered here since these aids are designed to improve the performance of the search system and only indirectly educate the user. Systems that translate search commands into lists of options from which the user may choose are called menu-driven systems. They are strictly aids to searching and not aids to learning how to search and thus are not discussed here.

CAL Programs Identified

Tutorials. Five of the CAL systems for users of online retrieval services have been expressly designed for developing online search skills before the search.

- National Library of Medicine (NLM) *MEDLEARN*: teaches basic capabilities of MEDLINE; on NLM computer; access is by direct dial, Tymnet, or Telenet for MEDLINE users.
- Congressional Research Service (CRS) Subject Content Oriented Retriever for Processing Information On-Line (SCORPIO) training: includes full SCORPIO training program; on Control Data Corp. (CDC) computer; access is limited to congressional and Library of Congress (LC) offices.
- University of Pittsburgh (UP), Carnegie-Mellon University (C-MU), TRAINER: teaches basic DIALOG and ORBIT capabilities; on UP computer; access is limited to UP community; also on C-MU computer; access limited to EDUNET member institutions; also independent installations at various locations; access varies.
- University of London, DIALOG with PET: teaches DIALOG system and generalized strategy building; available for purchase for use with Commodore PET microcomputer.
- Lockheed Information Systems, Online Training and Practice (ONTAP) files with TRAIN commands: guided practice in

search strategies; practice with particular commands; available when online to DIALOG service.

Search aids. Three systems have a similar long-range goal—to make online services more accessible to more users. They act as automatic assistants or as translators of command names or capabilities.

- Massachusetts Institute of Technology (MIT), Connector for Networked Information Transfer (CONIT): equates DIALOG, ORBIT, and MEDLINE commands to CONIT commands; teaching is limited to context-dependent messages while search is being made; user is constantly online to one or another of the target systems and to the MIT MULTICS computer.
- Drexel University (DU), Individualized Instruction for Data Access (IIDA): monitors user's interaction with DIALOG; intercepts DIALOG's error messages; diagnoses user difficulty; suggests ways to correct user strategies. User is constantly online to DIALOG and to IIDA computer.
- EURONET-DIANE, Common Command Language (CCL): expresses most important capabilities of all major retrieval services as CCL commands; CCL is intended to be individually integrated into each major retrieval service's software.

These systems also include direct and indirect training to some extent.

Explanations and error diagnostics. A third level of online training is built into the retrieval services as an optional "long form" of system messages or as diagnostic messages that respond to user errors or as "helps" or explanations that the user may request. These training aids are not considered here. However, they are an important part of the systems, and if properly developed would reduce the need for user training before the online search.

The Five Tutorial Systems

Here we consider those computer aids to learning online searching that attempt a tutorial role: *MEDLEARN*, SCORPIO training, TRAINER, DIALOG with PET, and ONTAP.

MEDLEARN. *MEDLEARN* is an outgrowth of the early ***MEDLEARN*** and is intended for beginning search specialists. The six bracketing asterisks were included in the name of the original tutorial system to distinguish it from MEDLARS (Medical Literature Analysis and Retrieval System). The current tutorial is distinguished from the early version by the use of only two bracketing asterisks. The 1972 ***MEDLEARN*** system followed the 1970 release of the MEDLINE database. It was intended for the end user and was tested successfully by novices (SOBEN & TIDBALL). *MEDLEARN* is operated by about 400 users per year logging 200 connect-hours per month (KASSEBAUM & LEITER). Teaching strategies include a tutorial dialog, drill and practice, testing, and simulation. *MEDLEARN* is divided into three courses or "tracks" that must be used in sequence. When the trainee is not using the *MEDLEARN* courses, he is expected to practice what he has learned in his regular library environment. The three tracks cover basic methods, advanced techniques, and new developments. Each topic is presented on two levels with alternate but comparable presentations for users who do not comprehend the initial coverage of a topic. Each of the two simulations allow the trainee to practice formulating and executing a search and to have it evaluated before performing it on MEDLINE. Student control is maximized on *MEDLEARN*. The trainee may use testing programs that check for immediate recall, general comprehension, and integration of knowledge.

Both ***MEDLEARN*** and *MEDLEARN* were the joint work of NLM and the George Washington University Medical Center. Development of *MEDLEARN* continues, with the addition of more sophisticated capabilities for advanced training and more database instruction. In addition, a *TOXLEARN* program is being developed. The *MEDLEARN* programs are maintained on the NLM computer; access is by direct dial or Tymnet or Telenet. The programs are written in PILOT.

SCORPIO training. The LC Automated Systems Office and the CRS (GRIFFITH & NORTON) are investigating the use of CAI in the teaching of both SCORPIO and the Multiple-Use MARC System (MUMS) retrieval systems. LC tested the possibility of doing its own CAI development, using IBM's Interactive Instructional System (IIS). IIS allows instructors to create their own CAI programs. LC staff developed a teaching module for the MUMS command *FIND*. That limited effort showed that much staff training and long development times would be required to create a training system of sufficient length for meaningful evaluation. This was a commitment of resources that LC was unwilling to make since it had not yet decided that CAI would meet its training needs. CDC was therefore hired to design a stand-alone introductory course in the use of SCORPIO. CDC uses a software system called PLATO, and the lessons it develops reside in CDC's computers in Minneapolis. The programs must be used with the special-purpose PLATO terminal, linked to Minneapolis over the CDC telecommunications network.

Use of the PLATO tutorial was begun in June 1980. It runs six to seven hours and covers the basic search techniques that are taught in a three-session, six hour traditional classroom course. Data for evaluating the program were collected during the summer of 1980 from 97 students. Results of the initial testing were positive in terms of content covered, user acceptance, user persistence (only 15% dropouts), and in the students' free use of varying pathways within the program. Objective testing for mastery of the content has yet to be completed, but 85% of users "feel" that they have completed practice searches satisfactorily. Cost parameters that seem to be competitive with the standard course will be analyzed more carefully. Restriction of program use to PLATO terminals was not judged to be a disadvantage since a central location was considered desirable for the training sessions. Most congressional offices proved to be inadequate learning environments for this type of training. However, this limitation does eliminate one of the most attractive capabilities for CAL—that of using the training when it is needed as opposed to scheduled sessions. It also limits the CAL's usefulness for a quick refreshing of skills when they will be used. The transfer of trained skills will be somewhat diminished since the training terminal is not the same as the searching terminal. The proved benefit of using a skill in the environment in which it was learned is also lost. Since the summer evaluation, the traditional teaching approach has been discontinued, and all SCORPIO training is being done with the online tutorial.

   TRAINER. TRAINER was developed at the University of Pittsburgh (UP) with funding from the Division of Science Information of the National Science Foundation (NSF). It was designed to train scientific and technical personnel in the use of bibliographic databases (E. CARUSO, 1977). There are seven tutorial modules that teach the most-used commands of DIALOG and ORBIT. File selection and search practice are guided by the tutorials and the printed manual using the two emulated systems, DIALOG and ORBIT. The emulators include fully developed basic commands of the two services. TRAINER is maintained at the Graduate School of Public and International Affairs (GSPIA) of UP, where it is used by students individually, by library staff, in formal classes that introduce the overall capabilities of computers to mid-career students of government, and in an experimental course for public-service officials who will deal with public crises and labor contract negotiations.

   TRAINER is also supported at Carnegie-Mellon University (C-MU), where it is a joint effort of the Hunt Memorial Library and the C-MU Computer Center as a service to the EDUNET network (E. CARUSO, 1979a). EDUNET is described more fully in the section on Distribution of CAL. Currently the emulators are being revised to reflect new capabilities of the DIALOG service. The tutorials are being similarly revised, and a new module is under development to focus on the characteristics and use of the Public Affairs Information Service (PAIS) database. The Bibliographical Center for Research at Denver, CO, is testing TRAINER as a possible addition to its training program for the seven midwest states that it serves (SEGAL). There is no institutional or governmental funding for TRAINER; it is supported in part by other projects. As use develops it will receive support from increased fees paid via EDUNET to the C-MU Computer Center.

   As part of the dissemination activities undertaken to comply with initial NSF funding, sample tape copies of TRAINER were distributed to 30 institutions in the United States and in five countries (E. CARUSO, 1981). The language in which the programs are distributed is the American National Standards Institute (ANSI) FORTRAN. Most computer systems must change file-loading statements and timing routines, and a character manipulation subroutine requires rewriting for computers other than those of Digital Equipment Corp. (DEC). A program for local revisions or additions to the tutorials is part of the software. Reports from tape users indicate wide variations in the use and extent of integration of the system into ongoing programs.

   CRAIG studied the costs of implementing and maintaining TRAINER on the C-MU DECsystem2060 prior to bringing it up on the C-MU system. She estimated use rates that could justify the allocation of computer storage, processing, and personnel required to keep TRAINER usefully abreast of the changes in the DIALOG and ORBIT services and to improve and expand its capabilities. Her formula is extremely sensitive to local costing figures and to estimates of the amounts of updating to be done. She estimates 1,000 users per year, averaging slightly under eight hours per user in online time.

DIALOG with PET. The Central Information Service of the University of London is developing a series of interactive simulation programs, using the Commodore PET microcomputer that will teach various aspects of online searching (VICKERY). A series of programs is planned, two of which are available on PET cassettes. The first program, DIALOG with PET, is a four-part, interactive, self-teaching program that introduces Lockheed Information System's command language, DIALOG. It is intended for new users, but the supplier suggests that it will be equally useful to those who wish to refresh their knowledge of DIALOG. A second program, Search Strategy, teaches search strategy design for online bibliographic information retrieval systems that use Boolean logic. It is intended for naive users and illustrates basic concepts that are independent of specific system command languages.

ONTAP with TRAIN. Lockheed's DIALOG system includes two kinds of tutorial elements: the Online Training and Practice (ONTAP) files and the TRAIN commands. The ONTAP files [for the Educational Resources Information Center (ERIC), Chemical Abstracts (CASEARCH), and Chemical Names (CHEMNAME) databases] are small files that are not updated and that anyone may use at the lower training rates. The ONTAP ERIC file includes a set of presearched questions of graduated difficulty, and the user may try to create the "best" search strategies. Recall and precision scores are calculated for each search. It is a very realistic experience; some of the best results may require more than one search strategy (LOCKHEED INFORMATION SYSTEMS). Other ONTAP files are planned, and more question sets will be included. All system features are available for practice in the ONTAP files except saving searches and printing offline.

Although ONTAP now resides in the DIALOG system, it originated at the ERIC Clearinghouse on Information Resources at Syracuse University. The original version was to be a self-help printed manual to be used by search specialists in training. The associated ONTAP ERIC file was viewed as a convenient supplement for drill and practice (MARKEY & ATHERTON). In practice, the user can achieve a complete learning experience, entirely in the online mode, without referring to the manual. The objectives of this self-contained "lesson" are much more limited than the goals of the ONTAP manual and seem quite appropriate for an end user or any beginner who has just learned the DIALOG commands. The proper use of ONTAP ERIC is simply practice in a real system—i.e., in creating search strategies that can be made more selective or more comprehensive.

A different approach to the use of the actual service in the tutorial mode is the recent inclusion of the TRAIN function. By issuing the *.ORDER TRAIN* or *.ORDERITEM TRAIN* commands the user can practice the commands that permit online orders to be placed, either for documents identified in the DIALOG database or for documents identified in other sources. Orders for DIALOG or non-DIALOG documents will not be placed. This kind of protected practice is certainly convenient, but because the user must pay for the online connection to DIALOG and because such use might overload the access ports or overwork the computer, the extension of this otherwise promising development may be limited.

Three Programs that Assist the Searcher

The three programs reviewed below—CONIT, IIDA, and CCL—do not make the learning a separate experience from online searching. They try to make the searching simpler by translating multiple command languages into a single common language or by interpreting user behavior and suggesting search tactics. However, by isolating the user from the system, they may obscure system capabilities and thus prevent the user from the independent growth that can develop with greater understanding of the system. Also any time saved in training may be offset by losses in effective use of the system. The principal value of these programs may lie in what they can teach us about an ideal system interface.

CONIT. The Laboratory for Information and Decision Systems at MIT developed CONIT as a computer interface between inexperienced users and the three retrieval systems: ORBIT, DIALOG, and MEDLINE as implemented at the State University of New York (SUNY) and at NLM (MARCUS & REINTJES). CONIT resides on the MIT computer system, and remote users can dial in directly or via Tymnet or Telenet. CONIT was designed for end users in the actual use mode. Because it has its own command language that can be used to operate any of the three retrieval services, CONIT users need not learn the other three command languages. Although CONIT is not designed as an instructional system, some online instructional features and online *HELP*s are used, and suggestions for likely options are given within the context of the search.

Experience with early versions of CONIT was used to improve its instructional features. Tutorial features were moved closer to where they are needed, and unduly repetitious messages were eliminated. For example, the technique for correcting spelling errors is given just once, after the first instance of a misspelled command name. MARCUS & REINTJES describe tutorial interactions in detail, illustrate online sessions, and summarize and analyze their experiences with six naive end users. The authors stress that the key to their success in getting inexperienced users to interact successfully with several existing bibliographic retrieval systems depends on suitable attention to simplicity of use and adequate online instruction.

The present CONIT system is the culmination of work begun in 1972 at the MIT Electronic Systems Laboratory with NLM cooperation. MARCUS & REINTJES project costs and benefits of an operational CONIT-type system, but the CONIT system remains a uniquely valuable but still experimental one. In summarizing the work on the instructional media and training modes used within CONIT, Marcus and Reintjes conclude that there is no clear advantage to either the online or offline modes in terms of search effectiveness. Although users generally prefer online aid, many also want printed guides. The content and quality of the instruction and its availability when needed, as in the online mode, are the most critical factors in effectiveness and user acceptance. Further tutorial improvements are suggested, and the need for a robust system, i.e., one that performs reliably, is underscored. Unreliable system performance is "especially pernicious" for users in the learning stage. Marcus and Reintjes list the well-developed online *HELP* messages and explanations that the user may request and some of the automatic instructions provided in problem situations—e.g., when the computer is slow to respond or when command syntax is incorrectly entered.

IIDA. IIDA began as a research project in 1976, and it was continued through April 1980 (MEADOW, 1979). The individualized instruction originally planned was dropped as project funds were allocated to the diagnostic and assistance effort (MEADOW, 1978). Today IIDA consists of four programs: three in the "exercise mode" and a fourth in the "assistance mode." The exercises consist of guided entry of DIALOG commands (MEADOW, 1979). LANDSBERG ET AL. report experience in the use of IIDA in an industrial environment (at Exxon Corp.). Significantly, there was great interest in online searching among both scientists and engineers. More than 300 volunteers responded to fill the 100 openings that were offered. Training time averaged two and one-half hours, with one-half hour added for a final search of the subject's own choosing. Statistical data on the experiment are reported by HEWETT & MEADOW. The difficulties of designing costly supportive materials for use with varying subject content are illustrated by IIDA: as the design was finalized prior to DIALOG's addition of the *SUPER SELECT* and *SELECT STEPS* commands, these are not included in IIDA. The Franklin Institute, which participated with Drexel University (DU) in developing IIDA, is marketing the assistance programs in a packaged system that includes a microcomputer, two terminals, and a printer.

CCL. The notion of using the computer to help the user learn several command languages has also been developed as a modular software package to be implemented within existing bibliographic retrieval systems (NEGUS & SNOWDEN). This software, tentatively dubbed CCL, does not obscure any important trait of existing major retrieval systems. CCL thus includes more functions than any one of the major systems. It is intended to be used selectively as it is integrated into an existing retrieval system—i.e., only the CCL commands required to express the commands of the particular system are added to that system.

LARRSON describes the integration of CCL into the 3RIP retrieval system at the Royal Institute of Technology Library in Stockholm. Specific CCL commands and their interaction with the operations of the 3RIP commands are detailed. Integration of CCL into the 3RIP means that users trained in CCL will automatically become 3RIP users and that present 3RIP users will not be inconvenienced. Unfortunately the fit is not perfect because CCL performs somewhat differently from 3RIP—e.g., the use of the carriage return does not interrupt current processing as it does in the CCL design. The CCL approach to the common interface for multiple systems eliminates the add-on cost of an additional computer in the man-to-database communication link that CONIT and IIDA entail, but it introduces CCL variations that would proliferate each time CCL is integrated with a new system. Instead of the different command languages of each system, one would have to deal with several new versions of CCL.

SUPPORT FOR CAL SYSTEMS

Support for CAL systems must be considered from two viewpoints: 1) resources for initial development and 2) revenues to maintain it, to make it known, and to continue its development. CAL is not like a book on a shelf that rests securely when it is not used. CAL programs exist in computer storage where they must compete for their continued existence on a week-to-week basis. If they are not used, they are removed.

Initial Support for CAL Development

Recognition of the need for CAL for online retrieval services and the commitment of resources have come from governmental agencies, computer service networks, and online services. The source of support has important effects on the content and quality of CAL, on its availability, and on its continuing development.

Computer aids developed with government funding in the academic environment tend to reflect user needs more completely than aids funded and developed by other sources because they are meant to be used with more than one retrieval service. In the United States the Division of Science Information of NSF sponsored some of the CAL systems reviewed here as part of a program to improve the communication of scientific information within that community. Individuals within the academic community are stimulated in the CAL effort by their need for assistance in teaching a new skill and by the new environment in which that skill is used. The commercial services seem motivated by the need to make the system more usable, while NLM and CRS are more responsive to the need to reduce the burden of training new users. Because commercial services recover at least a part of the cost of their traditional training sessions by charging fees, they are under less pressure to consider the economy of developing computer assistance programs. CAL should appeal to them as a marketing tool, however, because new customers could save travel and workshop expenses and because employers who send trainees would lose fewer working days.

Service-supported development. Four of the CAL systems discussed were developed by the retrieval services and thus are restricted to the retrieval system taught. *MEDLEARN* is useful to the 500 institutions that use the MEDLINE database and to individuals who are preparing to work in those institutions. The PLATO-SCORPIO tutorial of CRS is intended for members of Congress, LC, and a few other federal agencies that have established the right to use the SCORPIO database system. ONTAP, provided by DIALOG, teaches DIALOG users who have learned the basic DIALOG command language how to construct a logical strategy statement. CCL, commissioned by EURONET, is not restricted by design but is most likely to be used only with EURONET-DIANE member services.

Training developed within academic environments. CONIT, IIDA, TRAINER, and DIALOG with PET have more general intent than the CAL systems developed by the online services. They reflect the user's need for access to multiple systems, although none is a complete training program. DIALOG with PET is restricted to DIALOG users and trainees must have a Commodore PET microcomputer. This program from the University of London does have an open-ended design with respect to content. Like TRAINER, the design is hospitable to the addition of any retrieval service and to any database instruction. TRAINER is currently available with DIALOG, ORBIT, and the NTIS and ERIC databases.

The database industry and CAL development. The database industry is not represented among support sources for CAL development. It has been cooperative but rarely does more than provide sample tapes. This is a rich area for CAL development. The need for database training is at least as great as for the command language and search strategy CAL. The TRAINER/PAIS modules being developed represent the first CAL for database instruction, but the source of support is the professional group that will be served, the American Public Policy Personnel Association (PAVLAK & CARUSO).

Continuing Support for CAL

The source of economic support affects a CAL program more than just in controlling its content. Like any other service offered for public use, money is needed to keep CAL available and for needed improvements and changes. The services that develop their own CAL programs can continue to maintain them or not, as their perceived value dictates. CAL systems developed by government funding for use by the public must establish their own economic bases among their users once the research period has ended.

DISTRIBUTION OF CAL

Implementation Constraints Limit CAL Distribution

The source of support for initial CAL development and the assumed user population affect its physical manifestation—i.e., the computer system, the telecommunications requirements, and even the language in which the programs are written. One attribute of any CAL system that limits its distribution is the degree to which it depends on special arrangements with other systems or special equipment.

Training aids vary from stand-alone system-independent programs to those that are integrated into particular retrieval systems. Some examples in increasing order of system dependence are:

- TRAINER is a stand-alone aid that includes emulations of the DIALOG and ORBIT systems and databases so that the user can practice commands and explore their use.

- *MEDLEARN* is a system-oriented aid that assigns search tasks to be practiced when the user is connected to the MEDLINE systems.
- CONIT and IIDA are aids that are built into interfaces that exist between the user and the target system; to use these aids the user must be connected to a communications network, the computer where the aid is installed, and a retrieval system; this involves continuing overhead costs for every online search that is made.
- CCL is an aid developed outside the retrieval services that must be integrated into the software of the separate retrieval systems.
- ONTAP and TRAIN are aids developed by a retrieval service as part of their overall software system.

The User–CAL Connection

The ultimate goal of CAL distribution efforts is that the CAL program should be operational on a computer system and that the user should have a terminal on which to run the program. Three methods have been used, sometimes in combination, to achieve this goal:

- Distribute copies of the CAL programs to be adapted as necessary to the user's computer system;
- Build a computer system that includes all needed components, including the computer and the programs, ready to run at the turn of a key—i.e., a "turnkey" system; and
- Sell the use of the programs as a service, keeping them running on one computer system, with users accessing them from their own terminals over a network.

The most important factors in choosing among these methods include local computing facilities and expertise and the expected amount of use of the CAL (CRAIG). The question is whether it is cheaper to buy or to rent, with high maintenance costs for the former vs. the cost of the total subscribed service for the latter. However, no system presently offers this choice. The question is really one of choosing the system that offers the needed training.

All modes of use present problems; the turnkey approach emphasizes simple startup. Changing the CAL program and adding to it may lead to the problems encountered when adding to or changing programs in any computer system.

Services such as the CONDUIT center are evolving as clearinghouses where CAL authors can deposit their creations for editing and evaluation. Programs are sold to users who want and need them and who have the proper resources. CONDUIT attempts to guarantee that a program it sells will run on the buyer's system, and it will stay with the buyer until it does. Such services, like good publishers, also help to develop the revenue base for the product, stimulating interest and assisting the users.

Another approach to the difficulties of making computer aids available is the facilitating network, as exemplified by the recently activated EDUCOM project, EDUNET (HELLER; MAGARRELL). The programs remain at one computer installation where they are kept online, maintained, updated, revised, and extended. Problems of transporting software to other computer environments do not constrain development or use. Users make no investment in acquisition, loading and adapting, or in computer storage allocations. Access is arranged at the host system simply by membership in the network, and payment is based on hours of use only. Users do not need extensive computer expertise or experience; they need only to provide enough terminals for student use and to understand the appropriate use of the programs. This method of distribution brings CAL to individuals in institutions of higher education if the institution is an EDUNET member. Commercial networks, open to anyone, could vastly extend the potential user population.

Users of CAL for Online Services

The successful distribution of CAL programs depends on adequate identification of the user population. Anyone who uses an online service is a possible CAL user, but who are these users? This question has been debated within the library profession as one of the end user vs. the intermediary. Should the person who needs the information search for it himself, or should a specially trained intermediary do the searching? Continuing education programs to introduce practicing librarians to online searching and to refresh and update their skills are not presently a focus of much attention, although user groups affiliated with specific services do perform this function. As the need grows, a centrally maintained CAL service might be very useful to this group.

Where the intermediary approach is endorsed, as it is at NLM, it is seen as a rigid requirement because of the complexity and variability of the search services–database developer environment (DOSZKOCS ET AL.). Proponents of end-user searching are just as adamant in defending the need for the end user to do his or her own searching; they cite the ultimate inability of an intermediary to meet the needs of the various kinds of end users. Doszkocs et al. take the position that the multiple retrieval service command languages are too difficult for the non-specialist. A recent experiment by SEWELL & BEVAN using MEDLINE with naive medical personnel, introduces some evidence to refute that position. They did not assume any need for mastery of multiple command languages or databases. Seven pharmacists and nine pathologists learned only the MEDLINE commands and only the MEDLINE and TOXLINE databases. Sewell looked at several indicators to assess the effect of introducing non-mediated online searching, including: 1) changes in the proportion of users who used mediated and non-mediated searches; 2) repeat use of the non-mediated search; 3) correlation of search activities with professional activities of the searchers; 4) the adequacy of the search vocabulary used; and 5) problems with the search system. She concluded that

methods of user training present the greatest barrier to non-mediated searching but that end users will use online searching if it is "readily available."

N. CARUSO drew up a plan for introducing specific databases and online
searching into the curricula of the graduate professional schools of the
University of Pittsburgh (UP). He likens the present pattern of end-user access
to the evolution of the public telephone system, with the elimination of the
human operator as a necessary condition to full access by the end user, who is
the real revenue base of the service. E. CARUSO (1979a) sees all users starting out as naive users, with the first level of competency being appropriate for
either end users or beginning specialists. The end user needs basic competence
in the most-used commands and general database understanding. Then he
requires more complete comprehension of the one or several database files of
particular interest. The intermediary, however, goes on to learn more files and
more retrieval services and studies the efficiencies and economies of online
searching in depth.

The Research Libraries Group (RLG), in its planning for online library
catalogs, regards the inclusion of the library patron doing his own searching as
a necessary condition of the online catalog, or an economic fact of life.
Douglas Ferguson, Manager of RLG's Patron Access Project, says: "Now we
are at the point of using the computer to deliver information directly to
people. . . .a giant step forward from being solely a library resource to being a
public resource" (HATTERY). ELIAS ET AL. (1980), reporting on a design
study for end-user education, talk about end users who have "access control."
When information sources were few and inexpensive, the end user was the
sole mediator of his own access. As the bulk and cost of literature increased,
the end user lost both control and access to the primary sources as well as to
the indexing and abstracting publications. ELIAS ET AL. foresee the end
users' regaining access control in the not too distant future as technological
and economic conditions become more favorable.

While the debate goes on within the information profession, end users may
be taking matters into their own hands. The TRAINER evaluation drew
experimental subjects from 50 UP chemists who sought out the project. A
mixed group of faculty, including one librarian, at Muskingum College, Ohio,
sought the same training, using specially rented telephone lines to the UP
computer (E. CARUSO, 1979a). Three hundred Exxon scientists and engineers responded when 100 subjects were needed to test IIDA (LANDSBERG
ET AL.). MALLOY, for the British Library, is investigating the introduction
of online searching to public school children. The British Library is taking the
position that the online search be taught within the subject curricula, rather
than as a separate subject in itself (BRAKE).

ASSESSING CAL FOR ONLINE SERVICES

The first line for comparing CAL for online services is the subject content
being taught. Availability of the CAL, in terms of investments of money,
equipment, and expertise required for use, must be considered next. These

aspects have been covered in earlier sections. The quality and effectiveness of
CAL programs are surveyed here.

CAL is a much-studied but little-used medium. Many studies have been
made of the failure of computer technology to meet instructional needs in
formal educational programs. Questions of substantive content and of the
quality and effectiveness of the available programs have been raised. The
appropriateness of the computer as an aid or instructional medium is another
subject for investigation. LIPSON lists seven recommendations with respect
to content and quality that would help educators meet their "crucial responsibility" for integrating information technology into formal education.
HEINES, in response, makes the point that no such improvements will make
much difference until courseware "be produced in multiple formats so that it
can be transported directly (that's 'directly,' i.e., 'immediately,' not 'easily' or
'with minor revisions') to all major systems currently in use in our schools."

Evaluation of specific CAL systems. All of the tests that could be applied
to any educational material or methods could be applied to CAL for online
services. E. CARUSO (1979a) reports "real-world" use of TRAINER with 23
chemists whose performance was tested against a set of behavioral objectives.
Simple statistics of use for several hundred student users of TRAINER are
also reported. SEGAL is undertaking a major test of TRAINER as a substi-
tute for workshop training of beginning online searchers in the seven-state
area served by the Bibliographical Center for Research. LANDSBERG ET AL.
report similar testing of IIDA in a commercial setting by 100 scientists and
engineers. HEWETT & MEADOW report the statistical details of the IIDA
test. Statistics of use for *MEDLEARN* are reported by EISENBERG ET
AL. MARCUS & REINTJES report on six users of the final version of CONIT.
These reports are useful in studying the individual systems but are of little
value in comparing CAL programs. In fact, no comparisons can be made,
when no common set of learning goals has been established.

SUMMARY

The need for training for online searching is not fully defined. Information
professionals recognize their own need for training, but the need also seems
to exist in public schools and in higher education institutions. In graduate
professional schools the need is beginning to be articulated and addressed,
particularly in scientific and engineering programs. Industrial scientists and
engineers have shown that they recognize the value of doing their own searching.

Computer programs can assist the learning process. They include substantial amounts of content and skills training. Through them, motivated learners
can master certain skills and build logical constructs. The programs must be
rigid enough to ensure that all "bases are touched" but flexible enough to
skip over teaching and practice when it is not needed. There is an unusual
extra benefit to be gained in the use of CAL designed for online search training; the learner is not just learning the computer skills he will need but is

actually using them. The traditional reluctance of formal education to adopt new media and methods may be overcome in teaching online searching because there are few competing teaching resources for this new skill.

CAL can meet much of the need for online search training, but its potential users need to be made aware of it and it must be readily available. It is usually designed for individual use, but it can also serve as a resource for the teacher of database services. It can assist in repetitive skill development exercises and serve as a centrally updated resource for keeping up with the changing services and for refreshing seldom-used skills. CAL can be the ideal continuing education resource for practitioners in any area since it can be used at the place of work as needed.

The development of CAL systems can be a trivial undertaking, but when any substantial and complex body of content is used, it becomes difficult and costly. CAL systems must be reliable and easy to use. When these requirements are added to the demand for substantial content and sophisticated teaching strategies, the problem becomes greater and little work has been done in this area. The costs of successful CAL must be shared by many users. Distributing the CAL to enough users to make it economically feasible is essential to the continuing existence of up-to-date CAL for online services. It is now possible economically and technically to distribute CAL within institutions of higher education through use of facilitating networks. Statistical data on use and results, which can be collected for networked CAL use, provide evidence that may become the basis for recognition of the value of CAL.

BIBLIOGRAPHY

BELLARDO, TRUDI; JACKSON, M. VIRGINIA; PIKOFF, HOWARD. 1979. Education and Training for On-Line Searching; A Bibliography. Reference Quarterly. 1979 Winter; 19(2): 137–142. ISSN: 033-7072.

BOURNE, CHARLES P.; ROBINSON, JO. 1980. Education and Training for Computer-Based Reference Services: Review of Training to Date. Journal of the American Society for Information Science. 1980 January; 31(1): 25–35. ISSN: 0002-8231.

BRAKE, T. G. H. 1980. Information Skills in the Curriculum Research Unit. Available from: the author, Inner London Education Authority, Center for Learning Resources, 275 Kennington Lane, London SE 11 5QZ, UK 01-582-9207.

CARUSO, ELAINE. 1977. Training Modules for Users of Scientific and Technical Information Services: A Hands On Trainer for Online Bibliographic Retrieval. Pittsburgh, PA: University of Pittsburgh, 1977 December. 134p. NTIS: PB 277973.

CARUSO, ELAINE. 1978a. Hands on Online: Bringing It Home. Online Review. 1978 September; 2(3): 251–268. ISSN: 0309-314x.

CARUSO, ELAINE. 1978b. Online Training for Searching Online. In: 2nd International Online Information Meeting; 1978 December 5–7;

London, England. Oxford England: Learned Information; 1978. 37-48. ISBN: 0-904933-15-6.

CARUSO, ELAINE. 1979a. TRAINER: Computer Assisted Learning and Practice for Users of DIALOG and ORBIT. Pittsburgh, PA: University of Pittsburgh, 1979 August. 201p. ERIC: ED 178101.

CARUSO, ELAINE. 1979b. Resource Review: TRAINER at CMU. EDUNET News. 1979 Winter: 4. ISSN: 0146-1788.

CARUSO, ELAINE. 1981. TRAINER. Online. 1981 January; 5(1): 36-38. ISSN: 0146-5422.

CARUSO, ELAINE; GRIFFITHS, JOHN. 1977. A TRAINER for Online Systems. Online. 1977 October; 1(4): 28-34. ISSN: 0146-5422.

CARUSO, NICHOLAS C. 1979. A Perspective on Long Range Directions for the University's Commitment to Computer-Based Data and Information Retrieval Services. 1979 July 11. 12p. Available from: the author, University of Pittsburgh Graduate School of Public and International Affairs, Pittsburgh, PA 15260.

CONDUIT. 1979. What is Conduit? 1979. Available from: Conduit, University of Iowa, P. O. Box 388, Iowa City, IA 52244.

CRAIG, FRANCES. 1979. Evaluation of TRAINER. 1979. 8p. Available from: Carnegie-Mellon University Computer Center, User Services, Schenley Park, Pittsburgh, PA 15213.

DOSZKOCS, TAMAS E.; RAPP, BARBARA; SCHOOLMAN, HAROLD M. 1980. Automated Information Retrieval in Science and Technology. Science. 1980 April 4; 208(4439): 25-30. ISSN: 0036-8075.

EDSTROM, MALIN E.; WALLIN, MARIE A. 1978. Implementation of a New Interactive On-Line Information Retrieval System: 3RIP. In: Schwartz, Stephan; Carlsson, Gunnar; Froberg, Gudmund, eds. Library Services in Transition. Stockholm, Sweden: Royal Institute of Technology Library; 1978. 135-149. ISSN: 0348-0585.

EISENBERG, LAURA J.; STANDING, ROY A.; TIDBALL, CHARLES S.; LEITER, JOSEPH. 1978. *MEDLEARN*: A Computer-Assisted Instruction (CAI) Program for MEDLARS. Bulletin of the Medical Library Association. 1978 January; 66(1): 6-13. ISSN: 0025-7338.

ELIAS, ARTHUR W.; MCDONALD, T.; LANG, C. 1977. Media Selection for Information User Training. Philadelphia, PA: BioSciences Information Service; 1977 January 21. 54p. NTIS: PB 282 172/6GA.

ELIAS, ARTHUR W.; VAUPEL, NANCY; LINGWOOD, DAVID. 1980. End User Education: A Design Study. Online Review. 1980 June; 4(2): 153-162. ISSN: 0309-314X.

GUY, R. FREDERICK; LARGE, J. ANDREW; ARMSTRONG, CHRISTOPHER J. 1981. Microcomputer Simulations of Online Bibliographic Systems for Teaching Purposes. In: Proceedings of the 2nd National Online Meeting; 1981 March 24-26; New York, NY. Oxford, England: Learned Information; 1981. 261-270.

GRIFFITH, JEFFREY C.; NORTON, NANCY PROTHO. 1981. A Computer Assisted Instruction Program for End Users of an Automated Information Retrieval System. 1981 February 4. 10p. Available from: the authors, U.S. Library of Congress, Washington, DC; or Oak Ridge National Laboratory, Oak Ridge, TN.

HARDY, NANCY F. 1979. Maximizing the Effectiveness of Online Searching: A Training and Education Model. 1979. 10p. ERIC: ED 185971.

HARTER, STEPHAN P. 1979. Assessment of Instruction Provided by Library Schools in Online Searching. Information Processing & Management. 1979; 15(2): 71-75.

HATTERY, LOWELL H., ed. 1980. Commitment to Public Use of Library Computer Systems. Information Retrieval and Library Automation. 1980 September; 1:1. ISSN: 0020-0220.

HEINES, JESSE M. 1980. Courseware Development and the NSF: A Commentary on Dr. Joseph Lipson's Perceptions of "Technology in Science Education: The Next Ten Years." Bedford, MA: Digital Equipment Corp.; 1980. 20p. Also available in: Computer. 1980 July. ISSN: 0018-9162.

HELLER, PAUL S. 1978. Network Permits 150 Universities to Share DP-Based Instruction and Research Resources. Computerworld. 1978 November 27.

HEWETT, THOMAS T.; MEADOW, CHARLES T. 1981. A Study of the Measurement of User Performance. In: Divilbiss, J. L., ed. Public Access to Library Automation. Proceedings of the 1980 Clinic on Library Applications of Data Processing; Urbana-Champaign, IL. University of Illinois, Graduate School of Library and Information Science; 1981. 49-76. ISBN: 0-87845-065-3.

KASSEBAUM, LAURA; LEITER, JOSEPH. 1978. Training and Continuing Education for On-Line Searching. Medical Informatics (England). 1978 September; 3(3): 165-175. ISSN: 0307-7640.

LANCASTER, F. W.; FAYEN, E. G. 1973. Instruction and Training of Users. In: Lancaster, F. W.; Fayen, E. G. Information Retrieval On-Line. Los Angeles, CA: Melville Publishing Co.; 1973. 315-330. ISBN: 0-471-51235-4.

LANDSBERG, M. KAREN; LAWRENCE, BARBARA; LORENZ, PATRICIA A.; MEADOW, CHARLES T. 1980. A Joint Industrial-Academic Experiment: An Evaluation of the IIDA System. In: Benenfeld, Alan R.; Kazlauskas, Edward John, eds. Communicating Information: Proceedings of the American Society for Information Science (ASIS) 43rd Annual Meeting: Volume 17; 1980 October 6-9; Anaheim, CA. White Plains, NY: Knowledge Industry Publications Inc.; 1980. 406-408. ISBN: 0-87715-412-0; ISSN: 0044-7870.

LARRSON, ROLF. 1980. On Implementing the Common Command Language within 3RIP. Stockholm 70, Sweden: Royal Institute of Technology Library; 1980. 18p. (Report: TRITA-LIB-4067).

LIPSON, JOSEPH I. 1980. Technology in Science Education: The Next Ten Years. 1980. Available from: the author, Director, Division of Science Education Development and Research, National Science Foundation, Washington, DC 20550.

LOCKHEED INFORMATION SYSTEMS. 1980. ONTAP. Chronolog: Monthly Newsletter of the DIALOG Information Retrieval Service. 1980 October; 8(10): 7. Available from: Lockheed Information Systems, Palo Alto, CA 94304.

MAGARRELL, JACK. 1978. National Computer Network Now Links U.S. Universities. Chronicle of Higher Education. 1978 November 20; 1:1. ISSN: 009-5982.

MALLOY, IAN. 1979. Current R&D Projects in User Education. Unpaged. 1979. Available from: the author, Information Officer for User Educa-

334   ELAINE CARUSO

tion, Loughborough University of Technology, Loughborough LE11 3TU, Leicestershire, UK.

MARCUS, RICHARD S.; REINTJES, J. FRANCIS. 1979. Experiments and Analysis on a Computer Interface to an Information Retrieval Network. Cambridge, MA: Massachusetts Institute of Technology Laboratory for Information and Decision Systems; 1979 April. 127p.

MARKEY, KAREN. 1979. The Anatomy of a Search. Paper presented to: The Virginia Library Association; 1979 November 10; Hot Springs, VA. 31p. ERIC ED 184528.

MARKEY, KAREN; ATHERTON, PAULINE. 1978. ONTAP: Online Training and Practice Manual for ERIC Data Base Searchers. Syracuse, NY: Syracuse University; 1978 June. 182p. Available from: Syracuse University Printing Services, 125 College Place, Syracuse, NY 13210. ERIC: ED 16019.

MCCARN, DAVIS B. 1978. Online Systems—Techniques and Services. In: Williams, Martha E., ed. Annual Review of Information Science and Technology: Volume 13. White Plains, NY: Knowledge Industry Publications, Inc.; 1978. 85-124. ISSN: 0066-4200.

MEADOW, CHARLES T. 1978. Computer Assistance in the Performance of Interactive Bibliographic Searching. Paper presented to: American Society for Engineering Education; 1978 June 18-22; Vancouver, BC. 1978. 11p. Available from: the author, Drexel University, Philadelphia, PA 19104.

MEADOW, CHARLES T. 1979. Individualized Instruction for Data Access. Philadelphia, PA: Graduate School of Library Science, Drexel University; Franklin Institute Research Laboratories; 1979 March. 33p. ERIC: ED 179195.

MOSTELLER, FREDERICK. 1981. Innovation and Evaluation. Science. 1981 February 27; 211(4485): 881-886. ISSN: 0036-8075.

NEGUS, ALAN; SNOWDEN, ANDREW E. 1979. EURONET-DIANE, User's Guide (Common Command Language); Draft for Comment. 1979. Unpaged. Available from: Scicon Consultancy International Ltd., London, UK.

PAVLAK, THOMAS; CARUSO, ELAINE. 1981. Online Scholars Save Time and Dollars. 1981. 5p. Submitted for publication to the PAE (Public Administration Education) Report. Available from: the authors, Graduate School of Public and International Affairs (GSPIA), University of Pittsburgh, Pittsburgh, PA 15260.

SEGAL, JO AN. 1980. New Methods for Teaching Online Searching of Computerized Databases: Abstract of the Research Proposed. 1980. Available from: the author, Bibliographical Center for Research, 245 Columbine St., Denver, CO 80206.

SEWELL, WINIFRED; BEVAN, ALICE. 1976. Nonmediated Use of MEDLINE and TOXLINE by Pathologists and Pharmacists. Bulletin of the Medical Library Association. 1976 October; 64(4): 382-391. ISSN: 0025-7338.

SIMMONS, PETER. 1979. Satellite Television and Training for On-Line Computer Searching. Journal of Education for Librarianship. 1979 Spring; 19(4): 312-317. ISSN: 0022-0604.

SOBEN, PHYLLIS; TIDBALL, CHARLES S. 1974. ***MEDLEARN***: An Orientation to MEDLINE. Bulletin of the Medical Library Association. 1974 April; 62(2): 92-94. ISSN: 0025-7338.

VICKERY, ALINA. 1980. The CIS Software Series. 1980. 1p. Available from: the author, Central Information Service, Room 504, Senate House, University of London, Malet St., London WC1E 7HU, UK.

WANGER, JUDITH. 1979a. Education and Training for Online Systems. In: Williams, Martha E., ed. Annual Review of Information Science and Technology: Volume 14. White Plains, NY: Knowledge Industry Publications, Inc.; 1979. 219-245. ISSN: 0066-4200.

WANGER, JUDITH. 1979b. Overview of Training Needs and Opportunities. American Society for Information Science (ASIS) SIG Newsletter. 1979 September; CRS-8: 5-14.

WASSERMAN, PAUL, ed. Newsletter on Education and Training Programs for Specialized Information Personnel. International Federation of Documentation, Education and Training Committee. Available from: the Committee, College of Library and Information Services, Undergraduate Library Building, University of Maryland, College Park, MD 20742.

Introduction to Index

Index entries have been made for names of individuals, corporate bodies, subjects and author names that have been included in the bibliography pages as well as those found in the text pages. The page numbers in the index referring to bibliography pages are set in italics and they are listed after the page numbers relating to the text pages. Thus, the user can readily distinguish references to bibliographic materials from references to text.

Postings to acronyms are listed either under the acronym or under the fully spelled-out form depending on which form is more commonly used and known. In either case a cross reference to the alternate form is provided. Postings associated with BALLOTS, for example, are listed under BALLOTS as few people are likely to remember that BALLOTS stands for Bibliographic Automation of Large Library Operations using a Time-sharing System. In a few cases, such as the names of programs, systems and programming languages, there is no spelled-out form either because there is none or because the meaning has been changed or is no longer used.

The index is arranged on a word-by-word basis. The sort sequence employed sorts on special characters, first, followed by alpha characters and then numeric characters. Thus, O'Neill precedes Oakman and 3M Company follows the Zs. Government organizations are generally listed under country name with *see* references provided from names of departments, agencies and other subdivisions.

Subject indexing is by concepts rather than by words. When authors have used different words or different forms of the same words to express the same or overlapping concepts, the terminology has been standardized. An effort was made to use the form of index entries for concepts that had previously appeared in *ARIST* indexes. Cross references have been used freely to provide broad access to subject concepts. *See also* references are used for overlapping or related (but not synonymous) concepts; *see* references are used to send the readers to the accepted form of a term used in the index.

The index was prepared by Laurence Lannom. The programs for online editing of the index, page number conversions, and formatting of output were written by Scott E. Preece. The overall direction and coordination of the index were provided by Martha E. Williams. The index was generated on the DEC System 10 at the Coordinated Science Laboratory, University of Illinois. Comments and suggestions are welcomed and should be directed to the Editor.

Index*

A&I services,
arts and humanities, 257
life sciences, 267-268
AACR2 (Anglo-American Cataloging
Rules, Second Edition),
MARC, 229
shared cataloging quality
control, 221-222
AAT, [see Art and Architecture
Thesaurus]
Abbess, J., 70, *83*
ABC-Clio Press,
databases in the arts and
humanities, 257
Abels, David M., *202*
Abelson, R. P., *136*
ABI/INFORM,
spelling errors, 181
Above 890 decision,
telephone service competition
development, 19
Abrahamsson, Sixten, 189, *194*
Abstracting and indexing services,
[see A&I services]
Academic libraries,
OCLC adoption impacts, 220
online searching, 182
professionalism 305
public access to bibliographic
utilities, 223
satellite use survey, 225
Accademia della Crusca (Florence),
machine-readable dictionaries,
252
Access points,
bibliographic utilities, 229
ACH, [see Association for Computers
and the Humanities]
Acquisitions,
interlibrary loan networks, 217
ACS (Advanced Communications
System),
data communications historical
development, 23

ACS (Advanced Communications
System), (cont.)
data communications prospects, 24
Adam, T. W., *26*
Adams, Arthur L., 154, 155, 183,
157, 194
Adams, J., 68, *75*
Adams, R. C., 117, *130*
Adaptive Information Management
System, [see ADMIN]
Adaptive Management System for
Special Libraries and
Information Bureaux, [see
ADLIB]
Adkisson, James W., *75*
ADLIB (Adaptive Management
System for Special Libraries and
Information Bureaux),
ADMIN comparison, 94
ADMIN (Adaptive Information
Management System),
ADLIB comparison 94
Advanced Communications System,
[see ACS]
Advanced Research Projects Agency
Network, [see ARPANET]
Adventure (game),
state vector representation, 122
AFP, [see Associative File
Processor]
Agarwal, Krishna K., *132*
Agenbroad, James E., 225, *232*
AGREP (Agricultural Research
Projects),
descriptive study, 276
AGRICOLA (Agricultural Online
Access; *formerly* CAIN
(Cataloging and Indexing
database)),
CAB comparison, 271, 273
descriptive study, 276
manual vs. online searching, 151
Agricultural Canada Libraries
Information Network, 274

Broadcast industry,
data communications potential, 8
telecommunications industry
components, 6
Brodart Industries,
CLSI interface, 218
Brodauf, H., 271, 277, *281*
Brodie, Michael L., 119, *130*
Brodie, Nancy, *239*
Brooks, H., 96, 99, *111*
Brooks, H. M., *158*
Brooks, Kristina, *281*
Brooks, Rep. Jack, 11
Brotman, Stuart, 69, *32, 76*
Brown, Carolyn P., 186, *200*
Brown, Charles R., 60, *76*
Brown, David C., *130*
Brown, Gretchen P., 124, *130*
Brown, J. S., 128, *130*
Brown, Mike, 102, *104*
Brown University Corpus, 253
Browsing,
search techniques and theory,
147-148
BRS (Bibliographic Retrieval
Services, Inc.), [*see also*
CROSS]
acquisition by IHS, 173
cost comparisons, 187
history of online retrieval, 173
MEDLINE, 176
private file service, 192
review of three major systems, 173
Brumfit, P. J., 71, *81*
Brunner, Theodore F., 252
Bryant, G., 273, *283*
BSDP, [*see* Bibliographic Services
Development Program]
Buchanan, B. G., 123, 129, *131,
137*
Buckland, Michael K., 150, *158,
309*
Building-block strategy, 142
search patterns study, 150
search strategy types, 183
Building Research Establishment
(U.K.),
STATUS application to library
records, 93
Bulletin Signaletique,
A&I services in the life
sciences, 268

Bullock, Alan Louis Charles, *262*
Bun, Jean, 66, *76*
Bunderson, C. Victor, *131*
Bunge, Charles A., 153, *159*
Buntrock, Robert E., 175, 183, *196*
Burgess, R. L., *281*
Burket, T. G., 126, *131*
Burkhardt, Margit, 153, *159*
Burkley, John H., 231, *234*
Burnard, Lou D., 258, *262*
Burr, B. J., *76*
Burr, Robert L., 305, 306, *309*
Burridge, M. J., 273, *281*
Burroughs B7805 computer,
WLN software, 225
Burrows, Suzetta, 176, *196*
Burstein, Mark H., 122, *133*
Burton, D. H., *287*
Burton, Ellen, *37*
Burton, Hilary D., 271, *282*
Burton, Michael L., *262*
Burton, R., 128, *130*
Burton, Sarah K., 247-266, *252*
Busa, Roberto, 251, *262*
Business and management schools,
education for information
management, 302-303
Bussom, Robert S., 302, *314*
Butler, Brett, 100, 180, *104, 196*
Butler, R. E., 14, *28*
Bylander, E. G., 57, 64, 69, *76*
Byte,
word processing reports, 117

CA Condensates,
manual vs. online searching, 151
CA Registry Numbers,
chemical databases, 176
CIS (Chemical Information
System), 178
CAB, [*see* Commonwealth Agricultural Bureaux]
Cable TV,
Channel 2000 experiment, 214
computer-based services in the
humanities, 259-260, 261
data communications potential, 8
local communications market
competition, 20
regulation, 13
telecommunications industry
components, 6

Johansen, R., 74, *79*
Johansen, Thomas, *162*
Johnson, Allan R., 150, *162*
Johnson, B. K., *288*
Johnson, B. W., *76*
Johnson, Leland L., 6, *35*
Johnson, Margaret, *243*
Johnson, Mike, 17, *35*
Johnson, Richard B., 6, *35*
Johnson, Robert A., 184, *201*
Johnston, Susan M., 151, *162*
Johnstone, A., 273, *284*
Jones, Alan, 250, *264*
Jones, C. Lee, 215, *237*
Jones, Colin, 179, *201*
Jones, Iorwerth, 64, *79*
Jones, Kevin P., 91, *103, 104*
Jones, Richard, 226, *237*
Jones, W. T., *35*
Jong, Steven, 117, *133*
Josel, Nathan A., Jr., 154, *163*
Josephine, Helen B., 186, *201*
*Journal of the American Society for
    Information Science (JASIS)*,
    literature of online systems, 173
Joyner, Virginia, *41*
Joysticks,
    uses, 61
Judicial branch, [*see* U.S.
    Judicial branch]
Juliana, Anthony, *77*
Jurgen, Ronald K., 17, *35*

Kaae, Soren, 149–150, *162*
Kaback, Stuart M., 175, *201*
Kadec, Sarah T., 185, *201*
Kahneman, D., 149
Kalba, Kas, 297, *312*
Kalba, Konrad K., 13, 28, *35*
Kamen Sciences Co.,
    online circulation systems
    interface to online search
    systems, 218
Kaminuma, Tsuguchika, 275,
    284
Kanarick, Arnold F., *76*
Kaneko, Ryuichi, *78*
Kang, Jong H., 224, *237*
Kanji, [*see* Japanese character set]
Kaplan, R. M., *130*
Kaplan, S. Jerrold, 127, *133*
Karches, Gerald J., *80*

Karsh, Michelle, *312*
Kaske, Neal K., 218, *237*
Kassebaum, Laura, 319, *333*
Katz, William A., 153, 156, *163*
Kaufman, Larry, 178, *201*
Kawano, M., *281*
Kay, M., *130*
Kayser-Threde,
    DOMESTIC project, 92
Kazlauskas, Edward John, *107, 311*
Keen, E. Michael, 150, *163*
Kelley, Daniel, *29*
Kelly, Alex M., 177, *205*
Kelly, Maureen C., 276, *284*
Kennington, Don, 154, *163*
Kent, Allen, 173, 300, *201, 312*
Kenton, Edith, 147, *163*
Keren, C., 92, *107*
Kestenbaum, Lionel, *35*
Keyboards,
    design and operation, 60–61
    usage, 71
Kidd, J. S., 187, *201*
Kieburtz, Bruce R., *35*
Kiechel, Walter, III, 172, *201*
Kilgour, Frederick G., *237*
Kilton, Tom D., 215, *237*
King, Donald W., 294, 295, 299,
    303, *310, 312*
King, James, 227, *237*
King, Kathryn L., 100, *110*
King, T., 69, *79*
Kinnucan, Paul, 117, *133*
Kirby, Richard C., *35*
Kirby, Sharon, *27*
Kirchner, Jake, *35*
Kirk, Sam A., *130*
Kissman, Henry M., 270, 272, *284*
Kittross, John M., *35*
Klawiter-Pommer, J. H. T., *281*
Kleiman, Dena, 254, *264*
Klement, Susan, 306, *312*
Klempner, Irving M., 302, *312*
Klie, Robert H., *36*
Klingensmith, Patricia J., *198*
KLONE (Knowledge Language One),
    semantic data nets, 120
Klugman, Simone, 182, *201*
Knapp, Sara D., 182, *201*
Knight, S. J. T., 273, *285*
Knowledge Language One, [*see*
    KLONE]

Searching, [*see also* Databases;
Online systems; Online vendors;
Search aids; Search services;
Search strategy]
online, (cont.)
end-user access, 179-180, 328-329
equipment, 185-186
evaluation, 181
heuristics, 154-155
history of online retrieval, 171-174
library professionalism, 306
machine enhancement, 144
machine-readable output, 192-193
manual vs. online cost
analysis, 187
microcomputers, 97, 99-101
offline preparation, 99-100
testing alternative retrieval
techniques, 102
training, 95, 98-99
minicomputer bibliographic
database systems, 90-92
minicomputer personal file-
handling systems, 90
multi-database searching, 155, 271
pre- vs. postcoordinate indexing,
214-215
professionalism, 193
programming comparison, 180
psychology of searching, 148-150
query and search collections, 156
reference interview, 181-182
reference work, 182
research with implications for
search techniques, 150-152
search service management, 184
search strategy, 182
storage of retrieved data for offline
manipulation, 100
telephone conferencing, 185-186
texts, 156
unformatted records, 97
user interface, 179-184
1200 vs. 300 baud online
retrieval, 185
physical search techniques, 146-148
psychological aspects, 148-150

Searching, [*see also* Databases;
Online systems; Online vendors;
Search aids; Search services;
Search strategy] (cont.)
research with implications for
search techniques, 150-153
tactics, 154
texts, 156
Searle, R. H., *157*
Sears Roebuck,
videodisk catalog, 117
Seba, Douglas B., 184, *205*
Seeger, Thomas, 293, 298, *316*
Seelbach, H. E., *107*
Segal, H., 86, *110*
Segal, Jo An, 321, *334*
Seidewitz, L., 273, *287*
Seitz, Neal B., *40*
Selective dissemination of
information, [*see* SDI]
Self, D. A., *76*
Self-generating master, [*see*
SELGEM]
Self, P. C., *76*
SELGEM (self-generating master),
255
Selmon, John, *40*
Semantic data nets,
computer meaning representation,
120-121
links, 123
Semiautomatic Ground Environment,
[*see* SAGE]
Senate, [*see* U.S., Senate]
Serial searching,
hardware techniques, 95
minicomputer personal file-
handling systems, 90
Serials,
OCLC/Indiana University online
system, 213
records quality control, 220
Sewell, Winifred, 298, 328, *314, 334*
Shankle, James E., 66, *78*
Shapiro, Neil, 117, *137*
Shapiro, Stanley J., 185, *205*
Sharp,
hand-held microcomputer, 86
Shaughnessy, Thomas W., 301, *314*
Shaw, L. C., 61, *81*
Shaw, Mary, 300, *314*

Introduction to
Keyword and Author Index

The following section is an author and keyword index to *ARIST* chapters for Volumes 1 through 16. It has been produced to assist users in locating specific topics, chapters, and author names for all *ARIST* volumes to date. The index terms are sorted alphabetically and include all author names and content words from titles (a stop-word list of articles, conjunctions, and other non-content words was used). The sort word is followed by the author(s) name(s) and the *ARIST* citation.

Keyword and Author Index of *ARIST* Titles for Volumes 1-16

Application
    Beard, Joseph J. 6, p369
Applications
    Baruch, Jordan J. 1, p255; Blumstein, Alfred. 7, p471; Caceres, Cesar
    A.; Weihrer, Anna Lea, and Pulliam, Robert. 6, p325; Levy, Richard P.
    and Cammarn, Maxine R. 3, p397; Raben, Joseph and Widmann, R. L.
    7, p439; Silberman, Harry F. and Filep, Robert T. 3, p357; Smith,
    Linda C. 15, p67; Spring, William C., Jr. 2, p311; Vinsonhaler, John F.
    and Moon, Robert D. 8, p277.
Architectures
    Hollaar, Lee A. 14, p129
ARIST Staff
    ARIST Staff. New Hardware Developments. 1, p191
Artandi, Susan
    Artandi, Susan. Document Description and Representation. 5, p143
Artificial
    Smith, Linda C. 15, p67
Arts
    Raben, Joseph and Burton, Sarah K. 16, p247
Aspects
    Atherton, Pauline and Greer, Roger. 3, p329; Farradane, J. 6, p399;
    Harvey, John F. 2, p419; Shera, Jesse H. and McFarland, Anne S. 4,
    p439; Taylor, Robert S. 1, p15.
Assisted
    Larson, Signe and Williams, Martha E. 15, p251
Atherton, Pauline
    Atherton, Pauline and Greer, Roger. Professional Aspects of Informa-
    tion Science and Technology. 3, p329
Automated
    Becker, David. 16, p113; Bobrow, D. G., Fraser, J. B. and Quillian,
    M. R. 2, p161; Damerau, Fred J. 11, p107; Kay, Martin and Sparck
    Jones, Karen. 6, p141; Montgomery, Christine A. 4, p145; Salton,
    Gerard. 3, p169; Simmons, Robert F. 1, p137; Walker, Donald E. 8,
    p69
Automation
    Alper, Bruce H. 10, p199; Avram, Henriette. 6, p171; Bierman, Kenneth
    J. 9, p123; Black, Donald V. and Farley, Earl A. 1, p273; Griffin, Hillis
    L. 3, p241; Grosch, Audrey N. 11, p225; Kilgour, Frederick G. 4, p305;
    Markuson, Barbara Evans. 2, p255; Martin, Susan K. 7, p243; Parker,
    Ralph H. 5, p193; Reed, Mary Jane Pobst and Vrooman, Hugh T. 14,
    p193; Simmons, Peter. 8, p167; Veneziano, Velma. 15, p109
Avram, Henriette
    Avram, Henriette. Library Automation. 6, p171
Awareness
    Wente, Van A. and Young, Gifford A. 5, p259

Ballou, Hubbard W.
    Ballou, Hubbard W. Microform Technology. 8, p121
Baruch, Jordan J.
    Baruch, Jordan J. Information System Applications. 1, p255